TABLE D Mathematical Signs

MATHEMATICAL SIGNS

Add; positive	$+$
Subtract; negative	$-$
Multiply	$\times$ or $\cdot$
Divide	$\div$
Plus or minus	$\pm$
Equals	$=$
Does not equal	$\neq$
Is approximately equal to	$\cong$ or $\approx$
Is less than	$<$
Is much less than	$\ll$
Is greater than	$>$
Is much greater than	$\gg$
Is greater than or equal to	$\geqq$ or $\geq$
Is less than or equal to	$\leqq$ or $\leq$
Absolute value	$\lvert \quad \rvert$
Perpendicular	$\perp$
Right angle	$\llcorner$
Angle	$>$ or $\angle$
Parallel	$\parallel$
Therefore	$\therefore$
Change of	$\triangle$
Proportional to	$\propto$
Infinity	∞

MATHEMATICS FOR ELECTRONICS

PRENTICE-HALL, Englewood Cliffs, New Jersey

MATHEMATICS

Charles M. Thomson

formerly
Senior Dean of Instruction Wentworth Institute and
Wentworth College of Technology, Boston, Mass.

FOR

ELECTRONICS

Library of Congress Cataloging in Publication Data

THOMSON, CHARLES M
   Mathematics for electronics.

   1. Electronics—Mathematics. I. Title.
TK7835. T48   510′ .2′462138   75–31921
ISBN 0–13–562629–3

MATHEMATICS FOR ELECTRONICS
Charles M. Thomson

10   9   8   7   6   5   4   3   2   1
Printed in the United States of America

PRENTICE-HALL INTERNATIONAL, INC., *London*
PRENTICE-HALL OF AUSTRALIA, PTY. LTD., *Sydney*
PRENTICE-HALL OF CANADA, LTD., *Toronto*
PRENTICE-HALL OF INDIA PRIVATE LIMITED, *New Delhi*
PRENTICE-HALL OF JAPAN, INC., *Tokyo*
PRENTICE-HALL OF SOUTH-EAST ASIA PTE. LTD., *Singapore*

for Dorothy

CONTENTS

3
OPERATIONS
WITH SIGNED NUMBERS 15

4
OPERATIONS
INVOLVING ALGEBRAIC
EXPRESSIONS 28

5
EQUATIONS
AND FORMULAS 37

6

SCIENTIFIC NOTATION, MEASUREMENTS AND UNITS 52

7

RESISTANCE 66

8

SERIES CIRCUIT 80

PREFACE

The study of electronics requires a sound knowledge of mathematics. This text is designed to provide such a background. It is a specialized mathematics text, in that the content is mathematics for electronics. The subject matter, arrangement, and development is directed toward one end—that of establishing the mathematical skills required for the study of electronics.

It is essential that students become knowledgeable in the language—mathematics—that is used in their field of specialization. This text provides more than just the necessary theory of mathematics: it is designed to establish a working knowledge of the mathematics of electronics.

The mathematical topics are blended with many practical applications and examples. The subject matter is developed in a logical and systematic manner. The content is arranged to follow the development of concurrently offered electronic theory courses of most program curricula. The book is, however, flexible in its arrangement, to provide for program variations and to meet the needs of the individual instructor.

This text is principally for technical institute and community college programs. It should also meet the needs of many technical high schools and preparatory schools that offer programs in electronics. It will find use, as well, in industrial electronics training programs. Although not intended primarily for self-instruction, the subject arrangement and presentation should make it suitable for that purpose.

The text provides a short review of arithmetic theory and procedures. The necessary algebraic background is then provided to support electronic theory as it is developed. Considerable time is spent in building a sound foundation in the methods, procedures, and techniques of handling dc and ac circuit operations and analysis. To assist in these methods, such topics as determinants and logarithms, and their applications are presented. A chapter on number systems has been provided because of the increased emphasis on the computer in the electronics curriculum.

The study of electronics will prove to be a fascinating one for most students. The study of mathematics, so interwoven with electronics theory, should also prove intriguing. It is hoped that this text will make these topics both interesting and rewarding.

The author is indebted to Mary Ellen Hatfield, Barbara Baum, and Joan Peters for their work on the manuscript.

CHARLES M. THOMSON

MATHEMATICS FOR ELECTRONICS

1

INTRODUCTION

Many mathematics texts are currently available. They vary in terms of level and content. They vary in terms of emphasis and direction. This text is written primarily for the student and the technician in the field of electronics. The level is directed toward the community college and the technical institute. The contents and emphasis are such that they will provide the necessary mathematical background for such educational programs.

1-1 MATHEMATICS—THE LANGUAGE OF ENGINEERING

Mathematics is the language of engineering—a precise language. With mathematics we can construct a tunnel several miles long, starting at each side of a mountain and meeting in the center with an error amounting to only a fraction of an inch. The language of mathematics enables space vehicles to land men on the moon and return them safely to earth with pinpoint accuracy.

Such examples point out the exact nature of mathematics as a language, a science that has developed through the centuries in a logical and systematic manner. From man's first counting procedures in the distant past to the blinding speed of the modern computer, the language of mathematics has evolved.

As you become more experienced with mathematics as an engineering technician you will find that your methods, procedures, and perhaps even your personality will change. You will become more systematic and logical. You will become more careful in drawing conclusions and accepting assumptions. In many ways, the precise and exact nature of mathematics, its logic, and its orderly procedures will "rub off" on you.

Exactness and precision will develop and you will take on some of the characteristics of this language. Some engineers are difficult to live with and work for because of their precise nature and their need to strive for perfection. To a lesser extent such traits affect the engineering technician. Although not usually a problem with which to be concerned, it does help to understand the behavior of ourselves and others in this field.

1-2 STUDY TECHNIQUES

Often an instructor, at the first meeting of a course, will outline the content and coverage of the entire program. At that time many of the topics mentioned will not be familiar. Such an introduction does provide the student with an idea of the nature and scope of the course. It will show you where you are now and where your studies will take you.

It will be helpful for you to examine the general content of the entire text, in a manner similar to the course introduction. In this way, you will become familiar with the arrangement of topics provided by the chapter headings. Examination of the detailed chapter breakdown will then show how the subject matter is presented. It should be observed that individual chapters and segments of chapters are developed in the same logical manner that the instructor outlined the course.

The above comments indicate that a systematic examination and analysis are desired. This is the most important procedure to follow in a homework assignment, a quiz, or a final examination. Such a systematic approach is often difficult to establish at first. It is, however, absolutely essential to develop such a study-and-evaluation technique if you want to make your work easier. A seemingly difficult problem will, when approached in this manner, yield a solution much more readily. With training and experience, such a systematic approach will become instinctive. At that point you will be well on your way to mastering the language of mathematics and establishing your competence as an electronic technician.

1–3 EXAMPLES

Numerous examples are used throughout the text. They serve to illustrate the particular procedure or method. You should pay close attention to these examples. They will be most helpful in understanding the specific subject and the technique involved.

It should be noted that the examples are chosen to illustrate a particular method. They should only be considered to be *typical* of the method used or the principle involved. In practice, many variations of a particular type of problem may exist. To provide examples of each would be time consuming and unnecessary. Your instructor will usually give you a quiz problem that is not an exact duplicate of a text example but a variation of the example. The basic principle involved in the solution is the same, however. In the process, the analysis and logical approach of the reader is desired. Through this process a practical reinforcement is obtained of the method and the principle involved.

1–4 PROBLEMS

As with examples, problems are used to show many of the variations of situations that can exist. Completion of the problem provides experience in the solving method. A problem is often related to a classroom theory or laboratory experiment. The problem thus serves to illustrate and emphasize a principle or an application. It should be evident, then, that it is to the reader's advantage to complete as many problems as possible. Solving problems:

1. Provides experience in problem-solving techniques.
2. Establishes a system of logical analysis that in time becomes instinctive.
3. Provides a reinforcement of classroom and laboratory theory and procedures.
4. Establishes a firm foundation for developing solutions to more complicated problems.
5. Provides a sound background for the solution of quiz and examination problems.

1–5 REVIEW

It is very helpful to review the material after a particular section of the text has been completed. In going through the material initially, the overall scheme may be missed. A review provides a way to look back to see how all the pieces fit in place. The material covered can then be put in its proper perspective as a part of the whole.

In a language course, learning a new word requires its repeated use. Lectures, examples, problems, and reviews are steps that are required in learning a new mathematical method or technical relationship. All are important in the process, but a review takes on the added significance of "putting it all together."

1–6 STANDARDIZATION

In many fields there are symbols, abbreviations, units, and shorthand methods. When a physician writes a prescription, he uses a number of symbols and abbreviations. These make the writing easier and enables the pharmacist to accurately fill the medical order.

In the electronics field similar practices are commonly used. There is not complete uniformity or agreement, however, on many of the symbols, abbreviations, units, and so on, used. In fact, agreement has not been reached on such basic ideas as the use of current or electron flow in electric circuits.

In this text we shall generally use the standards of the Institute of Electrical and Electronic Engineers (IEEE). This will provide a consistent treatment throughout the text. Although not uniformly accepted, these standards do perhaps have the widest acceptance of any used at the present time. You will no doubt find adequate examples of nonuniformity in other texts that you may currently be using. The important thing is to be aware of this situation and guard against misinterpretation of symbols, units, and conventions.

In this text, an accuracy of three significant figures will normally be more than adequate. This should be easily obtained in slide-rule operation. The small hand type of calculator, now replacing the slide rule, will provide accuracies far greater than are generally necessary.

Components in electronic circuits usually have tolerances that range from 5 to 20 percent. Transistors, vacuum tubes, and other devices also have wide operational variations. These are dependent on such things as temperature, age, circuit voltage, and normal production variations. These devices, when connected to their associated components, often produce circuit variations well in excess of individual tolerances. As a result, circuit-design procedures often approach "cut-and-try" methods. It should be obvious that for most procedures, carrying answers out beyond three places is generally a waste of time. In certain operations, greater accuracy is required; in such cases, the number of significant figures will be specified.

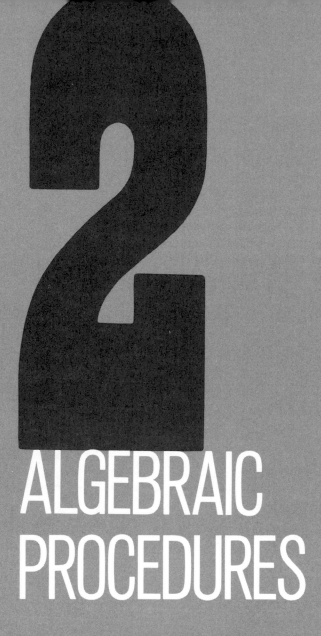

ALGEBRAIC
PROCEDURES

The arithmetic that you mastered in elementary school will not be adequate for the study of electricity and electronics. For this purpose, a background in the processes and procedures of algebra will be required. Algebra is essentially an extension of many of the basic principles of arithmetic. The use of algebra will allow the electrical and electronic circuits in our study to be analyzed and evaluated.

Algebra is a basic tool of the technician and engineer. Without algebra, many of the wonders in the world would not have been possible.

2-1 NUMBERS

In previous studies you have become familiar with the Roman *numeral* and the Arabic *number*. You know that the symbols V, VI, and VIII are the Roman-numeral representations of the numerical quantities 5, 6, and 8, which, in turn, are examples of Arabic number symbols.

2-2 LITERAL NUMBERS

The Arabic and Roman symbols represent a specific numerical value. In algebra, we shall be using letters or symbols to represent quantities. The value of these letters or symbols will be literal; that is, the numbers will have a general value, which may or may not be known. Such numbers are referred to as *literal numbers* or *general numbers*.

The resistance in a segment of an electrical circuit is represented by the letter R. This is shown in Figure 2-1. The letter R represents the general or literal value of the resistances shown in the circuit of Figure 2-1.

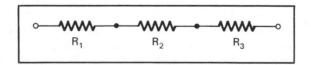

FIGURE 2-1
Schematic Representation of a Segment of an Electrical Circuit

The use of literal numbers permits an electrical law or circuit relationship to be stated easily. Ohm's law, a basic circuit theorem, states that the resistance of a circuit is directly proportional to the circuit voltage and inversely proportional to the circuit current. Using literal numbers, this may be expressed as

$$R = \frac{E}{I}$$

where the letters represent: R, resistance; E, voltage; and I, current. A written expression is lengthy and often difficult to understand. Expressed with literal numbers it is concise and much more easily understood.

2-3 EXPRESSIONS

As noted above, a mathematical relationship may be written using literal numbers. Such a relationship may also include numerical quantities. These written relationships are referred to as *algebraic expressions*. Such an expression may include numbers alone, literal numbers alone, or combinations of both. Examples:

$$3 + 5 - 7, \qquad 3A - 4B + C, \qquad A + C - D$$

2-4 SIGNS

In arithmetic we use the *signs* $+$, $-$, $\times$, and $\div$. These signs designate the operation involved. The same signs are used in algebra and have the same meaning. In algebra the symbol $\cdot$ may also be used to denote multiplication. Multiplication may also be indicated without using these two symbols, such as $x = wyz$. Multiplication, designated by each method described above, is shown in the following examples:

$$W = 2 \times P \times R$$
$$W = 2 \cdot P \cdot R$$
$$W = 2PR$$

An electrical circuit or an algebraic expression may use literal numbers to indicate different components of the same type. A circuit may require several hundred resistors, for example. A distinction between them is usually made by using subscripts, primes, or a combination. A subscript is a number or letter written as R_1, I_A, L_{302}, X_B. Primes are written R', X'', C'''.

2-5 TERMS

A *term* is that part of an algebraic expression that is not separated by a $+$ or $-$ sign. The term may consist of a numerical quantity, literal numbers, or a combination. In the expression

$$3 + 2A - CD$$

3, 2A, and CD are terms.

The number of terms in an algebraic expression results in the following designations:

MONOMIAL——*an expression with one term*

Examples: abc, $2x$, and $3cd$

BINOMIAL——*an expression with two terms*

Examples: $2ab + cd$ and $xy - 4z$

TRINOMIAL——*an expression with three terms*

Examples: $6xy + zb - 2A$ and $ab - bc + d$

POLYNOMIAL——*a general definition for expressions with two or more terms. It should be noted that the binomial and trinomial may be correctly designated as a polynomial.*

Examples: $2a + 3b$, $c + de - fg$, and $2h - jk + 3y + z$

2–6 COEFFICIENTS

In the examples of terms given above, the numerals that precede the literal number are known as *coefficients*, as in 6xy and 3b. A term without a numerical coefficient is understood to have a numerical coefficient of 1. For example, the term zb is understood to be 1zb.

2–7 FACTORS

In the term 3xy, a multiplication process is indicated. The numerical coefficient 3 and the literal numbers x and y are to be multiplied together to form a product. Any of these quantities, 3, x, or y, are designated as *factors of the product* 3xy. More specifically, when two or more numbers are multiplied together to form a product, those numbers are referred to as factors of the product.

2–8 SEQUENCE OF OPERATIONS

In giving directions for the operation of an electronic device, it is essential that the directions be accurate and that the reader interpret them *only* in the correct manner. This is also true in mathematics. For example, the evaluation of the following expression is shown.

$$A \times B + C$$

where $A = 2$, $B = 4$, and $C = 5$. Substitution of the numerical values is made. This then becomes $2 \times 4 + 5$. One might interpret this as meaning

---

2×4, which would be added to 5, which would result in a value of 13

Another might consider that

$4 + 5$ should be added first and then multiplied by 2; this would result in a value of 18

Obviously, then, a sequence for performing mathematical operations must be established. This will permit a common interpretation of meaning. As a result, the following rule must be followed:

> IN A SEQUENCE OF MATHEMATICAL OPERATIONS:
> FIRST PERFORM THE MULTIPLICATIONS AND DIVISIONS AND
> THEN THE ADDITIONS AND SUBTRACTIONS.

Following this sequence, in the expression

$$20 \times 5 + 6 - 5 + 10 \div 2$$

multiplication would first be performed. This would result in

$$100 + 6 - 5 + 10 \div 2$$

Next, division would produce

$$100 + 6 - 5 + 5$$

Then the addition and subtraction would result in an expression value of

$$106$$

2–9 SIGNS OF GROUPING

While previous procedures spelled out clearly the sequence in which operations are to be performed, these are often not sufficient. Suppose, for example, in the expression $2 \times 4 + 5$ that we actually wanted 4 to be added to 5 and the sum multiplied by 2. This could be done by using; ( ), *parentheses*; [ ], *brackets*; { }, *braces*; or ——, the *bar* or *vinculum*.

We could then write this expression as

$$2 \cdot (4 + 5) \text{ or } 2(4 + 5)$$

Using any of these signs of grouping enables us to treat the "group" as a whole. The operation indicated within the grouping is performed before any other procedure is carried out. An example is

$$\frac{(3 + 4)}{[6 - 3] - \{10 - 8\}}$$

Here all four signs of grouping are used. It should be observed that the vinculum or bar enables the fraction parts to be treated as a group. Evaluating this example we have

$$\frac{(3 + 4)}{[6 - 3] - \{10 - 8\}} = \frac{7}{3 - 2} = \frac{7}{1} = 7$$

The signs of grouping in an expression may be removed, if desired, by following these rules:

SIGNS OF GROUPING MAY BE REMOVED
IF PRECEDED BY A + SIGN, REMOVE THE GROUPING SIGN, LEAVING UNCHANGED THE SIGNS OF THE TERMS WITHIN.
IF PRECEDED BY A − SIGN, REMOVE THE GROUPING SIGN, CHANGING ALL THE TERMS WITHIN TO THE OPPOSITE SIGN.

The previous example will be used to show how the signs of grouping are removed. The signs of grouping will be removed prior to combining the terms within. The vinculum in this example, indicating division, could not be removed in such a manner. Using the original expression,

$$\frac{(3 + 4)}{[6 - 3] - \{10 - 8\}}$$

removing the signs of grouping following the rules above would produce

$$\frac{3 + 4}{6 - 3 - 10 + 8}$$

Evaluating,

$$\frac{7}{-13 + 14}, \quad \frac{7}{1}, \quad 7$$

As is seen, the evaluation of the expression is the same.

In some instances it may be easier to remove the grouping signs first. In other situations, it may be more convenient to perform the indicated procedures within the grouping signs.

The insertion of signs of grouping is a reverse procedure to the removal. A check for the correctness of insertion would be the removal, which must return the expression to the exact original form.

It must be remembered that the grouping signs are for a purpose and are not used haphazardly. The grouping signs direct that the terms within are to be treated as a group and that the operations indicated be performed in a particular manner.

2–10 EXPONENTS

An *exponent* is a number written above and to the right of a second number called the *base*: such as R^3, where 3 is the exponent or power and R is the base. The use of exponents merely means that the base is taken as a factor the number of times designated by the exponent. For example, Z^5 means $Z \cdot Z \cdot Z \cdot Z \cdot Z$. The use of exponents provides a much more convenient means of expression.

At this point it would be well to point out that any base or number (except zero) that has a zero exponent is equal to 1. For example, $2^0 = 1$, $3^0 = 1$, $x^0 = 1$.

2–11 RECIPROCALS

Reciprocals will often be used in electronics. Examples of reciprocals may be represented as $\frac{1}{R}, \frac{1}{C}$, and $\frac{1}{X_L}$. A *reciprocal*, then, is merely 1 divided by the particular number involved.

2–12 RADICAL SIGNS

In your previous mathematical studies you became familiar with the *radical sign*, $\sqrt{}$. It was used to designate the root of a number, such as $\sqrt{81}$, $\sqrt[3]{27}$, and $\sqrt[h]{x}$. These would be expressed as the square root of 81, the cube root of 27, and the hth root of x. In algebra the radical sign is treated as it was in elementary mathematics.

An algebraic expression is made up of numerical and literal numbers. It may include any or all of the signs, symbols, and operations previously discussed. The *evaluation* of an algebraic expression merely means determining its numerical value. In this process, the designated operations in the indicated sequence must be performed after a substitution of values for the literal numbers is made. The end result is to obtain a numerical value for the expression.

example 2-1   Determine the value of $6\pi D$ when $D = 2$ and $\pi = 3.14$.

solution: $6\pi D = 6 \cdot 3.14 \cdot 2 = 37.68$

example 2-2   Determine the value of $(15xy - 4xz)$, where $x = 2$, $y = 3$, and $z = 4$.

solution: $15xy - 4xz = 15 \cdot 2 \cdot 3 - 4 \cdot 2 \cdot 4 = 90 - 32 = 58$

example 2-3   Evaluate $\dfrac{1}{R} + \sqrt{16} - Rx$, where $R = 2$ and $x = 1$.

solution: $\dfrac{1}{R} + \sqrt{16} - Rx = \dfrac{1}{2} + 4 - 2 \cdot 1 = 0.5 + 4 - 2$

$$= 2.5$$

example 2-4   Evaluate $3xy + 2x_1y_1 + x^2$, where $x = 2$, $y = 3$, $x_1 = 4$, and $y_1 = 5$.

solution: $3xy + 2x_1y_1 + x^2 = 3 \cdot 2 \cdot 3 + 2 \cdot 4 \cdot 5 + 2^2$
$$= 18 + 40 + 4 = 62$$

EXERCISE   2-1   Evaluate the following expressions.
1.   If $x = 3$, $y = 4$, $z = 5$:
$x + 4y - 3z + 6x$

2.   If $A = 4$, $B = 5$, $C = 6$:
$A + B^2 + \sqrt{C^2}$

3.   If $x = 5$, $y = 7$, $z = 8$:
$(x + y) - 6(y + z)$

4.   If $A = 2$, $B = 4$, $C = 8$:
$(C - B)^2 + (C + A)^2$

5.   If $x = 6$, $y = 7$, $z = 10$:
$\sqrt{(z^2 - x^2)} + x^2 + (x + 2y^2)$

6.   If $A = 12$, $B = 14$, $C = 13$:
$(A + 3B)(B - A)^2 + 3AB^2C$

7. If $x = 0.25$, $y = 1.62$, $z = 3.40$:
$$\frac{3x^2y^2z^2}{x^3}$$

8. If $A = 1\frac{5}{8}$, $B = 0.72$, $C = 4.1$:
$$\frac{1}{A^2} + \frac{2}{B^2} + \frac{3}{C} + 2AB$$

3

OPERATIONS WITH SIGNED NUMBERS

In electricity and electronics, negative quantities must often be used. Your previous studies of mathematics probably did not involve negative numbers. Of necessity, then, a familiarity with mathematical operations involving both positive and negative numbers must be established. These are called *signed numbers*. This chapter will deal with the addition, subtraction, multiplication, and division of signed numbers.

3-1 CONCEPT OF NEGATIVE NUMBERS

Sea level is used as reference from which to express the height of mountains. Using this same reference, the depths under the ocean may also be expressed. Rather than indicate the height or depth as so many feet above or below sea level, positive or negative numbers—signed numbers—may be used. For example, a mountaintop may be +2800 feet (ft) while a particular ocean depth may be −850 ft.

In our home thermometers, one reference level used is 0° F. The temperature on a warm day might be +80° F. Normally, the + is understood and not used. A very cold day would be ten degrees below zero, −10° F.

In electronics an often-used device is a voltage divider. A typical arrangement is shown in Figure 3–1. Point B in the figure is chosen as the reference level, or ground. Point A is +200 volts (V) above this reference. Point C is −200 V below, and point D is −400 V below.

It is important to observe that a quantity is considered positive or negative relative to the reference point chosen. In the voltage divider of Figure 3–1, point B was chosen as the reference. Point C, or any other point in the circuit, could have as easily been used as the reference. Figure 3–2 shows the voltages with C used as the reference point. This change of reference point results in +400 V existing between points A and C, +200 V between B and C, and −200 V between C and D.

At this point it would be well to bring up the concept of absolute values. The *absolute value* of a number is its numerical value without concern for sign. The absolute value of the voltages in Figure 3–2 between points CB and CD would be 200 V. Often absolute values are designated by vertical bars, such as |200|.

It is important to remember that the voltage shown in these figures is a potent force whether considered positive or negative. The magnitudes, represented by the absolute values, are useful voltages. They are available for chosen electronic operations. It also should be added that a voltage, regardless of the positive or negative designation,

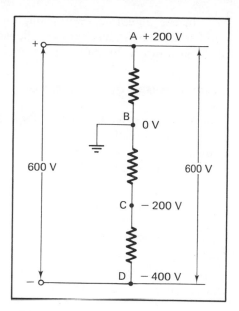

FIGURE 3-1
Typical Voltage Divider

is a dangerous and possible lethal force. In this regard, a technician or engineer is always concerned with the absolute value of voltage, as it represents the magnitude of this force.

FIGURE 3-2
Voltage Divider with Point *C* as Reference

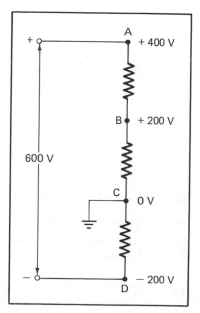

In the algebraic relationships used in electronics, the negative number, as shown, has both significance and purpose. This is also true of the absolute value of the number.

3–2 ADDITION OF SIGNED NUMBERS WITH LIKE SIGNS

It is helpful in explaining operations involving signed numbers to use a graphical approach. In Figure 3–3 numbers with positive signs are shown to the right of the zero reference, and numbers with negative signs are shown to the left.

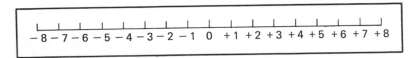

FIGURE 3–3
Graphical Representation of Signed Numbers

The addition of two numbers, each of which has a positive sign, is shown in Figure 3–4. As in arithmetic, we simply add one quantity to the other. This is shown by adding +2 and +6, which of course results in 8.

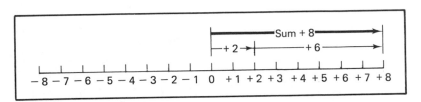

FIGURE 3–4
Graphical Addition of +2 and +6

The addition of two negative numbers, −3 and −4, is shown in Figure 3–5. As with positive signed numbers, the total is obtained in a similar manner. Only the direction is changed.

FIGURE 3–5
Graphical Addition of −3 and −4

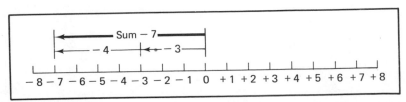

From these examples the following rule is developed:

> ADDITION OF SIGNED NUMBERS OF LIKE SIGN:
> ADD THE NUMBERS AND PREFIX THE COMMON SIGN.

Using this rule, complete the following exercise. Check the results graphically if desired.

EXERCISE 3–1 Add the following signed numbers.

1. $+11$
   $+\ 8$

2. -16
   -32

3. -53
   -24

4. $+14$
   $+39$

5. $+82$
   $+12$

6. -41
   -41

7. $+402$
   $+\ \ 36$

8. $+176$
   $+301$

3–3 ADDITION OF SIGNED NUMBERS WITH UNLIKE SIGNS

Figure 3–6 shows how -7 and $+9$ are added. The -7 is first placed on the scale as indicated. From the -7 point, the $+9$ is placed in the positive direction. This results in a $+2$ sum.

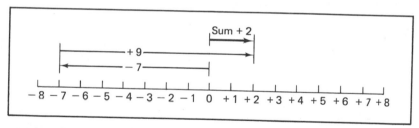

FIGURE 3–6
Graphical Addition of -7 and $+9$

The addition of $+6$ and -9 is shown in Figure 3–7. The solution is obtained in a manner similar to that shown in Figure 3–6. This results in a sum of -3.

It should be noted that either quantity may be placed on the graph first. In Figure 3–7, the -9 quantity could have been placed initially, followed by the $+6$. The result would, of course, be the same, -3.

From these examples, the following rule results:

> ADDITION OF SIGNED NUMBERS OF UNLIKE SIGN:
> SUBTRACT THE NUMBER WITH THE SMALLER ABSOLUTE
> VALUE FROM THE LARGER, AND PREFIX THE RESULT WITH THE
> SIGN OF THE NUMBER WITH THE LARGER ABSOLUTE VALUE.

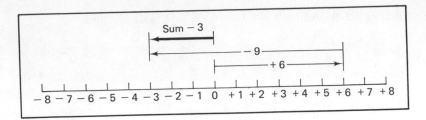

FIGURE 3–7
Graphical Addition of +6 and −9

EXERCISE 3–2 Add the following signed numbers.

1. $+\ 8$
   -12

2. -32
   $+\ 3$

3. $+15$
   -15

4. -37
   $+85$

5. -23
   $+\ 2$

6. $-\ 74$
   $+107$

7. $+56$
   -57

8. $+\ 66$
   -126

If it is desired to add more than two numbers with unlike signs, it is merely necessary to add all the numbers with like signs together and then proceed as above.

For example:

$$-20$$
$$+32$$
$$-47$$

Solution: Adding the two negative numbers,

$$-20$$
$$-47$$
$$-67$$

we then have

$$-67$$
$$+32$$

which results in −35

EXERCISE 3–3 Add the following signed numbers.

1.   − 20
     − 24
     + 2

2.   + 7.28
     − 23.2
     + 30.1

3.   − 7
     − 12
     − 14
     + 30

4.   + 6.2
     − 7.5
     − 7.0
     + 8.3

5.   + 107
     − 103
     + 74

6.   − 6
     − 76
     + 12
     + 4

7.   − 32
     + 15
     + 17
     + 16

8.   − 16
     − 47
     + 55
     − 65

3–4 SUBTRACTION OF SIGNED NUMBERS

In elementary school, subtraction is usually considered to be a procedure for determining what number has to be added to the subtrahend to equal the value of the minuend. The number that has to be added is called the *remainder*. As an example,

7 minuend
3 subtrahend
4 remainder

where 4 was found to be the number that had to be added to 3 to equal the minuend, 7.

The same procedure is used to perform the subtraction of signed numbers. Figure 3–8 shows how graphical procedures are used in the subtraction (+7) − (+3). First measure seven units positive and then three units positive. The number that must be added is found by counting the difference between the 3 and the 7 units. The answer, the remainder, is 4.

This graphical procedure may also be used with negative signed numbers. As an example, (−8) − (+2), where

− 8 minuend
+ 2 subtrahend
    remainder

FIGURE 3–8
Graphical Subtraction (+7) − (+3)

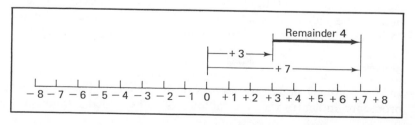

As before, measure off eight units in the negative direction and then two units in the positive direction (Figure 3–9). Measure the difference between the −8 and the +2. The answer is 10. In this instance the remainder is a −10, because a −10 has to be added to the subtrahend to equal the minuend.

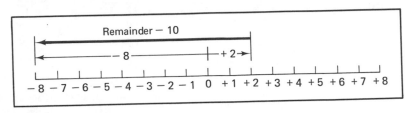

FIGURE 3–9
Graphical Subtraction (−8) − (+2)

Examination of the graphical procedures shown results in the following rule for subtraction of signed numbers:

> SUBTRACTION OF SIGNED NUMBERS:
> CHANGE THE SIGN OF THE SUBTRAHEND AND THEN ADD.

EXERCISE 3–4   Complete the following problems.

1.
$$\begin{array}{r} 56 \\ -20 \end{array}$$

2.
$$\begin{array}{r} -36 \\ 27 \end{array}$$

3.
$$\begin{array}{r} -72 \\ -51 \end{array}$$

4.
$$\begin{array}{r} 67.52 \\ -35.07 \end{array}$$

5.
$$\begin{array}{r} 45\frac{3}{8} \\ -32\frac{5}{8} \end{array}$$

6.
$$\begin{array}{r} 0.0752 \\ -1.370 \end{array}$$

7. In the voltage divider of Figure 3–1, what voltage difference exists between points A and C?

8. What temperature variation occurred in White Lake, Ontario, if the lowest winter temperature was −62° F and the highest summer temperature was +102° F?

3–5 MULTIPLICATION OF SIGNED NUMBERS

As in arithmetic, multiplication is essentially a process of adding a number the indicated number of times. Here, however, we will refer to the numbers to be multiplied together as factors (see Section 2–7).

example

In 3×5, the 3 and 5 are factors of the product. The multiplication procedure indicates that the factor 5 is to be added 3 times, $3 \times 5 =$

$5 + 5 + 5 = 15$, which is called the *product*. In 5×3 this would mean:
$5 \times 3 = 3 + 3 + 3 + 3 + 3 = 15$.

We will now show how multiplication would be depicted graphically. As an example, 2×4 would be shown as in Figure 3-10.

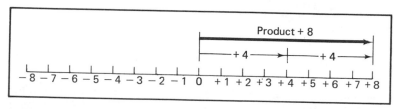

FIGURE 3-10
Graphical Multiplication +2 × +4

If one of the signed numbers were negative, as in 2×-4, this would be shown graphically as in Figure 3-11.

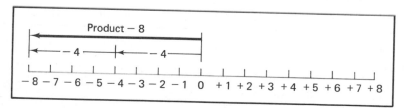

FIGURE 3-11
Graphical Multiplication +2 × -4

If, instead, we had to multiply $-4 \times +2$, this would be a problem to depict graphically. However, $+4 \times +2$ could be multiplied, which is easily shown on a graph as in Figure 3-12.

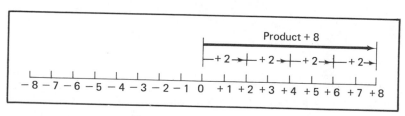

FIGURE 3-12
Graphical Multiplication +4 · +2

What would be the result if we multiplied this product by -1? This could be represented as $+8 \times -1$ and shown graphically as in Figure 3-13.

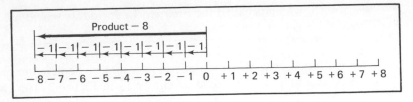

FIGURE 3–13
Graphical Multiplication +8 · −1

As a result of this procedure, we have only changed the graphical direction of the product from + to −. The magnitude remains unchanged, and the answer to −4 × +2 is −8. In effect, the multiplication by −1 caused a rotation on the graph of 180°. This procedure of rotation will be very useful in later work.

The process described permits multiplication to be depicted graphically. Adding 2 −4 times would not be possible graphically. The multiplication by −1 changes only the graphical direction and permits us to show this multiplication graphically. This process may be used whenever convenient.

The following rules for multiplication result from the preceding examples:

> MULTIPLICATION OF TWO FACTORS
>   WITH LIKE SIGNS: RESULTS IN A POSITIVE PRODUCT.
>   WITH UNLIKE SIGNS: RESULTS IN A NEGATIVE PRODUCT.

If three or more factors are involved, the above rules may be used successively, or, for simplicity:

> MULTIPLICATION OF THREE OR MORE FACTORS WITH AN ODD NUMBER OF NEGATIVE FACTORS RESULTS IN A NEGATIVE PRODUCT.
>
> MULTIPLICATION OF AN EVEN NUMBER OF NEGATIVE FACTORS (OR IF ALL FACTORS ARE POSITIVE) RESULTS IN A POSITIVE PRODUCT.

EXERCISE 3–5   Multiply the following factors.

1. −32, −26
2. −13.5, +12.2
3. −327, −26, −16
4. −37, −16, −14, −12
5. −12, +12, −2
6. −0.72, −0.36
7. +3, −7, +2, −16
8. −2.5, −4.5, −6.75

In Section 2–8, exponents were discussed. It was explained that Z^5, Z to the fifth power, means $Z \cdot Z \cdot Z \cdot Z \cdot Z$. If we were to multiply $Z^5 \cdot Z^4$, this would mean $Z \cdot Z \cdot Z \cdot Z \cdot Z \cdot Z \cdot Z \cdot Z \cdot Z = Z^9$, and $x^2 \cdot x^4$ would be $x \cdot x \cdot x \cdot x \cdot x \cdot x$, a result equal to x^6. From this, the following rule results:

> MULTIPLICATION OF POWERS WITH THE SAME BASE:
> ADD THE EXPONENTS, AS IN $X^a \cdot X^b = X^{a+b}$.

EXERCISE 3–6 Multiply the following powers with the same base.

1. $X^5 \cdot X^6 \cdot X^7$ 2. $X \cdot X^2 \cdot X^4$ 3. $2^x \cdot 2^y$ 4. $w^5 \cdot w^6$

5. $5^3 \cdot 5^8$ 6. $Z^y \cdot Z^x$ 7. $4^2 \cdot 4^y \cdot 4^x$ 8. $a^2 \cdot a^3$

As with arithmetic, in algebra, division is the inverse of the process of multiplication. This reverse process may, if desired, be depicted graphically. However, the following discussion should make this unnecessary.

Recalling from arithmetic, the following represents the division process:

$$\frac{\text{dividend}}{\text{divisor}} = \text{quotient}$$

In dividing $\frac{12}{3} = 4$, it is known that the divisor, 3, multiplied by the quotient, 4, must equal the dividend, 12. From the relationships of the multiplication process, the rules for the division of signed numbers may be developed.

In multiplication it is known that:

$$+3 \cdot +4 = +12$$

$$-3 \cdot +4 = -12$$

$$+3 \cdot -4 = -12$$

$$-3 \cdot -4 = +12$$

Then in division:

$$\frac{+12}{+3} = +4$$

$$\frac{-12}{-3} = +4$$

$$\frac{-12}{+3} = -4$$

$$\frac{+12}{-3} = -4$$

This results in the following rule:

> THE DIVISION OF SIGNED NUMBERS WITH LIKE SIGNS:
> RESULTS IN A POSITIVE QUOTIENT.
>
> THE DIVISION OF SIGNED NUMBERS WITH UNLIKE SIGNS:
> RESULTS IN A NEGATIVE QUOTIENT.

EXERCISE 3–7   Divide the following signed numbers.

1. -31 by -27
2. $-\frac{3}{5}$ by $-\frac{1}{8}$
3. -0.72 by -4.7
4. $+6.56$ by 3.75
5. $+E$ by $+R$
6. $+1.72$ by $+0.34$
7. -6.42 by -3.50
8. -15.07 by -16.27

At this point, it would be well to point out that division by zero has no significance. In the example,

$$\frac{+12}{0} =$$

it is known in multiplication that there is no number that we can multiply by 0 which will equal 12.

3–8   DIVISION INVOLVING EXPONENTS

In Section 3–7, it was observed that $Z^5 \cdot Z^4 = Z^9$. The division of $\frac{Z^5}{Z^4}$ may be written

$$\frac{Z^5}{Z^4} = \frac{Z \cdot Z \cdot Z \cdot Z \cdot Z}{Z \cdot Z \cdot Z \cdot Z}$$

which, if the common factors in the numerator and denominator are canceled, would result in

$$\frac{Z^5}{Z^4} = Z^1 \quad \text{or} \quad = Z$$

In checking the division, the multiplication of the quotient times the divisor, $Z^1 \cdot Z^4$, must equal the dividend, Z^5, which of course it does.

From this relationship, the following rule results:

> DIVISION OF POWERS WITH THE SAME BASE: SUBTRACT THE EXPONENTS, AS IN $\frac{X^a}{X^b} = X^{a-b}$

EXERCISE 3–8 Divide the following powers with the same base.

1. X^{17} by X^4
2. 5^3 by 5^2
3. 2^x by 2^y
4. w^{15} by w^{11}
5. a^{14} by a^{12}
6. Z^y by Z^x
7. 16^4 by 16^2
8. X^5 by X^3

3–9 DIVISION INVOLVING NEGATIVE EXPONENTS

If instead of $\frac{Z^5}{Z^4}$ as above, the example were $\frac{Z^4}{Z^5}$, we would have $\frac{Z \cdot Z \cdot Z \cdot Z}{Z \cdot Z \cdot Z \cdot Z \cdot Z}$. Canceling the common factors as above results in $\frac{Z^4}{Z^5} = \frac{1}{Z}$; or, put another way, by subtracting exponents $\frac{Z^4}{Z^5} = Z^{4-5} = Z^{-1}$.

It is seen that $\frac{1}{Z}$ is equivalent to Z^{-1}.

From this relationship, the following rule results:

> A BASE WITH A NEGATIVE EXPONENT MAY BE EXPRESSED AS THE RECIPROCAL OF THE BASE WITH A POSITIVE EXPONENT.

EXERCISE 3–9 Express the following powers in a different form.

1. Z^{-5}
2. 3^{-23}
3. $\frac{1}{3^{23}}$
4. X^{-15}
5. $\frac{1}{a^5}$
6. a^{-b}
7. $\frac{1}{14^3}$
8. b_1^{-16}

4

OPERATIONS INVOLVING ALGEBRAIC EXPRESSIONS

$\mathbf{W}$e shall now use the background developed in Chapter 3 involving signed numbers to establish a familiarity with single- and multiterm algebraic relationships. This chapter will deal with expressions that contain both numerical and literal quantities. These operations will involve algebraic expressions that contain a single term, the *monomial*; and two or more terms, the *polynomial*. We shall be involved with the addition, subtraction, multiplication, and division of these terms.

4–1 ADDITION OF ALGEBRAIC EXPRESSIONS

In arithmetic, quantities that are to be added must be the same: the addition of oranges and kilowatt-hours does not make sense. Neither does it make sense in algebra. The terms for algebraic addition must be the same. However, in algebra the addition of unlike terms may be indicated through the use of literal numbers, as in $E_T = I_1 R_1 + I_1 R_2$.

The addition of single- and multiterm expressions follows the same rules as those developed for signed numbers. The following examples show the addition of monomials with like terms.

example 4–1	$6xyz$	*example 4–2*	$4abc$	*example 4–3*	$-6pq$
	$-3xyz$		$-8abc$		$-4pq$
solution:	$+3xyz$		$-4abc$		$-10pq$

The following examples show the addition of monomials with unlike terms.

example 4–4	$-4AB$	*example 4–5*	$8xyz$
	$6BC$		$-10xyz$
	$10AB$		$3zy$
solution:	$6AB + 6BC$		$-2xyz + 3zy$

example 4–6	$3A$
	$-4B$
	$6C$
solution:	$3A - 4B + 6C$

The addition of polynomials follows similar rules. Care must be used, however, to group similar terms where possible.

The following examples show the addition of polynomials:

example 4–7

$$\begin{array}{r} 6AB + 4BC \\ -3AB - 2BC \\ \hline \end{array}$$

solution: $3AB + 2BC$

example 4–8

$$\begin{array}{r} 5CD + 4D - EF \\ -14CD - 2D + 3EF \\ \hline -9CD + 2D + 2EF \end{array}$$

example 4–9

$$\begin{array}{r} 4x + 2y - 3z \\ 6x - 4z \\ \hline \end{array}$$

solution: $10x + 2y - 7z$

EXERCISE 4–1   Add the following expressions.

1. $3a - 4y,\ -6a + y$

2. $a + 6b,\ -3a - 6b$

3. $16x - 4y,\ -12x + 3y + z$

4. $2m - 3n + 6p,\ -3m + 4p,\ 2m - 2n - p$

5. $10R - 6Z,\ -5R + 4T - 5Z,\ 4T - 10R$

6. $12x - 3y + 4z,\ -3x - 3y + 4z,\ 15x - 7y - 8z$

7. $0.25R - \frac{3}{5}X + 1.27V,\ -3.50V + 17R - \frac{50}{5}X$

8. $3A - 4D + C,\ 2B - 6C + 2F$

4–2 SUBTRACTION OF ALGEBRAIC EXPRESSIONS

As with addition, subtraction follows the rules for signed numbers developed previously. Here also, where possible, like terms must be grouped.
    The following are examples of the subtraction of monomials.

example 4–10

$$\begin{array}{r} -6ay \\ -4ay \\ \hline \end{array}$$

solution: $-2ay$

example 4–11

$$\begin{array}{r} 13azy \\ 12azy \\ \hline azy \end{array}$$

example 4–12

$$\begin{array}{r} 12ax \\ -16ax \\ \hline 28ax \end{array}$$

The following are examples of the subtraction of polynomials.

example 4–13

$$\begin{array}{r} 3a + 3b \\ -a + 2b \\ \hline \end{array}$$

solution: $4a + b$

example 4–14

$$\begin{array}{r} 6x - 3y + z \\ -4x - y + z \\ \hline 10x - 2y \end{array}$$

example 4–15

$$\begin{array}{r} 6c - 4d + e \\ -c + 5e \\ \hline \end{array}$$

solution: $7c - 4d - 4e$

example 4–16

$$\begin{array}{r} 5a + 6c \\ 6a - 4b - c \\ \hline -a + 4b + 7c \end{array}$$

EXERCISE 4-2 Perform the indicated operations.

1. Subtract $6a - 4b$ from $-16a + 16b$.
2. Subtract $-3ab + 2bc - 3cd$ from $-16ab - 16bc - cd$.
3. Subtract $-3ac$ from ac.
4. Subtract $16a - 15b - 16c$ from $a + b + c$.
5. Subtract $15x + 14y$ from $12x - 2y + 17z$.
6. Subtract $4c + 2d - 6e$ from $-7c - 17e$.
7. Subtract $2a - 6b + 4c - 2d$ from $-16a + 2d$.
8. Subtract $37xyz - 12z$ from $17z - 27xyz$.

4-3 MULTIPLICATION OF ALGEBRAIC EXPRESSIONS

The rules that were developed previously for the multiplication of signed numbers apply here also. The following example shows the multiplication of two monomials.

example 4-17 Multiply $6x$ by $-3x^2$.

solution: *First:* multiply the signed numbers (the numerical co-efficients) together, following the rules for signed numbers. *Second:* the literal factors are multiplied together following the rules for multiplication of exponents. *Third:* the results of the first and second operations are combined:

$$6x \cdot -3x^2$$

First: multiply 6 by $-3 = -18$.
Second: multiply x by $x^2 = x^{1+2} = x^3$.
Third: combine: $-18x^3$

example 4-18 $-16a^2b^2 \cdot -2a^3b^2$.

solution: First: $-16 \cdot -2 = 32$
Second: $a^2b^2 \cdot a^3b^2 = a^{2+3} \cdot b^{2+2} = a^5b^4$
Third: $32a^5b^4$

example 4-19 $-4ax^2 \cdot -3x^3$.

solution: $12ax^5$

EXERCISE 4-3 Perform the following operations.

1. $2x \cdot -13x^2$
2. $-2a \cdot -3a$
3. $-12xyz \cdot 3x^2y^2z^2$
4. $ab \cdot ab^2$

5. $-3ax \cdot 16a^2y$

7. $3b^2c \cdot -4b \cdot 3abc^2$

6. $-15ay \cdot 4a^2yz$

8. $(4x)^2 \cdot -3x$

The multiplication of a polynomial by a monomial is a successive procedure. Each of the terms of the polynomial is multiplied by the monomial in succession. This is really the multiplication of monomials by monomials, in successive steps. When completed, the individual products are combined.

example 4–20 Multiply $3a - 4b$ multiplicand
                      by $3a$ multiplier

solution: This would result in $9a^2 - 12ab$ product

example 4–21 Multiply $-2x - 3y + 4z$
                      by $-3xy$

solution: $6x^2y + 9xy^2 - 12xyz$

EXERCISE 4-4 Multiply the following expressions.

1. $3x - 4y$ by $-2y$

2. $3xy + 4z$ by -3

3. $-2a + 4b - 3c^2$ by $-3ab$

4. $-b - c - d$ by $3a$

5. $3x - 4y$ by $(2x)^2$

6. $7ab + 8cd - ef + gh^2$ by $-4aef$

7. $6a^2b^2c^2 + 15a^3b^4c^5$ by $-a^5b^4c^6$

8. $12ax^3 + 3y^2 - 6z + 2xz$ by $3azy$

The multiplication of a polynomial by a polynomial is also a successive procedure. Here each term of multiplicand is multiplied successively by each term of the multiplier. The results are combined in the product.

example 4–22 Multiply $3a + 4b$ by $-3a - 4b$.

solution:

$$3a + 4b$$
$$-3a - 4b$$
$$\overline{-9a^2 - 12ab} \qquad \text{multiplication of } 3a + 4b \text{ by term } -3a$$
$$\quad -12ab - 16b^2 \quad \text{multiplication of } 3a + 4b \text{ by term } -4b$$
$$\overline{-9a^2 - 24ab - 16b^2} \quad \text{combined resultant product}$$

example 4-23 Multiply $5x - 6y - 7z$ by $-x + 3y$.

solution:
$$
\begin{array}{l}
5x \;-\; 6y \;-\; 7z \\
\underline{ -\; x \;+\; 3y} \\
-5x^2 \;+\; 6xy \;+\; 7xz \\
\underline{ +\; 15xy -\; 18y^2 \;-\; 21yz} \\
-5x^2 \;+\; 21xy \;+\; 7xz \;-\; 18y^2 \;-\; 21yz
\end{array}
$$

EXERCISE 4-5 Multiply the following expressions.

1. $3x + 4y$ by $-x - y$
2. $3a + 2b$ by $-a + 6b$
3. $x + y + z$ by $3a + 4b$
4. $a + 2$ by $a - 2$
5. $x + 3y - 2$ by $x + y$
6. $a^2 + b^2$ by $a^2 - b^2$
7. $x + y + z^2$ by $x - y^2$
8. $3a + 4b + c$ by $a - b + c$

4-4 DIVISION OF ALGEBRAIC EXPRESSIONS

The division of algebraic expressions is an extension of the division procedures developed for signed numbers and exponents.

The division of the monomial $48x^4y^5z^6$ by $-12x^2y^3z^3$ requires

First: division of the numerical coefficients, the signed numbers, prefixing the resulting sign.

Second: division of individual literal numbers using the rules for the division of powers, and writing the resulting exponent.

Third: combining.

example 4-24 Divide $48x^4y^5z^6$ by $-12x^2y^3z^3$.

solution:
First: divide 48 by $-12 = -4$.
Second: divide $x^4y^5z^6$ by $x^2y^3z^3 = x^2y^2z^3$.
Third: combine: $-4x^2y^2z^3$

example 4-25 Divide $35a^5b^3c^4$ by $-5a^3b^2c^6$.

solution:
First: divide 35 by $-5 = -7$.
Second: divide $a^5b^3c^4$ by $a^3b^2c^6 = a^2bc^{-2}$.
Third: combine: $-7a^2bc^{-2}$

example 4-26 Divide $40d^6e^7f^3$ by $-8d^2e^5f^8$

solution:
First: divide 40 by $-8 = -5$
Second: divide $d^6e^7f^3$ by $d^2e^5f^8 = d^4e^2f^{-5}$
Third: combine: $-5d^4e^2f^{-5}$

Here it would be more appropriate to express the negative exponent of f as a positive exponent as $\dfrac{-5d^4e^2}{f^5}$.

example 4-27 Divide $-15m^3p^4t^3$ by $-3mp^2t^3$.

solution: $5m^2p^2$

EXERCISE 4-6   Divide the following expressions and express all answers with positive exponents.

1. $20a^7bc$ by $5a^5bc$ 2. $35.2d^2e^3f^6$ by $15.4d^3e^4f^5$

3. $0.7x^6y^5z^3$ by $0.3x^4y^3z^2$ 4. $-\frac{3}{5}a^2x^2z^3y^3$ by $-\frac{5}{6}a^2x^2z^3y^4$

5. $-14m^2n^2p^2$ by $-13m^3n^3p^3$ 6. $-0.625x^2y^3z^5$ by $0.327x^3y^4z^6$

7. $-0.0032a^3b^4d^5e^6f^7$ by $0.0017a^3b^5d^6e^3f^2$

8. $3.3xbe$ by $-4.35x^2b^2e^2$

The *division of a polynomial by a monomial* is a successive procedure. Here each of the terms of the polynomial, the dividend, is divided by the monomial, the divisor. The result of each division is written in succession, which of course is the quotient.

example 4-28 Divide $35x^5y^3 - 40x^4y^4$ by $-5xy$.

solution: First: divide $35x^5y^3$ by $-5xy = -7x^4y^2$.
Second: divide $-40x^4y^4$ by $-5xy = +8x^3y^3$.
Third: combine: $-7x^4y^2 + 8x^3y^3$

example 4-29 Divide $15a^4b^2c^6 - 5a^2bc^2$ by $5a^2bc^4$.

solution: First: divide $15a^4b^2c^6$ by $5a^2bc^4 = 3a^2bc^2$.
Second: divide $-5a^2bc^2$ by $5a^2bc^4 = -c^{-2}$.
Third: combine: $3a^2bc^2 - c^{-2}$

Expressed with positive exponents,

$$3a^2bc^2 - \frac{1}{c^2}$$

EXERCISE 4-7   Divide the following expressions and express all answers with positive exponents.

1. $-30a^2b^2c^2 + 10a^3b^3c^3$ by $5abc$ 2. $-15x^2y^2 + 3xy$ by $-3xy$

3. $-21a^4c^5x^6 - 28a^6c^5x^4$ by $-7a^5c^6x^7$

4. $-3a^2b^4c^6 + 4a^3b^5c^7 - 5a^4b^6c^8$ by $5a^2b^2c^2$

5. $3AB(B^2 + A^2B^2)$ by $-3AB$

6. $4xyz(-3x^2y^2z^2 - 12x^3y^3z^3)$ by $-3x^2y^2z^2$

7. $0.72xy^3 + 1.51xy^3 - 1.40xy^3$ by $0.32x^2y^5$

8. $4.7L_1^5L_2^6L_3^7 + 5.6L_1^8L_2^9L_3^6$ by $15L_1^2L_2^3L_3^4$

The division of a polynomial by a polynomial is similar to the process of long division in arithmetic. It will be recalled that in dividing

$$520)\overline{6520}$$

first 520 is divided into 652:

$$\frac{1}{520)\overline{6520}}$$
$$\underline{520\downarrow}$$
$$1320$$

Then multiply the quotient 1 by the divisor 520, subtract, and bring down a zero to form a new dividend.

$$12\frac{280}{520}$$
$$520)\overline{6520}$$
$$\underline{520}$$
$$1320$$
$$\underline{1040}$$
$$280$$

Next, dividing the new dividend by the divisor results in a new quotient figure, 2, which is multiplied by the divisor. This results in a remainder of 280, which is expressed as shown.

The divison of one polynomial by another is performed in the same manner.

example 4–30 Divide $5A^2 + 25A + 20$ by $A + 1$.

solution:

$$\begin{array}{r} 5A + 20 \\ A + 1)\overline{5A^2 + 25A + 20} \\ \underline{5A^2 + 5A} \\ 20A + 20 \\ \underline{20A + 20} \end{array}$$

As in arithmetic, to check a division the divisor is multiplied by the quotient. In this example, $5A + 20$ is multiplied by $A + 1$. This results in $5A^2 + 25A + 20$, the original dividend, which indicates the correctness of the division.

A further comment at this point: note that the dividend is arranged in descending powers. This should be done for both the divisor and dividend prior to division. If more convenient, you may arrange both the divisor and dividend in ascending powers of a common factor.

example 4-31 Divide $A^4 - 4$ by $A^2 - 2$.

solution:

$$
\require{enclose}
\begin{array}{r}
A^2 + 2 \\[-2pt]
\hline
A^2 - 2 \,\enclose{longdiv}{A^4 + \ldots + \ldots + \ldots - 4} \\
\underline{A^4 \qquad\quad -2A^2} \\
+2A^2 \qquad -4 \\
\underline{+2A^2 \qquad -4}
\end{array}
$$

Note that the terms A^3, A^2, and A are missing in the dividend and were replaced by blanks for convenience in division. This was not done with the divisor, but if it is helpful in the division process, it may also be so arranged.

example 4-32 Divide $A^4 + 7a^2 + 8$ by $A^2 + 1$.

solution:

$$
\begin{array}{r}
A^2 \qquad\quad +6 \quad \dfrac{2}{A^2+1} \\[-2pt]
\hline
A^2 + 1 \,\enclose{longdiv}{A^4 + \ldots + 7A^2 + \ldots + 8} \\
\underline{A^4 \qquad\quad +\ A^2} \\
6A^2 \qquad +8 \\
\underline{6A^2 \qquad +6} \\
+2 \quad \text{remainder}
\end{array}
$$

Note that the remainder is carried in the quotient exactly as it is in arithmetic.

EXERCISE 4-8 Divide the following expressions.

1. $9x^2 + 6x + 1$ by $x + 1$

2. $B^2 + 9B + 36$ by $B - 3$

3. $6Z^3 + 7Z^2 + 6Z + 7$ by $Z^2 + 1$

4. $x^2 + x - 6$ by $x - 2$

5. $C^3 - C^2D - CD^2 + D^3$ by $C - D$

6. $x^4 - x^2$ by $x - 1$

7. $D^3 + 2CD^2 + C^4 + C^3D + C^2D$ by $C + D$

8. $36A + 24A^2 + 12$ by $4A + 4$

5

EQUATIONS AND FORMULAS

In previous chapters, we established a familiarity with some of the basic principles and operations involving algebraic expressions. In this chapter, we will obtain a working knowledge of one of the most important tools of mathematics and engineering—the equation.

5-1 EQUATIONS

The very word *equation* provides the reader with a clue to its meaning—"equal" or "equality." An equation is

A mathematical statement that two algebraic expressions or quantities are equal.

Ohm's law, a relationship that is used very often in electronics is often written $E = IR$. This is a mathematical statement that the quantity E is *equal to* the product of the quantities I and R. The equality sign, =, is the means of stating that the quantities on one side of the equation are equal to the quantities on the other.

An equation such as

$$3x + 5x = 8x$$

is referred to as an *identity* or an *identical equation*. This is an equation that is equal for any numerical value inserted for the literal numbers.

For example, if the value of 2 is substituted for the literal number, x, in this equation, the result is

$$3 \cdot 2 + 5 \cdot 2 = 8 \cdot 2 \quad \text{or}$$
$$6 + 10 = 16 \quad \text{or} \quad 16 = 16$$

Using the value of 5 for x, the result is

$$3 \cdot 5 + 5 \cdot 5 = 8 \cdot 5 \quad \text{or}$$
$$15 + 25 = 40 \quad \text{or} \quad 40 = 40$$

In this equation, then, it is seen that whatever value is used for the literal number x, the equality will always exist.

Another type of equation is the *conditional equation*: for example,

$$4x = 16$$

With this equation, it is seen that there is only one number, 4, which when substituted for the literal number x will satisfy the equation. The equation is then said to be conditional or to be satisfied *only* when the value of x is equal to 4.

The most important fact to remember about any equation is that the algebraic quantities on one side of the equality sign must always be equal to the algebraic quantities on the other side. Any changes or manipulations we perform on an equation *must never change this equality*.

A number of procedures will be useful in working with equations. They will permit the equation to be handled more easily or to be more readily evaluated. One of these rules is:

> EQUAL NUMBERS MAY BE ADDED TO OR SUBTRACTED FROM EACH SIDE OF AN EQUATION WITHOUT CHANGING THE EQUALITY.

As an example, in the equation

$$x + 4 = 10$$

it is seen that substituting a value of 6 for x is required to have both sides of the equation equal.

If 5 is added to both sides of the original equation, it becomes

$$x + 4 + 5 = 10 + 5 \quad \text{or}$$
$$x + 9 = 15$$

Once again, $x = 6$ in order to satisfy the equation.

Therefore, *adding the same number* to each side *has not changed the equality*, and the value of the literal number, x, remains unchanged.

If 2 were subtracted from each side of the original equation, it would produce

$$x + 4 - 2 = 10 - 2 \quad \text{or}$$
$$x + 2 = 8$$

It is seen that, once again, $x = 6$. Therefore, *subtracting the same number* from each side *has not changed the equality*.

Another rule for handling equations is as follows:

> MULTIPLYING OR DIVIDING EACH SIDE OF AN EQUATION BY EQUAL NUMBERS WILL NOT CHANGE THE EQUALITY.

Using the equation of the original example, $x + 4 = 10$, and multiplying each side of the equation by 2 would produce

$$2(x + 4) = 10 \cdot 2 \quad \text{or}$$

$$2x + 8 = 20$$

Again it is seen that the value of x must be equal to 6. So *multiplying both sides* of the equation *by the same number has not changed the equality.*

Dividing both sides of the equation in the example by 2 results in

$$\frac{x + 4}{2} = \frac{10}{2} \quad \text{or}$$

$$\frac{x}{2} + \frac{4}{2} = \frac{10}{2} \quad \text{or}$$

$$\frac{x}{2} + 2 = 5$$

On examination, it is again seen that a value of $x = 6$ is the only quantity that satisfies the equation. Hence *dividing both sides* of an equation *by the same number has not changed the equality.*

Once again, it is essential to repeat that the equality of an equation must never be changed. What is done to one side of an equation must be done to the other. For example, both sides of an equation may be *squared* or *raised to the same power* without changing the equality. Similarly, the *square root*, or *any root*, may be taken of one side of an equation, provided that exactly the same operation is performed on the other side. In the equation $4 = 4$, for example, squaring both sides, $4^2 = 4^2$, will produce $16 = 16$, and the equality will be unchanged. Taking the square root of each side of $4 = 4$, $\sqrt{4} = \sqrt{4}$, will result in $2 = 2$, and again the equality is unchanged.

Another procedure that may be used when convenient, without changing the equality of an equation, is to change the signs of all terms on each side. This is shown in the following example:

example 5-1 $-x + 4 = 12$

---

solution: Subtracting 4 from each side,

$$-x + \cancel{4} - \cancel{4} = 12 - 4$$

$$-x = 8 \quad \text{or, if the signs on each side were changed}$$

$$x = -8$$

If all the signs of the original equation were changed,

$$x - 4 = -12$$

Adding 4 to each side,

$$x - \cancel{4} + \cancel{4} = -12 + 4$$

$$x = -8$$

It is seen that this process does not change the solution of the equation. As with the previous procedures, this will provide a useful tool to be used in the solution of more involved equations.

5–2 STATING EQUATIONS

We shall now investigate the process of expressing written statements in mathematical terms. In our previous example, $x + 4 = 10$, the equation could be stated in words as: four added to a certain number is equal to ten.

The use of the mathematical terms provides a concise and easy-to-understand means of expressing a technical problem or a formula. As the equations and problems become more involved, it will become obvious that using mathematical terms provides a means of expression that would be difficult or nearly impossible to convey in words. For example, think of the words required to express what is stated in the equation

$$\frac{6x}{2} - 3x + 7x = (x + 3)^2 + (x^2 + 4)^2$$

This would take a paragraph to express in words. In addition, in written form it would be extremely difficult to understand the meaning and what was required. Again, the use of mathematical terms provides a concise method of expressing what is meant and having others understand exactly what is meant.

A great deal of practice will be required in writing equations, stating in mathematical terms, what is being stated in words. The following will provide an example of this procedure.

example 5–2 Express the written statement in mathematical terms; use x as the unknown.

	WORDS	ANSWER
1.	One plus a number equals seven.	$1 + x = 7$
2.	A number less twelve equals four.	$x - 12 = 4$
3.	Four times a number plus four equals twenty.	$4x + 4 = 20$
4.	Three times a number less one equals twice the number plus two.	$3x - 1 = 2x + 2$
5.	Five times a number plus four equals eight plus three times the number.	$5x + 4 = 8 + 3x$

EXERCISE 5-1 In each case, write the equation; use x as the unknown.

1. Four times a number less five equals twice the number plus ten.

2. Three added to a number equals the number squared.

3. One half a number plus two equals sixteen.

4. A number plus four equals one half the number less two.

5. What number less two equals one half the number plus two?

6. A number divided by four equals the number plus twelve.

7. · What number divided by three equals the number minus two?

8. Four times a number less twelve equals the number plus twenty-one.

5-3 SOLVING EQUATIONS

In the preceding exercises, experience was gained in writing an equation from a written statement. Now the process of evaluating or solving an equation will be examined. In previous sections, procedures were established that could be used to manipulate an equation. These methods will permit us to obtain more readily the solution of an equation.

In time, and with experience, these procedures will become mechanical. At this point, however, each step in the process of solving an equation will be explained. The student should make certain that each step in the process is clearly understood.

It is necessary also to work the exercises and problems. Much of our future work in electronics will involve similar exercises and problems. It is absolutely essential, therefore, that a sound foundation in equations and their solution be established at this point.

In the solution of the examples, exercises, and problems it is necessary to place the unknown literal number on one side of the equation and the numerical quantities on the other. The solution procedures will be directed toward this end. In this way the equation is "solved," in that the "unknown" is then equal to a numerical quantity.

It is often desirable to check the correctness of a solution. All that is necessary is to substitute the values obtained in the solution back in the original equation. If one side of the equation is equal to the other, the solution is correct.

example 5-3 Solve for A.

---

equation: $A - 4 = 3$

solution: Adding 4 to each side, $A - \cancel{4} + \cancel{4} = 3 + 4$, noting that the $+4$ and -4 on the left cancel.

answer: $A = 7$

check: Substitute $A = 7$ back in the original equation, which becomes $7 - 4 = 3$. The solution is correct, as $3 = 3$.

example 5–4 Solve for *x*.

equation:	$5 + x = 12$
solution:	Subtracting 5 from each side, $\cancel{5} + x - \cancel{5} = 12 - 5$.
answer:	$x = 7$
check:	$5 + 7 = 12$ or
solution correct:	$12 = 12$

example 5–5 Solve for *y*.

equation:	$\dfrac{y}{4} = 2$
solution:	Multiplying both sides by 4, $\cancel{4} \cdot \dfrac{y}{\cancel{4}} = 2 \cdot 4$.
answer:	$y = 8$
check:	$\dfrac{8}{4} = 2$
solution correct:	$2 = 2$

example 5–6 Solve for *M*.

equation:	$4M = 16$
solution:	Dividing both sides by 4, $\dfrac{\cancel{4}M}{\cancel{4}} = \dfrac{16}{4}$.
answer:	$M = 4$
check:	$4 \cdot 4 = 16$
solution correct:	$16 = 16$

The previous solutions involved only one step—addition, subtraction, multiplication, or division. The next examples, which will be a little more difficult, will involve several steps.

example 5–7 Solve for *B*.

equation:	$\dfrac{B}{2} + 4 = 8$
solution:	Step 1: Subtracting 4 from each side, $\dfrac{B}{2} + \cancel{4} - \cancel{4} = 8 - 4$,
	which results in $\dfrac{B}{2} = 4$.
	Step 2: Multiply both sides by 2: $\cancel{2} \cdot \dfrac{B}{\cancel{2}} = 4 \cdot 2$.
answer:	$B = 8$
check:	$\dfrac{8}{2} + 4 = 8$
solution correct:	$8 = 8$

example 5–8 Solve for p.

---

equation: $4p + 4 = 2p - 2$

solution: Step 1: Subtract $2p$ from each side:

$$4p + 4 - 2p = 2\not{p} - 2 - 2\not{p}$$

$$2p + 4 = -2$$

Step 2: Subtract 4 from each side:

$$2p + \not{4} - \not{4} = -2 - 4$$

$$2p = -6$$

Step 3: Divide each side by 2: $\dfrac{2p}{\not{2}} = \dfrac{-6}{2}$.

answer: $p = -3$

check: $(4)(-3) + 4 = (2)(-3) - 2$

$$-12 + 4 = -6 - 2$$

solution correct: $-8 = -8$

example 5–9 Solve for w.

---

equation: $3(w + 3) - 2 = 4$

solution: Step 1: Remove parentheses by performing indicated multiplication: $3w + 9 - 2 = 4$.

Step 2: Simplify: combine numerical terms, $3w + 7 = 4$.

Step 3: Subtract 7 from each side: $3w + \not{7} - \not{7} = 4 - 7$; $3w = -3$.

Step 4: Divide each side by 3: $\dfrac{3w}{\not{3}} = \dfrac{-3}{3}$.

answer: $w = -1$

check: $3(-1 + 3) - 2 = 4$

$$3(2) - 2 = 4$$

$$6 - 2 = 4$$

solution correct: $4 = 4$

example 5–10 Solve for z.

---

equation: $3(z + 1) + 4 = 2(z - 2) - 1$

solution: Step 1: Remove parentheses by performing indicated multiplication: $3z + 3 + 4 = 2z - 4 - 1$.

Step 2: Simplify: combine numerical terms: $3z + 7 = 2z - 5$.

Step 3: Subtract 7 from each side:
$$3z + \cancel{7} - \cancel{7} = 2z - 5 - 7;$$
$$3z = 2z - 12.$$
Step 4: Subtract $2z$ from each side:
$$3z - 2z = \cancel{2z} - 12 - \cancel{2z}.$$

answer: $z = -12$

check: $3(-12 + 1) + 4 = 2(-12 - 2) - 1$
$$3(-11) + 4 = 2(-14) - 1$$
$$-33 + 4 = -28 - 1$$

solution correct: $-29 = -29$

In the previous examples, adding or subtracting a quantity to each side of an equation is equivalent to moving the term to the opposite side and changing its sign. This process is called *transposing*. For example, in the equation $A - 4 = 3$, adding 4 to each side resulted in

$$A - \cancel{4} + \cancel{4} = 3 + 4$$

The terms on the left-hand side cancel and $+4$ remains on the right-hand side. So the process of transposing, moving the -4 on the left to the right side and changing the sign, is nothing more than what has been done by adding 4 to each side. Subtracting a number from each side produces the same results. Transposing is a much easier procedure, but it is necessary that the process be understood.

The following example will show how the transposing method is used in the solution of an equation.

example 5–11 Solve for x: $3x + 5 = -2x - 20$.

solution: Transposing the $+5$ from the left to the right:
$$3x = -2x - 20 - 5.$$
Transposing the $-2x$ from the right to the left:
$$3x + 2x = -20 - 5.$$

combining: $5x = -25$

answer: $x = -5$

check: $3(-5) + 5 = -2(-5) - 20$

solution correct: $-10 = -10$

The rule for transposing is stated:

A TERM MAY BE TRANSPOSED FROM ONE SIDE OF AN EQUATION TO THE OTHER BY CHANGING ITS SIGN.

Canceling a term or terms in an equation may be performed if the same term, or terms with similar signs, occurs on each side of an equation.

---

example 5-12 Solve for x: $3x + 4y = 3x + 16$.

---

solution: The $3x$ terms may be canceled:

$$\cancel{3x} + 4y = \cancel{3x} + 16 \quad \text{or}$$
$$4y = 16 \quad \text{or} \quad y = 4$$

It should be noted that this, too, is essentially a transposing procedure. If in the original equation the $3x$ on the left side was transposed to the right side,

$$4y = \cancel{3x} + 16 - \cancel{3x}$$

the $+3x$ and $-3x$ terms would cancel and the solution would be as before.

EXERCISE 5-2   Determine the value of the unknown in each of the following equations.

1. $2x + 4 = 16$
2. $4 - 3y = -2y + 6$
3. $3a - 4 + 4 = -3a + 6$
4. $6b - 3 - 4b - 2 = 1$
5. $6c - 4 + 2 - 6c = c$
6. $13d + 4 = 13d + 4 - 3d + 12$
7. $3(e + 12) = 2(e - 12)$
8. $15x + 5 - 10x = -5x - 25$
9. $-16y + 12y + 4 - y = -1$
10. $12w - 5(2 + 2w) = -30$
11. $2(3w + 4) = 3(2w - 3) + w$
12. $12x - 1 = 3x(5 + 1) + 6(3 + 4) + 5$
13. $6a - 3 = -3 + 6a + 4a - 24$
14. $2(3b + 4b) - 3(b - 2b) = 3(1 + 6 + 4)$
15. $(c + 2)(c + 3) + 19 = c^2$
16. $(e - 1)(e - 3) = (e + 4)(e + 6) + 7$

5-4 FORMULAS

The inquisitive nature of man has led to many discoveries. The results of these discoveries are in the world for all to see. Man also found that many occurrences in nature follow a pattern. Events may have occurred on a regular or repeating basis or may have exhibited predictable characteristics. From such occurrences, observations, and experimentation, certain laws were developed.

In Section 5–1, we mentioned Ohm's law. This law, like other scientific laws and relationships, was developed as the result of observation, investigation, and experimentation. One form of Ohm's law states that the current through a resistor is equal to the voltage across the resistor divided by its resistance. In the same manner in which we previously converted a written statement to a mathematical one, Ohm's law may also be expressed as

$$I = \frac{E}{R}$$

At this point the units are not important. What is important is that a scientific law has been expressed in mathematical terms, using literal numbers. In this form it is called a *formula*.

Many such formulas are used in arithmetic. Examples of familiar ones are:

$$A = \pi R^2 = \frac{\pi D^2}{4} \qquad \text{area of a circle}$$

$$C = \pi D \qquad \text{circumference of a circle}$$

$$A = hw \qquad \text{area of a rectangle}$$

$$A = \tfrac{1}{2}bh \qquad \text{area of a triangle}$$

It will be noted that all the formulas are equations. These formulas are handled in exactly the same manner in which we handled previous equations.

example 5–13 If the area of a rectangle is 40 in² and the width is 10 in, what is the height?

solution: Using the formula for the area of a rectangle,

$$A = hw$$

It is observed that the area and the width are known. Solving for h results in

$$h = \frac{A}{w}$$

Substituting the known values and solving,

$$h = \frac{40}{10}$$

$$= 4 \text{ in}$$

example 5–14 Solve for R and E.
Using Ohm's law,

$$I = \frac{E}{R}$$

solution: Solving for R, $R = \frac{E}{I}$.

Solving for E, $E = IR$.

EXERCISE 5–3 Solve the following formulas.

		Determine
1.	$X_L = 2\pi f L$	f and L
2.	$X_c = \dfrac{1}{2\pi f C}$	f and C
3.	$\dfrac{1}{R_T} = \dfrac{1}{R_1} + \dfrac{1}{R_2}$	R_1 and R_2
4.	$I_1 N_1 = I_2 N_2$	I_1 and I_2
5.	$I_1 R_2 = I_2 R_3$	I_1 and I_2
6.	$t = CR$	C and R
7.	$P = I^2 R$	I and R
8.	$t = \dfrac{L}{R}$	L and R
9.	$F_R = \dfrac{1}{2\pi \sqrt{LC}}$	L and C
10.	$Z = \sqrt{R^2 + X_L^2}$	R and X_L
11.	$A = \dfrac{h}{2}(b_1 + b_2)$	h
12.	$R_T = \dfrac{R_1 R_2}{R_1 + R_2}$	R_1 and R_2
13.	$P = I^2 Rt$	t
14.	$\dfrac{P_1}{P_2} = \dfrac{V_2}{V_1}$	V_2 and V_1

15. $x^2 + y^2 = z^2$ $\qquad\qquad\qquad$ x and y

16. $s = \frac{1}{2}gt^2$ $\qquad\qquad\qquad$ g and t

A *ratio* may be defined as the quotient of two similar quantities. To form a ratio, it is only necessary to compare the two quantities in this manner. For example, the ratio of 3 V to 30 V may be expressed as

$$\frac{3}{30} \quad \text{or} \quad \frac{1}{10}$$

Similarly, the ratio of 5 ohms (Ω) to 20 Ω may be written

$$\frac{5}{20} \quad \text{or} \quad \frac{1}{4}$$

The ratio, the relationship that exists between two similar quantities, will find many practical applications in electronics. It should be observed that a ratio has no units. It merely expresses how one quantity is related to another, similar quantity.

Often, a ratio of two quantities, equal to a ratio of two other quantities, will be used. This is called a *proportion*. For example, in the discussion of ratios above, a ratio of 3 V to 30 V was set up as

$$\frac{3}{30} \quad \text{or} \quad \frac{1}{10}$$

If an equality sign was placed between these two terms, it would be called a proportion. That is,

$$\frac{3}{30} = \frac{1}{10}$$

If, for example, the ratio of A to B were said to be equal to the ratio of C to D, the proportion would be written

$$\frac{A}{B} = \frac{C}{D}$$

Here, the equality of ratios of literal numbers is expressed in this proportion. As an equation, the methods and procedures apply that were developed previously in this chapter.

Setting up a proportion involves establishing the two ratios involved. Normally, one term of one ratio in the proportion is unknown.

example 5–15 If an automobile required 1.8 gallons (gal) of gas to travel 30 miles (mi), how many miles could be traveled on a full tank of 22 gal?

solution A proportion would be established as

$$\frac{1.8 \text{ gal}}{22 \text{ gal}} = \frac{30 \text{ mi}}{x \text{ mi}}$$

Using the relationships developed for equations, this becomes

$$1.8x = 30 \cdot 22 \quad \text{or} \quad x = 366.6 \text{ mi}$$

This proportion also may have been written

$$\frac{1.8 \text{ gal}}{30 \text{ mi}} = \frac{22 \text{ gal}}{x \text{ mi}}$$

$$x = 366.6 \text{ mi}$$

The proportion used in the second part of this example results in the same answer as previously. However, in the definition of a ratio it was specified that a ratio was the relationship that existed between *two similar quantities*. Actually, where the proportion is written in the form above, *it is* a comparison between two similar quantities. In this proportion, the units gallons/mile are used on each side of the equation. So writing the proportion in this form is perfectly proper. Again, the ratio of the quantities that are set up on one side of a proportion must be equal to those on the other side.

In addition to using ratios and proportions, it will often be indicated that a quantity is directly or inversely proportional to another. For example, in Ohm's law,

$$I = \frac{E}{R}$$

Here the current, I, may be said to be *directly* proportional to the voltage, E, and *inversely* proportional to the resistance, R. What is meant, then, is that as the voltage increases, the current will increase in the same proportion. If the voltage were doubled, the current would also be doubled.

The current being inversely proportional to the resistance means that as the resistance increases, the current will decrease in the same proportion. Then, if the resistance is doubled, the current would be decreased by this factor, or halved.

Often this proportionality may be expressed using the symbols $\propto$ or k. The first indicates *proportionality*, and the second is called the *constant of proportionality*. For example, again using Ohm's law, it could be written that $I \propto E$ and $I \propto \dfrac{1}{R}$.

A circuit relationship used often in electronics is $X_L = 2\pi f L$. The 2π is a constant, so this equation could be written $X_L = kfL$, using the constant of proportionality.

EXERCISE 5–4   Determine the value of the unknown.

1. $\dfrac{2}{32} = \dfrac{4}{x}$

2. $\dfrac{x}{40} = \dfrac{5}{70}$

3. $\dfrac{3}{x} = \dfrac{50}{1,200}$

4. $\dfrac{1}{4} = \dfrac{x}{8}$

5. $\dfrac{3.25}{6.17} = \dfrac{x}{17.25}$

6. $\dfrac{0.25}{3.17} = \dfrac{3.75}{x}$

7. $\dfrac{3.78}{x} = \dfrac{0.74}{0.26}$

8. $\dfrac{4.5}{0.32} = \dfrac{x}{0.45}$

Express the following as a proportionality or an equation.

9. The resistance varies directly with the voltage, E.

10. The resistance is inversely proportional to the current, I.

11. The area of a circle, using its radius and the constant of proportionality; and its diameter and the constant of proportionality.

12. The capacitive reactance X_c, of a circuit varies inversely with the frequency, f; the capacitance, C; 2; and π.

13. The inductive reactance, X_L, of a circuit varies directly with the frequency, f; the inductance, L; 2; and π.

14. The power, P, consumed in a circuit varies directly with the voltage, E; and the current, I.

SCIENTIFIC NOTATION, MEASUREMENTS, AND UNITS

$\mathbf{W}$ith the advent of the integrated circuit and the subsequent development of the small hand-held calculator, it would appear that the slide rule will become much less important than it has been. For that reason, a lengthy discussion of slide rules will not be presented in this text. The small calculator will be to the engineers and technicians of the future what the slide rule has been in the past—an extremely versatile and necessary tool.

In electronics, calculations will often involve extremely large, as well as extremely small, quantities. In many instances the hand calculator that will be used will not have the capacity to handle these quantities. It is for this reason, and others that will be seen in later chapters, that it is desirable to develop a background in engineering shorthand or scientific notation.

Very closely tied to this subject is the use of units and measurements. The need in mathematical calculations for reduction, conversion, interpretation, and approximation of values and results makes these very important topics indeed.

6–1 SCIENTIFIC NOTATION—POWERS OF 10

The use of *scientific notation*, or powers of 10, enables the technician and the engineer to handle with ease extremely large and small numbers. These procedures will permit an easy approximation of results using only simple arithmetic operations. Essentially what will be involved is to express these large or small quantities as a number, usually between 1 and 10, multiplied by 10 raised to an appropriate power.

For example, the number 81 could be expressed as 8.1×10, 810 could be expressed as $8.1 \times 10 \times 10$, and 8,100 could be expressed as $8.1 \times 10 \times 10 \times 10$. Rather than writing these numbers in these forms,

TABLE 6–1 Powers of 10 for Numbers 1 and Greater

NUMERICAL VALUE	EXPONENTIAL VALUE	EXPRESSION
1	10^0	Ten to the zero
10	10^1	Ten to the first
100	10^2	Ten to the second
1,000	10^3	Ten to the third
10,000	10^4	Ten to the fourth
100,000	10^5	Ten to the fifth
1,000,000	10^6	Ten to the sixth

we would write them in exponential form as shown in Table 6–1. In the previous examples, using the table,

81 would be expressed as 8.1×10^1
810 would become 8.1×10^2
8,100 would be 8.1×10^3

In a similar manner, *any* number 1 or larger could be expressed as a number between 1 and 10 multiplied by the appropriate power of 10. If the above process is examined, it would be observed that the decimal point has been moved to the *left* the number of places indicated by the exponent. For example, with 8,100 written as 8.1×10^3, the decimal point has been moved three places to the *left*.

From these observations the following rule results:

> TO EXPRESS A NUMBER LARGER THAN 1 IN SCIENTIFIC NOTATION (POWERS OF 10):
> 1. MOVE THE DECIMAL POINT TO THE LEFT UNTIL A NUMBER BETWEEN 1 AND 10 RESULTS.
> 2. COUNT THE NUMBER OF PLACES THE DECIMAL POINT HAS BEEN MOVED, AND USE THIS NUMBER AS THE POWER OF 10 EXPONENT.

example 6–1   Express 3,150,000 in powers of 10.

solution: First: the decimal point will be moved to the left to form 3.15, a number between 1 and 10. Second: in this process the decimal point was moved six places, so the number is expressed as 3.15×10^6.

example 6–2   Express 453,000,000 in powers of 10.

solution: Form 4.53, obtained by moving the decimal point eight places. The result in scientific notation is 4.35×10^8.

EXERCISE 6–1   Express the following numbers in scientific notation.

1. 3,250
2. 65,000
3. 3,575,000
4. 15,250
5. 42,500,000,000
6. 367,000
7. 453,000,000
8. 27,000,000,000

Small numbers may also be expressed in scientific notation. They are handled in a manner similar to large numbers. For example, the numbers

0.62 could be expressed as $6.2 \div 10$

0.062 could be expressed as $6.2 \div (10 \times 10)$

0.0062 could be expressed as $6.2 \div (10 \times 10 \times 10)$

As previously, it is much more convenient to write these numbers in exponential form. Table 6–2 lists powers of 10 for numbers smaller than 1. Using the table, the numbers in the previous example become:

0.62 would be expressed as 6.2×10^{-1}

0.062 would become 6.2×10^{-2}

0.0062 would be 6.2×10^{-3}

TABLE 6-2 Powers of 10 for Numbers Less Than 1

NUMERICAL VALUE	EXPONENTIAL VALUE	EXPRESSION
0.1	10^{-1}	Ten to the minus one
0.01	10^{-2}	Ten to the minus two
0.001	10^{-3}	Ten to the minus three
0.0001	10^{-4}	Ten to the minus four
0.00001	10^{-5}	Ten to the minus five
0.000001	10^{-6}	Ten to the minus six

In a similar manner, *any* number smaller than 1 may be expressed as a whole number between 1 and 10, multiplied by the appropriate negative power of 10. Examining the above process, it is seen that the negative exponent indicates the number of places the decimal point has been moved to the *right*.

Accordingly, the following rule may be written:

TO EXPRESS A NUMBER BETWEEN ZERO AND 1 IN SCIENTIFIC NOTATION (POWERS OF 10):
1. MOVE THE DECIMAL POINT TO THE RIGHT UNTIL A NUMBER BETWEEN 1 AND 10 RESULTS.
2. COUNT THE NUMBER OF PLACES THE DECIMAL POINT HAS BEEN MOVED, AND USE THIS NUMBER AS THE NEGATIVE POWER OF 10 EXPONENT.

example 6-3 Express 0.000532 in powers of 10.

solution: First move the decimal point to the right to form 5.32, a number between 1 and 10. In this process the decimal point was moved four places. The number is then expressed as 5.32×10^{-4}.

example 6–4 Express 0.0000027 in powers of 10.

solution: Form 2.7, obtained by moving decimal point six places. The answer is 2.7×10^{-6}.

EXERCISE 6–2 Express the following in scientific notation.

1.	0.037	**2.**	0.530
3.	0.0067	**4.**	0.000045
5.	0.074	**6.**	0.000000074
7.	0.0037	**8.**	0.0565

At this point it would be well to indicate that changing a number expressed in scientific notation to conventional numerical form is a reverse procedure. It would involve merely moving the decimal point, either right or left, the number of places indicated by the exponent.

example 6–5 Express 5.75×10^6 as a conventional number.

solution: Moving the decimal point six places to the right would produce 5,750,000.

example 6–6 Express 3.27×10^{-4} as a conventional number.

solution: The decimal point would move four places to the left: 0.000327.

EXERCISE 6–3 Express the following as conventional quantities.

1.	6.28×10^4	**2.**	5.31×10^{-2}
3.	6.32×10^0	**4.**	8.75×10^{-5}
5.	$1,422 \times 10^{-4}$	**6.**	57.62×10^6
7.	107.1×10^{-5}	**8.**	0.25×10^3

6–2 SCIENTIFIC NOTATION—ADDITION AND SUBTRACTION

The addition and subtraction of both large and small numbers may be performed using scientific notation. It is necessary to remember that the quantities must be expressed in similar terms, in the same manner as with literal numbers. That is, the powers of 10 must be identical. This is shown in the following examples.

example 6–7 Add 3,000,000 and 425,000.

solution: These could, of course, be added in their present form or be converted to scientific notation: 3×10^6 and 4.25×10^5.

Converting to similar terms, 3×10^6 and 0.425×10^6, and adding, we have 3.425×10^6.

example 6–8 From 1,650,000 subtract 325,000.

solution: $1.65 \times 10^6 - 3.25 \times 10^5$, or $1.65 \times 10^6 - 0.325 \times 10^6$, or 1.325×10^6.

Addition and subtraction using powers of 10 are not particularly useful procedures. They were presented to show that these procedures may be performed using scientific notation. The processes of multiplication and division, which follow, will be much more useful in calculations.

6–3 SCIENTIFIC NOTATION—MULTIPLICATION

It was learned previously that multiplication involving exponents required the addition of exponents, such as $x^a \cdot x^b = x^{a+b}$. With scientific notation, both large and small numbers are expressed using exponents of the powers of 10. It follows, then, that the previous rules for exponents apply here also.

The following example is used to illustrate this method.

example 6–9 Multiply 2,000,000 by 1,500.

solution: First: express the numbers in scientific notation: as $2.0 \times 10^6 \times 1.5 \times 10^3$.
Second: multiply 2×1.5 and then add the exponents.
Result: 3.0×10^9

example 6–10 Multiply 3,200 by 0.0002.

solution: $3.2 \times 10^3 \times 2 \times 10^{-4}$ in scientific notation; on multiplying and adding exponents this becomes 6.4×10^{-1}.

It should be noted that this process permits the multiplication of large and small quantities using only basic arithmetic. All that is involved in these examples is the multiplication of two numbers expressed between 1 and 10, and then the addition of the exponents.

EXERCISE 6–4 Multiply the following numbers using scientific notation.

1. $350 \times 4,200$
2. $46,500 \times 2,300$
3. $15,200,000 \times 3,700$
4. $25,600 \times 0.003$
5. $2,500 \times 1,500 \times 20,000$
6. $13,500 \times 14,000 \times 0.037$
7. $16,200,000 \times 0.007 \times 1,500$
8. $3,250,000 \times 12,000 \times 2,500$

In a previous chapter, we found that division, involving exponents, required the algebraic subtraction of exponents, such as $\frac{x^a}{x^b} = x^{a-b}$. It follows, then, that in division, using powers of 10, this rule is applicable.

example 6–11 Divide 300,000 by 2,000.

solution: Expressed in scientific notation we have

$$\frac{3.0 \times 10^5}{2.0 \times 10^3}$$

Dividing, and subtracting exponents: $1.5 \times 10^{5-3}$, or 1.5×10^2.

example 6–12 Divide 24,000 by 0.0012.

solution: $\frac{2.4 \times 10^4}{1.2 \times 10^{-3}}$ in powers of 10; dividing, $2 \times 10^{4-(-3)}$, or

2×10^7.

EXERCISE 6–5 Divide the following numbers using scientific notation.

1. 35,000 by 2,700
2. 625,000 by 100,000
3. 3,250,000 by 152,000
4. 2,300 by 1,500,000
5. 3,600 by 0.0002
6. 0.365 by 0.0005
7. 1,536,000 by 0.25
8. 0.0062 by 0.000031

6–5 SCIENTIFIC NOTATION—MIXED MULTIPLICATION AND DIVISION

The previously developed methods of multiplication and division will now be successively applied. These steps will be performed in the manner most convenient to solving the problem.

example 6–13 Perform the indicated operations:

$$\frac{325,000 \times 25,000}{16,200,000 \times 200}$$

solution: First: convert to scientific notation:

$$\frac{3.25 \times 10^5 \ \times \ 2.5 \times 10^4}{1.62 \times 10^7 \ \times \ 2 \times 10^2}$$

Second: the indicated multiplication would result in

59

Sec. 6–5
SCIENTIFIC
NOTATION—
MIXED
MULTIPLICATION
AND DIVISION

$$\frac{8.12 \times 10^9}{3.24 \times 10^9}$$

Third: division results in 2.51.

example 6–14 Perform the indicated operations:

$$\frac{672,000 \times 1,500 \times 20,000}{150,000 \times 0.0003}$$

solution: $\dfrac{6.72 \times 10^5 \times 1.5 \times 10^3 \times 2 \times 10^4}{1.5 \times 10^5 \times 3 \times 10^{-4}}$

$\dfrac{20.16 \times 10^{12}}{4.5 \times 10^1}$ on multiplication

4.48×10^{11} on division

example 6–15 Perform the indicated operations:

$$\frac{1}{0.032 \times 35,000 \times 1,500}$$

solution: $\dfrac{1}{3.2 \times 10^{-2} \times 3.5 \times 10^4 \times 1.5 \times 10^3}$

$\dfrac{1}{16.8 \times 10^5}$

0.059×10^{-5} or

5.9×10^{-7}

EXERCISE 6–6 Evaluate the following expressions using scientific notation.

1. $\dfrac{3,500 \times 1,500}{1,500,000 \times 2,500}$

2. $\dfrac{250 \times 1,200 \times 54,000}{350,000 \times 27,000}$

3. $\dfrac{0.0074 \times 0.000052}{0.0000065 \times 0.003}$

4. $\dfrac{1}{6.28 \times 15,000 \times 27,000}$

5. $\dfrac{3,000,000 \times 0.0075 \times 0.70}{1,500 \times 10^3 \times 0.25 \times 10^{-4}}$

6. $$\frac{3,000 \times 10^{12} \times 150,000}{250 \times 10^{-4} \times 14,000 \times 10^3}$$

7. $$\frac{0.072 \times 10^6 \times 1,500 \times 10^{-2} \times 0.070 \times 10^{-4}}{3,500,000 \times 15,000,000}$$

8. $$\frac{1}{6,500 \times 10^{-3} \times 15,000 \times 10^{-3} \times 0.002 \times 10^3}$$

6–6 MEASUREMENTS

To apply the methods previously developed in this chapter to practical situations, it is necessary that a familiarity with measurements be established. In electronics, as in other fields, the measurements used are often unique.

In previous examples the numerical answers obtained might well have been values of some unit. As such, they would have been part of a system of measurements. When expressed in this manner they would have a practical meaning, in that a certain quantity of a specific unit would be indicated.

Such terms as "by the mark, three," "hands," "stones," "gills," and "cubits" have been used in measurements. These were units applied to the particular measurement involved and were characteristic of their times. These terms are not generally used today.

Two measurement systems involving units appropriate to the needs of the modern world are the *English* and *metric systems.* At this writing there is pressure for the adoption of a single system of measurement. The metric system, also called the *meter–kilogram–second system,* is by far the most common one in use today. The United States and Canada, however, still use principally the English system, although Canada has already begun a slow conversion to metric units. A comparison of these systems is given in Tables 6–3 and 6–4.

TABLE 6–3 English System of Measurement

Length
12 inches (in) = 1 foot (ft)
3 feet (ft) = 1 yard (yd)
5,280 feet (ft) = 1 mile (mi)
Mass
16 ounces (oz) = 1 pound (lb)
2,000 pounds (lb) = 1 ton (t)
Time
60 seconds (s) = 1 minute (min)
60 minutes (min) = 1 hour (h)

TABLE 6-4 Metric System of Measurement

Length
1 millimeter (mm) = 0.001 meter (m)
1 centimeter (cm) = 0.01 meter (m)
1 kilometer (km) = 1,000 meters (m)
Mass
1 milligram (mg) = 0.001 gram (g)
1 gram (g) = 0.001 kilogram (kg)
Time
60 seconds (s) = 1 minute (min)
60 minutes (min) = 1 hour (h)

The English and metric systems form the basis of the measurement procedures used in electronics. The interrelation between the two systems is provided, in part, in Table 6–5.

TABLE 6-5 Measurement Conversion Factors
(Approximate)

1 inch = 2.54 centimeters
1 foot = 30.48 centimeters
1 centimeter = 0.3937 inch
1 meter = 39.37 inches
1 mile = 1.609 kilometers
1 kilometer = 0.6214 mile
1 ounce = 28.35 grams
1 pound = 453.6 grams
1 kilogram = 2.205 pounds

6-7 ELECTRICAL UNITS OF MEASUREMENT

At this point in our studies, no attempt will be made to provide a detailed explanation of the electrical units of measurement. Introducing these units here, however, will assist in the understanding of the terminology that will be applied to extremely large and extremely small levels of these basic units.

Table 6–6 provides a listing of common terms, abbreviations, and symbols used in electronics. In addition, a short explanation of the terms is provided.

TABLE 6-6 Electrical Units of Measurements

TERM	ABBREVIATION	SYMBOL	EXPLANATION
Volt	V	E or V	Electrical pressure
Ampere	A	I	Electrical current flow
Ohm	R or Ω	Ω	Opposition to current flow

TABLE 6-6   Electrical Units of Measurements (*cont.*)

TERM	ABBREVIATION	SYMBOL	EXPLANATION
Mho	mho	G	Reciprocal of resistance
Henry	H	L	Unit of inductance
Farad	F	C	Unit of capacitance
Watt	W	P	Unit of power
Hertz	Hz	$\sim$	Frequency (cycles per second)

As noted, extremely large and extremely small levels of these basic units are often required. This has resulted in the development of a group of unit prefixes that designate magnitude. These are shown in Table 6–7. The examples in Table 6–8 show how the prefixes would be used to designate unit levels. The table should provide the student with an understanding of how typical large and small values of a particular quantity are designated. The best procedure for establishing the prefix to use is to first express the quantity in scientific notation.

TABLE 6-7   Levels Represented by Unit Prefixes

PREFIX	SYMBOL	NUMBER REPRESENTED	SCIENTIFIC NOTATION
tera	T	1,000,000,000,000	10^{12}
giga	G	1,000,000,000	10^{9}
mega	M	1,000,000	10^{6}
kilo	k	1,000	10^{3}
—	Basic unit	1	10^{0}
milli	m	0.001	10^{-3}
micro	μ	0.000001	10^{-6}
nano	n	0.000000001	10^{-9}
pica	p	0.000000000001	10^{-12}

TABLE 6-8   Examples of Prefixes, Units, and Representation

EXAMPLE: UNITS	SCIENTIFIC NOTATION	ENGLISH REPRESENTATION	SYMBOL
3,200,000,000,000 hertz	3.2×10^{12}	3.2 terahertz	3.2 THz
5,650,000,000 ohms	5.65×10^{9}	5.65 gigaohms	5.65 GΩ
1,320,000 volts	1.32×10^{6}	1.32 megavolts	1.32 MV
4,250 watts	4.25×10^{3}	4.25 kilowatts	4.25 kW
3.25 amperes	3.25×10^{0}	3.25 amperes	3.25 A
0.0065 mho	6.5×10^{-3}	6.5 millimhos	6.5 mmhos
0.000002 henry	2×10^{-6}	2 microhenrys	2 μH
0.000000000003 farad	3×10^{-12}	3 picofarads	3 pF

example 6–16   Apply an appropriate prefix to 425,000 Ω.

solution: In scientific notation this could be expressed as

0.425×10^6 or

425×10^3

Applying an appropriate prefix would result in 0.425 MΩ or 425 kΩ.

This example was chosen to illustrate that it is often a matter of choice which prefix to use. It would also be optional whether or not to use a prefix. For example, 0.250 A could be suitable expressed in this form or as 250 mA. Either would be perfectly correct. The prefix chosen is often used on the basis of experience, convenience, or convention.

E X E R C I S E   6–7   Fill in the blanks. Provide answers between 1 and 10 in scientific-notation form.

		A		**B**	
1.	1,650,000 Hz = _____	MHz = _____		GHz = _____	
2.	56,000,000 Ω = _____	kΩ = _____		MΩ = _____	
3.	3,600 kV = _____	MV = _____		V = _____	
4.	3.2 A = _____	mA = _____		μA = _____	
5.	13.5 μW = _____	mW = _____		W = _____	
6.	1.4 H = _____	μH = _____		mH = _____	
7.	1.2 pF = _____	μF = _____		F = _____	
8.	1200 MW = _____	kW = _____		W = _____	

6–8   CONVERSION, REDUCTION, AND CALCULATIONS

In this section, a number of practical considerations involving measurements and units used in calculations will be presented. The process of changing from units in one system to units in another is called *conversion*. A limited table of conversion factors is provided in Table 6–5. Examples of conversions would be the changing of miles to kilometers, pounds to grams, and inches to meters. Changing units within a system is called *reduction*. Exercise 6–7 provided examples of the reduction procedure.

It is essential that when either of these processes is used, the resultant quantity have the appropriate units for the calculations involved. Care must also be exercised to include the units with each quantity.

example 6–17 Add 3.0 V and 1,300 mV.

solution: Reduction to the same units would produce

$$\begin{array}{r} 3.0\ \text{V} \\ \text{adding} \quad \underline{1.3\ \text{V}} \\ 4.3\ \text{V} \end{array}$$

example 6–18 Add 3.54 cm and 2.0 in.

solution: Conversion to similar units would be required. The answer could be obtained by converting both to centimeters:

$$2.0\ \cancel{\text{in}} \times 2.54\ \frac{\text{cm}}{\cancel{\text{in}}} = 5.08\ \text{cm}$$

$$\begin{array}{l} 3.54\ \text{cm} \\ \underline{5.08\ \text{cm}} \quad \text{adding} \\ 8.62\ \text{cm} \end{array}$$

or by converting both to inches,

$$3.54\ \cancel{\text{cm}} \times \frac{1\ \text{in}}{2.54\ \cancel{\text{cm}}} = 1.39\ \text{in}$$

$$\begin{array}{l} 1.39\ \text{in} \\ \underline{2.0\ \ \text{in}} \quad \text{adding} \\ 3.39\ \text{in} \end{array}$$

In certain operations it is desirable to express the results in terms of different units. For instance, pounds per square inch, ohms per mile, and inch-ounces.

example 6–19 Express in appropriate units.

solution: $$\frac{30\ \text{lb}}{5\ \text{in}^2} = 6\ \text{lb/in}^2$$

$$\frac{1,200\ \Omega}{2\ \text{mi}} = 600\ \Omega/\text{mi}$$

$$30\ \text{in} \times 5\ \text{oz} = 150\ \text{in-oz}$$

In many of the formulas that will be used in electronics, specific units are required. In Ohm's law, for example, in the form $I = \dfrac{E}{R}$, the current *must* be in amperes, the voltage *must* be in volts, and the resistance *must* be in ohms. If these quantities are expressed in different units, they *must* be reduced to the units required.

EXERCISE 6–8 Perform the indicated operation.

1. Convert 14 yd to centimeters.

2. Convert 452 mm to inches.

3. Reduce 35 mi/h to ft/min.

4. Convert 5,600 kg to tons.

5. Convert 305 oz to grams.

6. Using Ohm's law, determine the current in a circuit if the resistance is 5 kΩ and the voltage is 2.7 V.

7. Using Ohm's law, calculate the circuit resistance in megohms if the voltage is 500 V and the current is 300 mA.

8. Convert 200 lb/in² to kg/m².

7

RESISTANCE

In Chapter 6, a superficial introduction to electrical and electronic units was provided. In this chapter, a more detailed examination of one of these units, resistance, will be developed.

Resistance was defined previously as the opposition to current flow. Although this basic explanation is valid, in this chapter we shall provide a further explanation of this definition. We shall examine a number of factors that affect resistance. This will provide an understanding of the characteristics and effects of resistance when used later in electrical and electronic circuits.

The difficulty with which current flows in the circuit is, as observed, related to resistance. Similarly, the ease with which current flows is also related to resistance. This is referred to as *conductance* and was previously defined as the reciprocal of resistance, $\frac{1}{R}$.

In most situations, it is advantageous to make the path for current flow as low in resistance as possible. The path is called a *conductor*, *wire*, or *bus bar*. The cross-sectional area of conductors varies greatly. For example, a wire may have a diameter much less than a human hair or a diameter of several inches. Conductors also vary greatly in length. A printed circuit connection may require only a few thousandths of an inch, whereas a power transmission line may involve a length of several hundred miles.

Conductors may be made of a variety of materials, including aluminum, copper, silver, and gold. Operating temperatures may range from those of the frigid Arctic regions to those of a rocket reentering the earth's atmosphere.

Thus the factors of composition, length, cross-sectional area, and temperature of its location all affect the opposition or resistance that a conductor will provide to the flow of current. The effects of cross-sectional area will be examined first.

A garden hose would provide greater opposition to the flow of water than would a 6-in pipe. In the same manner, a wire with a smaller cross-sectional area creates a greater resistance to current flow than would a larger wire of the same material. This means, then, that as the cross-sectional area increases, the resistance decreases. The resistance is then said to be inversely proportional to the conductor area. This may be written

$$R = \frac{1}{A}$$

As many conductors are round in cross section, the area would be $A = \frac{\pi d^2}{4}$, where d is the diameter. Substituting in the above expression would produce

$$R = \frac{1}{\frac{\pi d^2}{4}}$$

Two conductors of the same material but with different cross sections would have resistances related to the cross-sectional areas that may be written

$$\frac{R_1}{R_2} = \frac{A_2}{A_1}$$

where R_1 and A_1, and R_2 and A_2, represent the resistance and cross-sectional area of each conductor.

The preceding equation may be written for a round conductor as

$$\frac{R_1}{R_2} = \frac{\frac{\pi d_2{}^2}{4}}{\frac{\pi d_1{}^2}{4}}$$

The $\frac{\pi}{4}$ is a constant and would cancel. The equation then becomes

$$\frac{R_1}{R_2} = \frac{d_2{}^2}{d_1{}^2}$$

From this relationship the following rules result:

> THE RESISTANCE OF A CONDUCTOR
> 1. VARIES INVERSELY WITH THE AREA.
> 2. IF ROUND, IT VARIES INVERSELY WITH THE SQUARE OF THE DIAMETER.

example 7-1 Determine the resistance of a wire with a cross section of 2 in² if a wire of similar material has an area of 1.5 in² and a resistance of 2 Ω.

solution: $\dfrac{R_1}{R_2} = \dfrac{A_2}{A_1}$, where $A_1 = 2$ in², $R_2 = 2\ \Omega$, $A_2 = 1.5$ in², and

$$R_1 = \frac{R_2 A_2}{A_1} = \frac{2\ \Omega \times 1.5\ \cancel{\text{in}^2}}{2\ \cancel{\text{in}^2}} = 1.5\ \Omega$$

example 7-2 Determine the area of a round wire with a resistance of 5.3 Ω if another round conductor of similar material has a resistance of 8.25 Ω and a cross-sectional area of 0.375 in². What is the diameter of each wire?

solution: $\dfrac{R_1}{R_2} = \dfrac{A_2}{A_1}$, where $R_1 = 5.3\ \Omega$, $R_2 = 8.25\ \Omega$, and
$$A_2 = 0.375\ \text{in}^2.$$

Solving for A_1,

$$A_1 = \frac{R_2 A_2}{R_1} = \frac{8.25\ \cancel{\Omega} \times 0.375\ \text{in}^2}{5.3\ \cancel{\Omega}} = 0.584\ \text{in}^2$$

Solving for the diameter of each wire,

$$A = \frac{\pi d^2}{4} \quad d^2 = \frac{4A}{\pi} \quad \text{or} \quad d = \sqrt{\frac{4A}{\pi}}$$

Then

$$d_1 = \sqrt{\frac{4 \times 0.584\ \text{in}^2}{\pi}} = \sqrt{0.744\ \text{in}^2} = 0.862\ \text{in}$$

$$d_2 = \sqrt{\frac{4 \times 0.375\ \text{in}^2}{\pi}} = \sqrt{0.477\ \text{in}^2} = 0.691\ \text{in}$$

example 7-3 Determine the diameter of a round wire with a resistance of 0.329 Ω if a wire of similar material has a resistance of 0.164 Ω and a diameter of 0.008 in.

solution: $\dfrac{R_1}{R_2} = \dfrac{d_2{}^2}{d_1{}^2}$, where $R_1 = 0.329\ \Omega$, $R_2 = 0.164\ \Omega$, and

$$d_2 = 0.008\ \text{in}.$$

Solving for $d_1{}^2$,

$$d_1{}^2 = \frac{d_2{}^2 R_2}{R_1} \quad \text{or} \quad d_1 = \sqrt{\frac{d_2{}^2 R_2}{R_1}}$$

$$d_1 = \sqrt{\frac{(0.008 \text{ in})^2 \times 0.164 \, \cancel{\Omega}}{0.329 \, \cancel{\Omega}}}$$

$$= \sqrt{0.00003.16 \text{ in}^2} = \sqrt{31.6 \times 10^{-6} \text{ in}^2}$$

$$= 5.62 \times 10^{-3} \text{ in} \quad \text{or} \quad 0.00562 \text{ in}$$

7–3 EFFECT OF CONDUCTOR LENGTH ON RESISTANCE

With a garden hose it would be found that the longer the length, the greater would be the resistance to the flow of water. Similarly, the longer a conductor, the greater will be its resistance to the flow of current. This means that the resistance is directly proportional to the conductor length. This may be expressed as

$$R \propto L \quad \text{or} \quad R = kL$$

From this relationship, the following rule results:

THE RESISTANCE OF A CONDUCTOR VARIES DIRECTLY WITH THE LENGTH.

Two conductors of the same cross-sectional area and material but of different lengths will have resistances directly related to their lengths. In equation form this becomes

$$\frac{R_1}{R_2} = \frac{L_1}{L_2}$$

where R_1 and L_1, and R_2 and L_2, represent the resistance and length of each conductor.

example 7–4 Determine the resistance of a wire with a length of 200 ft if a wire of the same material and cross section has a resistance of 57.5 Ω per 1,000 ft.

solution: $\dfrac{R_1}{R_2} = \dfrac{L_1}{L_2}$, where $L_1 = 200$ ft, $R_2 = 57.5 \, \Omega$, $L_2 = 1,000$, and

$$R_1 = \frac{R_2 L_1}{L_2} = \frac{57.5 \, \Omega \times 200 \, \cancel{\text{ft}}}{1,000 \, \cancel{\text{ft}}} = 11.5 \, \Omega$$

example 7–5 Determine the length of a wire whose resistance is 1.72 kΩ if a wire of similar material and cross section has a resistance of 200 Ω per 1,000 yd.

solution:

$$\frac{R_1}{R_2} = \frac{L_1}{L_2}, \text{ where } R_2 = 200 \text{ Ω}, L_2 = 1,000 \text{ yd } (= 3,000 \text{ ft}),$$

$$R_1 = 1.72 \text{ kΩ} = 1,720 \text{ Ω}$$

$$L_1 = \frac{R_1 L_2}{R_2} = \frac{1,720 \text{ Ω} \times 3,000 \text{ ft}}{200 \text{ Ω}} = 25,800 \text{ ft}$$

7–4 EFFECT OF CONDUCTOR MATERIAL ON RESISTANCE

The differences that exist in the atomic structure of metallic materials result in a wide variation in the ability of a material to conduct current. The reader will learn elsewhere how these differences in the atomic structure result in materials being classified as conductors, semi-conductors, or insulators. Only the characteristics of materials considered conductors will be examined in this text.

A measure of the resistance of a conductor is called its *specific resistance* or *resistivity*. This is a measure of the resistance of a unit length and unit cross-sectional area at a specific temperature. The diameter of the selected unit cross section is 0.001 in. This results in an area that is called a circular mil (cmil). This will be discussed in more detail later in the chapter. The unit length is chosen as 1 ft and the temperature at 20° Celsius, which is 68° Fahrenheit. The units for specific resistance are, then, ohms/circular mil foot, at 20° C. The Greek letter rho, ρ, is the symbol used to designate the specific resistance or resistivity.

Table 7–1 lists the specific resistance for some typical conductor materials. Note the wide variations.

TABLE 7–1 Specific Resistance, ρ, at 20° C

MATERIAL	ρ, Ω/CMIL FT
Silver	9.8
Copper	10.4
Aluminum	17.0
Tungsten	34
Iron (pure)	58
Magnesium	275
Nichrome II	660

7–5 EFFECT OF TEMPERATURE ON RESISTANCE

The designation of 20° C for the determination of the specific resistance, ρ, was a clue that there is, in fact, a change in resistance with temperature. All the conductor materials listed in Table 7–1 have an increase in resistance with an increase in temperature. This is found to be a linear variation from a temperature where the resistance is considered to be zero up to normal working temperature. The zero resistance point for copper is $-234.5°$ C. The following equation for copper results from this characteristic linear behavior:

$$\frac{R_2}{R_1} = \frac{234.5 + T_2}{234.5 + T_1}$$

where R_1 is the resistance in ohms at the °C temperature of T_1 and R_2 is the resistance in ohms at the °C temperature of T_2.

It should be stressed that the equation above is only for copper. While the variation or resistance with temperature of other conductor materials is also linear, the temperature where zero resistance occurs is different. As a result, the above relationship would not be correct.

example 7-6 The resistance of a copper conductor is 25 Ω at 30° C. What is the resistance at 46° C?

solution: $\dfrac{R_2}{R_1} = \dfrac{234.5 + T_2}{234.5 + T_1}$, where $R_1 = 25\ \Omega$, $T_1 = 30°$ C, and

$T_2 = 46°$ C:

$$\frac{R_2}{25} = \frac{234.5 + 46}{234.5 + 30} = \frac{280.5}{264.5}$$

$$R_2 = 25 \times 1.06 = 26.5\ \Omega$$

It would be well to point out here that not all materials have a linear increase in resistance with temperature. Some have nonlinear characteristics. One type of device in common use, called a thermistor, has a marked decrease in resistance with increasing temperature. This is also true for certain semiconductor devices.

7-6 CONDUCTOR MEASUREMENTS

In Section 7-4, a unit of measurement for conductors with a round cross section was introduced. This measure was called the circular mil. This concept will now be examined in greater detail.

The most common cross section for conductors is round. For this reason, the specific resistance is normally provided for round conductors. It was also necessary to set a standard temperature, length, and diameter for the measurement of this quantity. This uniformity establishes a common basis for comparison of the specific resistivity, ρ, for various round conductors.

These values are repeated for emphasis. The temperature chosen was 20° C. This is 68° F, often considered normal room temperature. The length chosen was 1 ft. The diameter selected was one-thousandths of an inch, 0.001 in, which is called a *mil*.

7–7 WIRE TABLES

Most conductors of electrical current are wires, and most wire is made of copper. A standard of wire measurement was required, and the *American Wire Gauge*, most frequently referred to as *AWG*, was established to provide such uniformity.

Table 7–2 shows a segment of the AWG tables. Actual wire tables provide much more information, but this material will serve the needs of this text. The AWG wire numbers shown run from size 0000 to size 40. Note that the smaller the AWG number, the larger the diameter and hence cross-sectional area.

TABLE 7–2 Wire Size and Diameters from AWG Tables

AWG NUMBER	DIAMETER, MILS	AWG NUMBER	DIAMETER, MILS
0000	460.0	19	35.89
000	409.6	20	31.96
00	364.8	21	28.46
0	324.9	22	25.35
1	289.3	23	22.57
2	257.6	24	20.10
3	229.4	25	17.90
4	204.3	26	15.94
5	181.9	27	14.20
6	162.0	28	12.64
7	144.3	29	11.26
8	128.5	30	10.03
9	114.4	31	8.928
10	101.9	32	7.950
11	90.74	33	7.080
12	80.81	34	6.305
13	71.96	35	5.615
14	64.08	36	5.000
15	57.07	37	4.453
16	50.82	38	3.965
17	45.26	39	3.531
18	40.30	40	3.145

If the area for each wire size were calculated, it would be found that the wire table was developed systematically. Examination would show that a decrease of one wire-gauge number would result in an approximate 25 percent increase in cross-sectional area.

If the data for one wire size were known using this information and that previously developed, the data for any other wire size could be approximated. Often wire size 10 is used as a standard of reference. It has approximate values of: diameter = 100 mils, area = 10,000 cmils, and resistance = 1 Ω/1,000 ft. For memory purposes, this size is ideal. The process of conversion using this procedure is rather cumbersome, however, and produces only approximate results. For most purposes, a wire table is more convenient and provides much more accurate data for calculations.

7–8 CIRCULAR MIL

The cross-sectional area of a round conductor is measured in circular mils. The *circular mil (cmil)* is the area of the round conductor, or wire, with its diameter measured in mils. Remember that a diameter of 0.001 in represents a diameter of 1 mil.

The area of a circle is found using the relationship

$$A = \frac{\pi d^2}{4}$$

The units of area are square inches if the diameter is in inches.

The circular mil is a unique unit of measurement. In much the same manner as the weighted line and "by the mark, three" evolved for the measurement of water depth, the circular mil was developed for a particular purpose.

In the calculation of an area of circular cross section, using the relationship above, it should be observed that $\frac{\pi}{4}$ is a constant. On this basis, $\frac{\pi}{4}$ is omitted in the calculation of the area in circular mils. The area using the $\frac{\pi}{4}$ relationship is in square units—square inches if the diameter is in inches, square feet if in feet, and so on. Omitting the $\frac{\pi}{4}$ results in a new unit of area measure, the circular mil. Hence in $A = d^2$, where the diameter is in mils, the area is in circular mils.

example 7-7 Determine the area in circular mils of a wire with a diameter of 0.012 in.

---

solution: $A = d^2$,   where $d = 0.012$ in = 12 mils
          $= 12^2$
          $= 144$ cmils

example 7-8 What is the diameter in inches of a wire with an area of 16,510 cmils?

solution: $A = d^2$, where $A = 16{,}510$ cmils
$d^2 = 16{,}510$
$d = 128.5$ mils
$= 0.1285$ in

EXERCISE 7-1 Calculate the area in circular mils of a wire with

1. $d = 0.027$ in
2. $d = 0.320$ mil
3. $d = 1$ cm
4. $d = 0.0032$ in

Determine the area in circular mils of a wire of

5. AWG #30
6. AWG #00

Determine the diameter of wire in inches if

7. cmils $= 520$
8. cmils $= 300{,}000$

7-9 SQUARE MIL

Another unit often used to measure a conductor cross section is the *square mil*. This is, in part, the result of the frequent use of a type of rectangular conductor called a bus bar.

The calculation of the cross-sectional area of a rectangular conductor is obtained by: area in square mils = width in mils × thickness in mils.

example 7-9 Determine the area in square mils of a bus bar 2 in wide and 0.012 in thick.

solution: area = width × thickness, where

width $= 2$ in $= 2{,}000$ mils

thickness $= 0.012$ in $= 12$ mils

$= 2{,}000 \times 12 = 24{,}000$ mils^2

example 7-10 What is the width in inches of a bus bar 0.025 in thick if it has an area of 37,500 square mils?

solution: $A =$ width × thickness, where $A = 37{,}500$ mils^2 and thickness $= 0.025$ in $= 25$ mils

$$\text{width} = \frac{A}{\text{thickness}}$$

$$= \frac{37{,}500}{25}$$

$$= 1{,}500 \text{ mils} = 1.50 \text{ in}$$

In the explanation of the circular mil in Section 7–8 it was stated that the $\frac{\pi}{4}$ factor was dropped from the calculation of the area of a round conductor. With this omitted, the area was designated in units of circular mils.

If the $\frac{\pi}{4}$ factor were not dropped, $A = \frac{\pi d^2}{4}$. If the diameter were measured in mils, the area would then be in square mils. We now have a means of comparing the circular mil with the square mil.

A circular mil is equal to $A = d^2$, whereas a square mil is equal to

$$A = \frac{\pi d^2}{4}$$

For a round conductor 1 mil in diameter the circular mil area is

$$\text{cmil area } A = d^2 = 1^2 = 1 \text{ cmil}$$

$$\text{mil}^2 \text{ area } A = \frac{\pi d^2}{4} = \frac{\pi \times 1^2}{4} = 0.7854 \text{ mil}^2$$

This establishes that the area of a round conductor, in square mils, is a factor $\frac{\pi}{4}$, or 0.7854 smaller than the area in circular mils. Then

$$A \text{ mils}^2 = 0.7854 \, A \text{ cmils} \quad \text{or}$$

$$A \text{ cmils} = \frac{A \text{ mils}^2}{0.7854}$$

This relationship provides a convenient means of converting from one unit to the other (see Figure 7–1). Although developed for a round conductor, this relationship between circular mils and square mils may be used for any conversion.

example 7–11 Determine the area in square mils of a round conductor with a diameter of 0.032 in.

solution: Calculating the area first in circular mils:

$$A = d^2, \quad \text{where } d = 0.032 \text{ in} = 32 \text{ mils}$$

$$= 32^2$$

$$= 1,024 \text{ cmils}$$

Then converting to square mils:

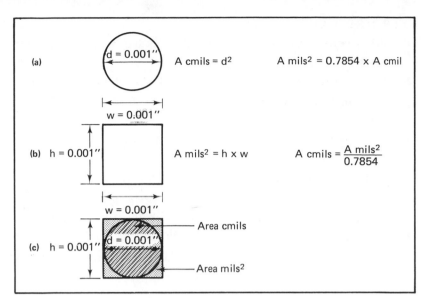

FIGURE 7–1
Circular Mil Compared with Square Mil (a) Circular Mil (b) Square Mil (c) Area
Comparison

$$A \text{ mils}^2 = 0.7854 \, A \text{ cmil}$$
$$= 0.7854 \times 1{,}024$$
$$= 804.2 \text{ mils}^2$$

example 7-12 Determine the area in square mils of a bus bar with an
area of 72,000 cmils. If the thickness is 0.025 in, determine the width in inches.

solution: $A \text{ mils}^2 = 0.7854A \text{ cmil}$

$A \text{ mils}^2 = 0.7854 \times 72{,}000$

$\qquad = 56{,}548.8 \text{ mils}^2$

$A \text{ mils}^2 = \text{width} \times \text{thickness}$

$\qquad \text{width} = \dfrac{A \text{ mils}^2}{\text{thickness}} \quad$ where thickness $= 0.025 \text{ in} = 25$
mils

$\qquad\qquad = \dfrac{56{,}548.8}{25}$

$\qquad\qquad = 2{,}261.9 \text{ mils}$

$\qquad\qquad = 2.262 \text{ in}$

EXERCISE 7-2

1. What is the area in square mils of a bus bar 3 in wide and 0.047 in thick?

2. What is the area of a wire in square mils if its diameter is 0.018 in?

3. Determine the area in square mils of AWG #14 and AWG #30 wire.

4. If a bus bar is 2 in wide and has an area of 39,500 cmils, determine the thickness.

5. Determine the area in circular mils of a bus bar 3 in wide and 0.365 in thick.

6. If a wire has an area of 16,000 cmils, what is its diameter?

7. A wire has an area of 40,000 mils². What is its diameter in inches?

8. Determine the area in circular mils and in square mils for AWG #20 wire. What is its diameter in inches?

7-11 CIRCULAR MIL FOOT

In Section 7-4, the concept of the specific resistance, ρ, was developed. The units for ρ are Ω/cmil ft. Subsequent sections provided experience with the circular mil. At this point it would be helpful to become more familiar with the circular mil foot.

A round conductor 1 ft long with a diameter of 1 mil is defined as a *circular mil foot* (cmil ft). This is sometimes referred to as simply a *mil ft*.

Previously, it has been established that the resistance of a conductor varies inversely with the area and directly with the length. In the circular-mil measure, the area varies as the square of the diameter. From these expressions, the following equation for wire results:

$$R = \rho \frac{l}{d^2}, \quad \text{where } \rho = \text{the specific resistance, } \Omega\text{/cmil ft}$$

$$l = \text{length, ft}$$

$$d = \text{diameter, mils}$$

$$R = \text{resistance, } \Omega$$

This relationship provides a convenient method of determining the resistance of a wire of any length, size, or material.

example 7-13 Determine the resistance, at 68° F, of an aluminum conductor 1 mile in length with a diameter of 10 mils.

solution: From Table 7-2, for aluminum, $\rho = 17$ Ω/cmil ft.

$$R = \rho \frac{l}{d^2}, \quad \text{where } l = 1 \text{ mi} = 5{,}280 \text{ ft}$$
$$d = 10 \text{ mils}$$

$$= 17 \frac{5{,}280}{10^2}$$

$$= 17 \times 52.8$$

$$= 897.6 \ \Omega$$

example 7–14 At room temperature a length of silver wire has a resistance of 3.25 Ω and a diameter of 0.0025 in. Determine the length in feet.

solution:

$$R = \rho \frac{l}{d^2}, \quad \text{where } \rho = 9.8 \ \Omega/\text{cmil ft}$$
$$d = 0.0025 \text{ in} = 2.5 \text{ mils}$$
$$R = 3.25 \ \Omega$$

Solving for l in this equation results in

$$l = \frac{Rd^2}{\rho}$$

$$= \frac{3.25 \times 2.5^2}{9.8}$$

$$= 2.07 \text{ ft}$$

EXERCISE 7–3

1. Determine the resistance of a copper conductor 5 mi long and 0.352 in in diameter.

2. What is the length of a copper conductor with a diameter 0.012 in if its resistance is found to be 727 Ω?

3. A conductor of unknown material has a length of 1,500 ft, a resistance of 450 Ω and a 0.010-in cross section. Determine the value of ρ.

4. A wire of pure iron has a length of 1,200 cm and a diameter of 0.25 ft. Determine its resistance.

5. What is the cross-sectional area in circular mils of an aluminum wire 7,500 ft long with a resistance of 18,200 Ω?

6. A length of Nichrome II wire has a diameter of 12.6 mils and a length of 15 ft. What is its resistance?

7. Determine the diameter in inches of a silver wire 1.5 m long and a resistance of 0.375 kΩ.

8. What is the length of a tungsten wire with a diameter of 0.032 in and a resistance of 420 Ω?

8
SERIES CIRCUIT

$\blacksquare$n earlier chapters, a number of definitions regarding electricity were presented. Ohm's law was used to demonstrate equations and their solution. Conductors and resistance concepts were developed in Chapter 7.

All of the above background is essential to understand the concepts of the electric circuit. In this chapter the most basic of these circuits, the direct current, dc, series circuit, will be presented.

Some basic electrical terms were presented in Chapter 6. A brief explanation of their meaning, abbreviations, and symbols were included. The terms of principal interest here are those of the volt, ampere, and ohm. For purposes of review this information is presented again in Table 8–1. The explanations are necessarily brief. A more detailed understanding of these terms will be presented in other courses of instruction.

TABLE 8–1 Electrical Terms

TERM	ABBREVIATION	SYMBOL	EXPLANATION
Volt	V	E or V	Electrical pressure
Ampere	A	I	Electric current flow
Resistance	R	Ω	Opposition to current flow

All three of these basic electrical terms are used in developing an understanding of the operation of an electric circuit. The voltage provides the electrical pressure, or *electromotive force (emf)*, as it is often called. The ampere is a measure of the electric current flow in the circuit. The resistance, in the form of a resistor or other electrical device, represents the opposition to the flow of current. The electric circuit provides a complete path for current to flow.

Figure 8–1 is a graphical or schematic representation of an electrical circuit, called a *circuit diagram*. All the necessary essentials are shown. The battery is the source of direct-current voltage or electromotive force. The resistor provides the opposition to current flow. Wires or electrical conductors, connecting the two, provide the complete electrical path or circuit for the current to flow. This, then, is the basic electric circuit.

Note that in the circuit diagram the direction of current flow is indicated. In this text, current will *always* be considered to flow from negative (−) to positive (+).

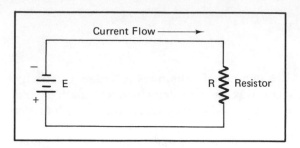

FIGURE 8–1
Electric Circuit

8–2 SERIES CIRCUIT

A *series circuit* is one in which the current is the same at any point in the circuit. Figure 8–2 represents a series circuit. The current flow that leaves the source passes through the resistors and returns unreduced in amount, back to the source. If the current were measured at any point in the circuit, it would be the same.

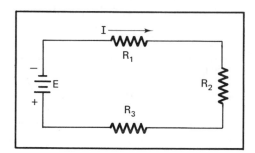

FIGURE 8–2
Series Circuit—Resistances in Series

The series circuit in Figure 8–2 has three resistances in series. As in Figure 8–1, the amount of current that leaves the source passes through each resistance in series and returns to the source. Once again, the current through resistances R_1, R_2, and R_3 is the same.

8–3 OHM'S LAW AND THE SERIES CIRCUIT

Ohm's law is stated in the form

$$R = \frac{E}{I}$$

where R is the resistance in ohms, E the voltage in volts, and I the current in amperes. Ohm's law may be also expressed in the following form:

$$I = \frac{E}{R} \quad \text{and} \quad E = IR$$

In the circuit shown in Figure 8–2, all the terms used in Ohm's law are present. If any two of the terms were known, the other could be determined using Ohm's law.

8–4 OHM'S LAW APPLIED—SIMPLE SERIES CIRCUIT

In this section, a number of practical applications of Ohm's law in the simple series circuit will be developed. These will provide the background that will be necessary in order to work with more complicated circuits. It is essential that the reader become thoroughly familiar with these basic procedures.

example 8–1 Determine the resistance in the circuit of Figure 8–3 if the voltage is 100 V and the current is 5A.

solution: Using Ohm's law,

$$R = \frac{E}{I} = \frac{100}{5} = 20 \ \Omega$$

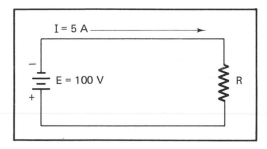

FIGURE 8–3
Circuit for Example 8–1

example 8–2 A dc generator (Figure 8–4) delivers 24 V to a resistor of 4,800 Ω. What current flows in the circuit?

solution: $$I = \frac{E}{R} = \frac{24}{4.8 \times 10^3} = 5 \times 10^{-3} \ \text{A} = 5 \ \text{mA}$$

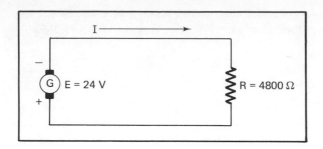

FIGURE 8–4
Circuit for Example 8–2

example 8–3 An ammeter placed in a circuit reads 4.2 μA (Figure 8–5). A resistor has a value of 2.2 MΩ. What would the voltmeter read when placed across the battery?

solution: $E = IR$

$$= 4.2 \times 10^{-6} \times 2.2 \times 10^{6}$$

$$= 9.24 \text{ V}$$

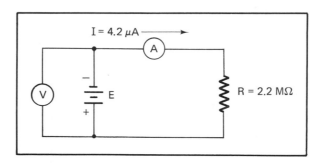

FIGURE 8–5
Circuit for Example 8–3

EXERCISE 8–1

1. What current would flow in the circuit if 150 V were placed across a resistor of 30,000 Ω?

2. Determine the size of a resistor in a circuit if $E = 500$ V and $I = 3$ A.

3. What voltage would be required to cause a current of 5.2 A to flow through a resistor of 2,300 Ω?

4. What current through a resistor of 4.2 kΩ would a voltage of 1.27 mV produce?

5. A generator that developed 0.05 kV, when connected to a motor, resulted in a current flow of 1,200 mA. What is the resistance of the motor?

6. What current would flow through an ammeter in a circuit if a voltmeter placed across a 1.2-mΩ resistor read 1.47 μA?

7. A resistor of what size would be required to limit the current flow in a circuit to 4.15 mA, if 1.36 V were applied?

8. A battery of what size would be required to cause 0.25 A to flow through a resistor of 0.024 kΩ?

8–5 OHM'S LAW APPLIED—RESISTANCES IN SERIES

A series circuit showing three resistances in series, similar to Figure 8–2, is shown in Figure 8–6. Recalling the definition of a series circuit, the current flow at any point is the same. This would, of course, mean that the current flow through resistors R_1, R_2, and R_3 would be the same.

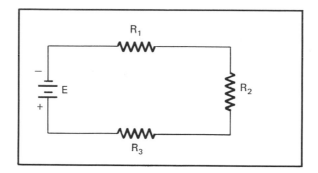

FIGURE 8–6
Series Circuit—Three Resistors in Series

In the circuit of Figure 8–7 values have been assigned to the supply voltage E, the current I, and resistors R_1, R_2, and R_3. In this circuit, the voltages E_{R_1}, E_{R_2}, and E_{R_3} that exist across R_1, R_2, and R_3 are not known. It should be observed that the supply voltage of $E =$ 100 V is placed across all three resistors connected in series.

From the series circuits examined previously, it was found that, using Ohm's law, the voltage across a resistance was a product of its current and its resistance, as $E = IR$. Applying this to resistors R_1, R_2, and R_3,

$$E_{R_1} = IR_1 = 1 \times 10 = 10 \text{ V}$$

$$E_{R_2} = IR_2 = 1 \times 40 = 40 \text{ V}$$

$$E_{R_3} = IR_3 = 1 \times 50 = 50 \text{ V}$$

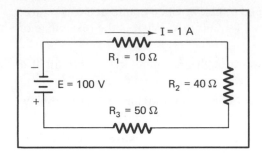

FIGURE 8-7
Circuit of Figure 8-6 with Values Shown

Upon examination, it will be seen that the supply voltage $E = 100$ V is equal to the sum of the voltages E_1, E_2, and E_3, or

$$E = E_1 + E_2 + E_3 = 10 + 40 + 50 = 100 \text{ V}$$

If the total circuit resistance, R_T, were to be determined, it would again be found by using Ohm's law,

$$R_T = \frac{E}{I} = \frac{100}{1} = 100 \text{ }\Omega$$

Examination will reveal that the total circuit resistance, $R_T = 100$ Ω, is equal to the sum of R_1, R_2, and R_3:

$$R_T = R_1 + R_2 + R_3 = 10 + 40 + 50 = 100 \text{ }\Omega$$

From these observations, the following rules may be written:

> FOR A CIRCUIT WITH RESISTANCES IN SERIES
> 1. THE SUM OF THE VOLTAGES ACROSS EACH RESISTANCE IS EQUAL TO THE SUPPLY VOLTAGE.
> 2. THE SUM OF THE INDIVIDUAL RESISTANCES IS EQUAL TO THE TOTAL CIRCUIT RESISTANCE.

example 8-4 Determine the supply voltage if the circuit current is 0.50 A and the three resistances in series have values of $R_1 = 200$ Ω, $R_2 = 600$ Ω, and $R_3 = 800$ Ω (Figure 8-8).

solution: Examination of this circuit shows that the resistance of each resistor and current flow through each resistor is known. Therefore,

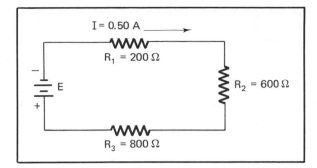

FIGURE 8–8
Circuit for Example 8–4

$$E_{R_1} = I \times R_1 = 0.50 \times 200 = 100 \text{ V}$$

$$E_{R_2} = I \times R_2 = 0.50 \times 600 = 300 \text{ V}$$

$$E_{R_3} = I \times R_3 = 0.50 \times 800 = 400 \text{ V}$$

and since $E = E_{R_1} + E_{R_2} + E_{R_3}$, then

$$E = 100 + 300 + 400 = 800 \text{ V}$$

Solved another way,

$$R_T = R_1 + R_2 + R_3$$

$$= 200 + 600 + 800$$

$$= 1{,}600 \ \Omega$$

and since $E = I \times R_T$, then

$$E = 0.50 \times 1{,}600$$

$$= 800 \text{ V}$$

example 8–5 Determine the supply voltage, the circuit current, and the voltage across resistors R_1 and R_2 (Figure 8–9).

solution: Examination of this circuit shows that while the total resistance R_T may be determined as $R_T = R_1 + R_2 + R_3$, the circuit current is unknown. However, this may be calculated with the information available from R_3:

$$I = \frac{E_3}{R_3} = \frac{180}{100} = 1.8 \text{ A}$$

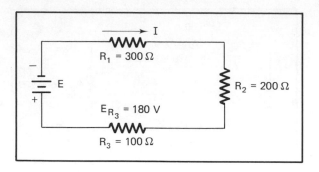

FIGURE 8-9
Circuit for Example 8-5

This common circuit current may then be used to determine E_{R_1} and E_{R_2}:

$$E_{R_1} = IR_1 = 1.8 \times 300 = 540 \text{ V}$$

$$E_{R_2} = IR_2 = 1.8 \times 200 = 360 \text{ V}$$

Therefore,

$$E = E_{R_1} + E_{R_2} + E_{R_3} = 540 + 360 + 180 = 1,080 \text{ V}$$

The voltage, E, may also be calculated from

$$E = IR_T \quad \text{where } R_T = R_1 + R_2 + R_3$$
$$R_T = 300 + 200 + 100 = 600 \text{ } \Omega$$

Then

$$E = 1.8 \times 600 = 1,080 \text{ V}$$

example 8-6 In the circuit of Figure 8–10, determine E, R_1, R_2, R_3, and R_T.

solution: Examination of the circuit shows that the voltage across each resistance is known, along with the current through the circuit. Therefore,

$$R_1 = \frac{E_{R_1}}{I} = \frac{50}{2} = 25 \text{ } \Omega$$

$$R_2 = \frac{E_{R_2}}{I} = \frac{60}{2} = 30 \text{ } \Omega$$

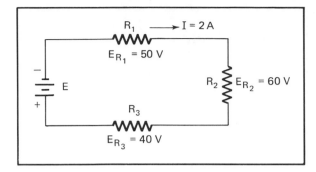

FIGURE 8–10
Circuit for Example 8–6

$$R_3 = \frac{E_{R3}}{I} = \frac{40}{2} = 20 \ \Omega$$

R_T may then be determined:

$$R_T = R_1 + R_2 + R_3 = 25 + 30 + 20 = 75 \ \Omega$$

The supply voltage is then found:

$$E = IR_T = 2 \times 75 = 150 \ \text{V}$$

It could also have been calculated as

$$E = E_{R_1} + E_{R_2} + E_{R_3} = 50 + 60 + 40 = 150 \ \text{V}$$

example 8–7 A dc generator supplies 1,800 V to a series circuit composed of three resistances, $R_1 = 100 \ \Omega$, $R_2 = 200 \ \Omega$, and $R_3 = 300 \ \Omega$ (Figure 8–11). Determine the circuit current and the voltage across each resistance.

solution: $R_T = R_1 + R_2 + R_3 = 100 + 200 + 300 = 600 \ \Omega$

$$I = \frac{E}{R_T} = \frac{1,800}{600} = 3 \ \text{A}$$

$$E_{R_1} = IR_1 = 3 \times 100 = 300 \ \text{V}$$

$$E_{R_2} = IR_2 = 3 \times 200 = 600 \ \text{V}$$

$$E_{R_3} = IR_3 = 3 \times 300 = 900 \ \text{V}$$

As a check,

$$E = E_{R_1} + E_{R_2} + E_{R_3} = 300 + 600 + 900 = 1,800 \ \text{V}$$

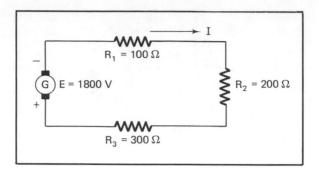

FIGURE 8-11
Circuit for Example 8-7

EXERCISE 8-2

1. The current flow through two resistors, $R_1 = 30\ \Omega$ and $R_2 = 60\ \Omega$ in series, is 5 A. Determine the voltage across each resistor and the line voltage.

2. The total resistance of a circuit composed of R_1 and R_2 in series is 200 Ω. The voltage across $R_1 = 100$ V and $R_2 = 200$ V. Determine the line voltage and line current.

3. For two resistors in series, R_1 and R_2, the voltage across R_2 is $E_{R_2} = 100$ V and the resistance of $R_1 = 60\ \Omega$. The line voltage is $E = 250$ V. Determine I, R_2, and E_{R_1}.

4. Three resistances, R_1, R_2, and R_3, are in series across a 200-V line, $R_1 = 200\ \Omega$, $R_2 = 300\ \Omega$, and $R_3 = 400\ \Omega$. Determine I, E_{R_1}, E_{R_2}, E_{R_3}, and R_T.

5. Three resistances, $R_1 = 50\ \Omega$, $R_2 = 60\ \Omega$, and $R_3 = 80\ \Omega$, are connected in series. The voltage across R_2 is $E_{R_2} = 300$ V. Find I, E_{R_1}, E_{R_3}, E, and R_T.

6. The total circuit resistance of R_1, R_2, and R_3 in series is 200 Ω. The resistance of $R_3 = 60\ \Omega$, $R_2 = 40\ \Omega$, and $E_{R_3} = 240$ V. Find E, E_{R_1}, E_{R_2}, and R_1.

7. In a series circuit, $R_1 = 50\ \Omega$, $R_2 = 40\ \Omega$, $R_3 = 20\ \Omega$, and $R_4 = 10\ \Omega$. The circuit current is 5 A. Determine E, R_T, E_{R_1}, E_{R_2}, E_{R_3}, and E_{R_4}.

8. What is the current I through a circuit composed of $R_1 = 30\ \Omega$, $R_2 = 40\ \Omega$, and $R_3 = x$? The circuit voltage is $E = 250$ V, and $E_{R_3} = 60$ V and $E_{R_1} = 90$ V.

8-6 POWER

Another electrical term briefly explained in Chapter 6 was the watt. The *watt* is a unit that is used as a measure of the rate of generation or the rate of utilization of energy. This is referred to as *power*. Power is usually measured in watts, kilowatts, or megawatts.

The measurement of the generation or consumption of power is normally made on an hourly basis. The power that a nuclear power plant produces would have its large generating capability rated in megawatt-hours. The homeowner, with his relatively low usage, would purchase his power on a kilowatt-hour basis.

In dc electrical circuits, power is measured using the following relationship:

$$P = EI \qquad (1)$$

where E is in volts, I is in amperes, and P is in watts.

The voltage and current terms in Equation (1) are also used in Ohm's law. This permits the development of a relationship between the two. In the power equation,

$$P = EI$$

while in Ohm's law,

$$I = \frac{E}{R} \qquad (2)$$

A comparison of the two equations shows that the current term I in Ohm's law may be substituted in the power equation. This results in

$$P = E\left(\frac{E}{R}\right) = \frac{E^2}{R} \qquad (3)$$

Ohm's law in one of its other forms is written

$$E = IR \qquad (4)$$

Substituting the value for E in the power equation produces

$$P = (IR)I = I^2R \qquad (5)$$

Another useful power term is the *horsepower*. This provides a relationship between mechanical and electrical energy. An automobile engine is rated in mechanical terms while its electrical generator or alternator is rated in electrical terms. The relation between the mechanical power and electrical power is expressed as

1 horsepower (hp) = 746 watts (W)

This provides a very convenient and useful means for comparing mechanical and electrical power.

8-7 EFFICIENCY

Men have sought in vain for the perpetual-motion machine. Such a search is doomed from the start because of the energy losses that always occur. A student will often question why the output of an electrical generator, once in operation, cannot be used to supply the electrical motor that is driving the generator. The student has not found a perpetual-motion process because of the losses that occur. These losses are the result of the fact that the electrical, mechanical, and magnetic processes involved are less than perfect.

A measure of how close a process or device is to perfection is called its *efficiency*. The long-sought perpetual-motion device with no losses would have an efficiency of 100 percent. All devices as noted fall short of this ideal. An electrical transformer has efficiencies in the 90 percent range, while the old steam locomotive had efficiencies in the order of 10 percent. It should be obvious that it is desirable to obtain as high an efficiency as possible. At 100 percent efficiency, the following condition would exist:

input = output

Losses present in all processes result in the following practical relationship:

input − losses = output

Efficiency is a comparison of the input power of a device to its output power. It is usually expressed as a percentage:

$$\text{efficiency} = \frac{\text{output}}{\text{input}} \times 100$$

Efficiency, then, is a ratio of the input to the output, and so the units of both must be the same. If the comparison is in mechanical units, both must be in horsepower, for example. If in electrical units, then if the input is measured in watts, the output must be in watts.

example 8-8 A refrigeration motor has an output of $\frac{1}{4}$ hp. The electrical input is 120 V and 2 A. Determine the efficiency and the losses.

solution: Output: $\frac{1}{4}$ hp × 746 W/hp = 186.5 W

Input: $P = EI = 120 \times 2 = 240$W

$$\text{Efficiency} = \frac{\text{output}}{\text{input}} \times 100 = \frac{186.5}{240} = 77.7\%$$

$$\text{Losses} = \text{input} - \text{output} = 240 \text{ W} - 186.5 \text{ W} = 53.5 \text{ W}$$

example 8–9 Determine the input current to a motor on 400-V lines. The output is 200 hp. The motor has an efficiency of 82.3 percent.

solution: Output: $200 \text{ hp} \times 746 \text{ W/hp} = 149,200 \text{ W} = 149.2 \text{ kW}$

$$\text{Input} = \frac{\text{output}}{\text{efficiency}} \times 100 = \frac{149.2}{82.3} \times 100 = 181.3 \text{ kW}$$

$$\text{Input } P = E \times I \text{ or } P_{\text{kW}} = \frac{E \times I}{1,000}$$

$$I = \frac{P_{\text{kW}} \times 1,000}{E} = \frac{181.3 \times 1,000}{440} = 412 \text{ A}$$

EXERCISE 8–3

1. On the basis of an average cost of 2.97 cents per kilowatt-hour, how much would an average daily consumption of 22 kilowatt-hours cost in a 30-day period?

2. Determine the amount of power consumed by a 120-V portable room heater, with a resistance of 12 Ω. How much would the cost of operation be if the unit ran for 3 hours (h) and the cost per kilowatt-hour was 2.07 cents?

3. Calculate the efficiency of an electric motor that has an input of 1,200 W and losses of 156 W.

4. A 1,200-hp diesel engine drives an electrical generator that has an output of 2,200 V and 320 A. Determine the losses in kilowatts and the efficiency.

5. If an electrical motor has an efficiency of 72 percent and the output is 24 hp, what is the input in watts?

6. Calculate the efficiency of a motor–generator set if the motor draws 52 A from 440-V lines. The generator operating at rated output delivers 781 A at 24 V. What are the losses in watts?

7. A 660-V generator receives 1,251.7 hp from a diesel engine. At rated load it has an efficiency of 86.2 percent. Determine the output current and the generator losses in watts.

8. Calculate the efficiency of a motor-generator set if the motor input is 35 hp and the generator delivers 49.5 A at 400 V.

9
PARALLEL CIRCUIT

roblems often occur when a number of electrical devices are placed in series. For this reason the series circuit is not suitable for many commercial applications. If a short circuit occurred in one device of a series, the full line voltage would then be across the remaining units. This overvoltage could result in damage to the remaining devices.

An open circuit occurring in one device of a series creates another type of problem. A check of each unit would be required to locate and remedy the fault. Think of the problem that this would create if series circuits were used for home lighting purposes. Each time a bulb failed, individual bulbs, often in different rooms and often in the dark, would have to be tested.

For the above reasons, and others, in many applications the series circuit has been replaced by the parallel circuit.

9–1 PARALLEL CIRCUIT

In the series circuit, the current is common to all circuit elements. In the *parallel circuit* the voltage is common to all circuit elements. A simple parallel circuit is shown in Figure 9–1. In this circuit the voltage, E, is common to both R_1 and R_2. In other words, each resistance has the full supply voltage E, connected across its terminals.

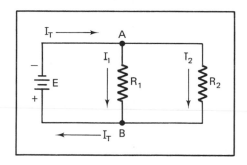

FIGURE 9–1
Parallel Circuit—Two Resistances in Parallel

The circuit current, I_T, divides when it reaches point A. Part of the current flows through resistance R_1 and is labeled I_1. The other part flows through R_2 and is labeled I_2. At point B the currents I_1 and I_2 combine, to again form I_T, which returns to the battery. In this type of circuit it is seen that an open-circuit failure in one unit would not affect the operation of the other unit.

Using Ohm's law in the form $I = \dfrac{E}{R}$, it is possible to determine the circuit current, I_T, and the current through each of the circuit branches, I_1 and I_2. The circuit current may be expressed as

$$I_T = I_1 + I_2$$

Using Ohm's law this may be written

$$\frac{E}{R_T} = \frac{E}{R_1} + \frac{E}{R_2}$$

If both sides of the equation are divided by E, the following relationship results:

$$\frac{1}{R_T} = \frac{1}{R_1} + \frac{1}{R_2}$$

R_T is often referred to as the *equivalent resistance* of the parallel circuit.

In a previous chapter, the reciprocal of resistance was called the conductance, G. So in the parallel circuit above, the circuit conductance is equal to the sum of the conductance of the branches or

$$G_T = G_1 + G_2$$

For a parallel circuit with two branches, a special relationship is developed. This may be helpful in problem-solving techniques. If the equation

$$\frac{1}{R_T} = \frac{1}{R_1} + \frac{1}{R_2}$$

is solved for R_T, the following equation results:

$$R_T = \frac{R_1 R_2}{R_1 + R_2}$$

Keep in mind that this equation *only applies* to a circuit with two branches. A similar relationship may be developed for three resistances in parallel or, for that matter, any number of parallel resistances. The larger the number, the more progressively involved the mathematical relationship becomes. As a result, the equation for two resistances in parallel is the only one commonly used.

example 9-1 Determine the total resistance of $R_1 = 100$ and $R_2 = 200$ in parallel.

solution:
$$\frac{1}{R_T} = \frac{1}{R_1} + \frac{1}{R_2} = \frac{1}{100} + \frac{1}{200}$$

$$\frac{1}{R_T} = 0.01 + 0.005 = 0.015$$

$$R_T = 66.6 \ \Omega$$

example 9-2 Calculate the total resistance of $R_1 = 10 \ \Omega$ and $R_2 = 6 \ \Omega$ when connected in parallel.

solution:
$$R_T = \frac{R_1 R_2}{R_1 + R_2} = \frac{10 \times 6}{10 + 6} = \frac{60}{16}$$

$$R_T = 3.75 \ \Omega$$

Examination of the above examples shows that the total circuit resistance is smaller than the smallest resistance in the circuit. This is *always true* in a parallel circuit. This relationship is helpful in providing a quick check of parallel-circuit-resistance calculations. If a calculation results in a circuit resistance larger than the smallest resistance, the results are in error and must be recalculated.

9-2 OHM'S LAW APPLIED—TWO PARALLEL RESISTANCES

In the solution of problems involving parallel circuits, it will be shown in the following examples that there are several methods of approach. Each is perfectly acceptable and correct. It is entirely optional which procedure is used.

In examining a problem before attempting a solution, it is helpful to remember that Ohm's law, in one of its forms, will probably be used. Using this relationship for the circuit, or for individual branches, two of the three literal numbers E, I, or R must be known or be able to be determined.

In conjunction with Ohm's law, the relationships for total circuit resistance are also available. These are also helpful in considering a solution prior to attempting it.

example 9-3 In the circuit shown in Figure 9-2, determine the circuit current, I_T, the branch currents, I_1 and I_2, and the total circuit resistance, R_T.

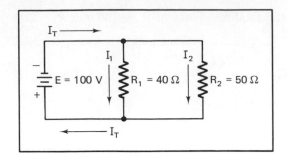

FIGURE 9–2
Circuit Diagram for Example 9–3

ANALYSIS:

The circuit shows the following:

	CIRCUIT		BRANCH 1		BRANCH 2	
	KNOWN	UNKNOWN	KNOWN	UNKNOWN	KNOWN	UNKNOWN
	E	I_T, R_T	E, R_1	I_1	E, R_2	I_2

Knowing both the resistance and voltage of each branch, the currents I_1 and I_2 may be determined. The circuit current I_T may then be found and R_T calculated.

solution:

$$I_1 = \frac{E}{R_1} = \frac{100}{40} = 2.5 \text{ A}$$

$$I_2 = \frac{E}{R_2} = \frac{100}{50} = 2 \text{ A}$$

$$I_T = I_1 + I_2 = 2.5 + 2 = 4.5 \text{ A}$$

$$R_T = \frac{E}{I_T} = \frac{100}{4.5} = 22.2 \ \Omega$$

Calculating R_T by the method

$$\frac{1}{R_T} = \frac{1}{R_1} + \frac{1}{R_2}$$

results in

$$\frac{1}{R_T} = \frac{1}{40} + \frac{1}{50} = 0.025 + 0.020$$

$$= 0.045$$

$$R_T = 22.2\ \Omega$$

Using the special relations for two resistances in parallel,

$$R_T = \frac{R_1 R_2}{R_1 + R_2}$$

results in

$$R_T = \frac{40 \times 50}{40 + 50} = \frac{2{,}000}{90} = 22.2\ \Omega$$

example 9-4 In the circuit shown in Figure 9–3, determine I_1, I_2, R_2, and R_T.

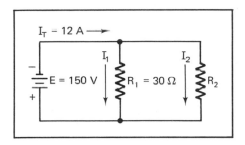

FIGURE 9–3
Circuit Diagram for Example 9–4

ANALYSIS:

The circuit shows the following:

CIRCUIT KNOWN	BRANCH 1 KNOWN	BRANCH 2 KNOWN
E, I_T	E, R_1	E
UNKNOWN	**UNKNOWN**	**UNKNOWN**
R_T	I_1	I_2, R_2

Examination of the above shows two solution procedures that may be used.

1. Knowing the voltage, E, and the resistance, R_1, of branch 1, I_1 may be determined. With I_T and I_1 known, I_2 may be calculated. Then calculating R_2, R_T may be found using R_1 and R_2. Note that R_T could have been determined initially using E and I_T.

2. Knowing the circuit E and I_T, R_T could be calculated. With R_T and R_1 known, R_2 could then be determined. I_1 and I_2 could then be found.

Each of these methods will be shown in the solution.

solution: *Method 1*

The current I_1 through the R_1 branch may be calculated, as E and R_1 are known:

$$I_1 = \frac{E}{R_1} = \frac{150}{30} = 5 \text{ A}$$

As the total current I_T and the branch current I_1 are known, the current I_2 may now be determined.

$$I_T = I_1 + I_2$$
$$12 = 5 + I_2$$
$$I_2 = 7 \text{ A}$$

With the voltage across R_2 equal to E and the current I_2 known, the value of R_2 may now be calculated:

$$R_2 = \frac{E}{I_2} = \frac{150}{7} = 21.4 \ \Omega$$

Calculating R_T from

$$R_T = \frac{R_1 R_2}{R_1 + R_2} = \frac{30 \times 21.4}{30 + 21.4} = \frac{642}{51.4} = 12.5 \ \Omega \quad \text{or}$$

$$R_T = \frac{E}{I_T} = \frac{150}{12} = 12.5 \ \Omega$$

solution: *Method 2*

Knowing E and I_T,

$$R_T = \frac{E}{I_T} = \frac{150}{12} = 12.5 \ \Omega$$

Calculating R_2 from

$$\frac{1}{R_T} = \frac{1}{R_1} + \frac{1}{R_2}$$

$$\frac{1}{12.5} = \frac{1}{30} + \frac{1}{R_2}$$

$$0.008 = 0.033 + \frac{1}{R_2}$$

$$\frac{1}{R_2} = 0.0467$$

$$R_2 = \frac{1}{0.047} = 21.4 \ \Omega$$

$$I_1 = \frac{E}{R_1} = \frac{150}{30} = 5 \ A$$

$$I_2 = \frac{E}{R_2} = \frac{150}{21.4} = 7 \ A$$

101
Sec. 9–3
OHM'S LAW
APPLIED—THREE
OR MORE
PARALLEL
RESISTANCES

9–3 OHM'S LAW APPLIED—THREE OR MORE PARALLEL RESISTANCES

The procedures developed for two resistances in parallel also apply to circuits where three or more resistances are in parallel. A circuit with three resistances is shown in Figure 9–4. As with all parallel circuits, the voltage is common to all branches. Here the supply voltage, E, is common to R_1, R_2, and R_3. The line current I_T flows from the battery, as shown. When point A is reached, the line current, I_T, divides, with a part, the current, I_1, flowing through resistance, R_1. The remainder flows to point B. At point B, this current divides, with I_2 flowing through resistance R_2 and I_3 flowing through resistance R_3. After passing through these resistances, currents I_2 and I_3 combine at point C and flow toward point D. At point D, the combined I_2 and I_3 join with I_1 to again form the line current, I_T, which returns to the supply.

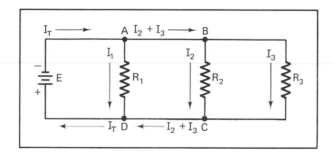

FIGURE 9–4
Parallel Circuit—Three Resistances in Parallel

The total resistance of the circuit is

$$\frac{1}{R_T} = \frac{1}{R_1} + \frac{1}{R_2} + \frac{1}{R_3}$$

and the total conductance is

$$G_T = G_1 + G_2 + G_3$$

If the parallel circuit contains more than three branches, then

$$\frac{1}{R_T} = \frac{1}{R_1} + \frac{1}{R_2} + \frac{1}{R_3} + \frac{1}{R_4} + \text{etc.} \quad \text{and}$$

$$G_T = G_1 + G_2 + G_3 + G_4 + \text{etc.}$$

example 9-5 In the circuit in Figure 9–5, determine the circuit current, I_T; the branch currents, I_1, I_2, and I_3; and the total circuit resistance, R_T.

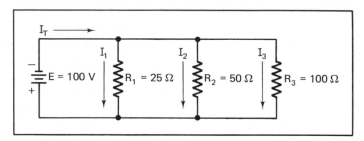

FIGURE 9-5
Circuit Diagram for Example 9–5

ANALYSIS:
The circuit shows the following:

CIRCUIT KNOWN	BRANCH 1 KNOWN	BRANCH 2 KNOWN	BRANCH 3 KNOWN
E	E, R_1	E, R_2	E, R_3
UNKNOWN	UNKNOWN	UNKNOWN	UNKNOWN
I_T, R_T	I_1	I_2	I_3

Knowing the resistance and voltage across each branch, I_1, I_2, and I_3 may be calculated. The line current, I_T, may then be determined. The circuit resistance R_T may be calculated using E and I_T or the resistances R_1, R_2, and R_3.

solution:

$$I_1 = \frac{E}{R_1} = \frac{100}{25} = 4 \text{ A}$$

103
Sec. 9–3
OHM'S LAW
APPLIED—THREE
OR MORE
PARALLEL
RESISTANCES

$$I_2 = \frac{E}{R_2} = \frac{100}{50} = 2 \text{ A}$$

$$I_3 = \frac{E}{R_3} = \frac{100}{100} = 1 \text{ A}$$

$$I_T = I_1 + I_2 + I_3 = 4 + 2 + 1 = 7 \text{ A}$$

$$R_T = \frac{E}{I_T} = \frac{100}{7} = 14.3 \ \Omega \quad \text{or}$$

$$\frac{1}{R_T} = \frac{1}{R_1} + \frac{1}{R_2} + \frac{1}{R_3} = \frac{1}{25} + \frac{1}{50} + \frac{1}{100}$$

$$= 0.04 + 0.02 + 0.01 = 0.07$$

$$R_T = \frac{1}{0.07} = 14.3 \ \Omega$$

example 9-6   In the circuit in Figure 9–6, determine I_1, I_2, I_3, R_2, and R_T.

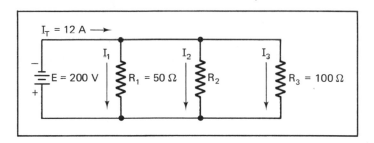

FIGURE 9–6
Circuit Diagram for Example 9–6

ANALYSIS:

CIRCUIT KNOWN	BRANCH 1 KNOWN	BRANCH 2 KNOWN	BRANCH 3 KNOWN
E, I_T	E, R_1	E	E, R_3
UNKNOWN	UNKNOWN	UNKNOWN	UNKNOWN
R_T	I_1	I_2, R_2	I_3

solution: Solving first for I_1 and I_3 using Ohm's law, $I = \dfrac{E}{R}$,

$$I_1 = \frac{200}{50} = 4 \text{ A}, \qquad I_3 = \frac{200}{100} = 2 \text{ A}$$

As $I_T = I_1 + I_2 + I_3$, I_2 may then be found:

$$12 = 4 + I_2 + 2$$

$$I_2 = 6 \text{ A}$$

Then

$$R_2 = \frac{E}{I_2} = \frac{200}{6} = 33.3 \ \Omega$$

and solving,

$$R_T = \frac{E}{I_T} = \frac{200}{12} = 16.6 \ \Omega$$

As a check,

$$\frac{1}{R_T} = \frac{1}{R_1} + \frac{1}{R_2} + \frac{1}{R_3} = \frac{1}{50} + \frac{1}{33.3} + \frac{1}{100}$$

$$\frac{1}{R} = 0.02 + 0.03 + 0.01 = 0.06$$

$$R_2 = 16.6 \ \Omega$$

EXERCISE 9–1

1. Calculate the circuit resistance of $R_1 = 100 \ \Omega$, $R_2 = 200 \ \Omega$ in parallel.

2. Determine the current flow, I_T, that would result if $R_1 = 24 \ \Omega$, $R_2 = 30 \ \Omega$, and $R_3 = 38 \ \Omega$ in parallel were placed across 120 V.

3. What is the size of R_1 required in parallel with R_2, to produce a circuit resistance $R_T = 100 \ \Omega$, if $R_2 = 400 \ \Omega$?

4. In a parallel circuit composed of R_1 and R_2, it is desired to limit the circuit current to 5.2 mA. What is the size of R_1 if $R_2 = 100 \ \text{k}\Omega$? The supply voltage is 50 V.

5. Calculate the circuit resistance of $R_1 = 20 \ \Omega$, $R_2 = 30 \ \Omega$, $R_3 = 40 \ \Omega$, and $R_4 = 50 \ \Omega$ in parallel.

6. Determine the circuit conductance of $R_1 = 35.2 \ \Omega$ in parallel with $R_2 = 57.5 \ \Omega$. What is the equivalent circuit resistance?

7. A circuit is composed of $R = 100 \ \Omega$, $R_2 = 200 \ \Omega$, and $R_3 = 600 \ \Omega$ in parallel. What would be the effect on the circuit resistance if R_3 became an open circuit?

8. In a circuit of $R_1 = 100\ \Omega$, $R_2 = 2,000\ \Omega$, and $R_3 = 60\ \Omega$, what would be the effect on the circuit resistance if a short circuit were placed across R_1?

9. The equivalent resistance of a circuit made up of R_1, R_2, and R_3 in parallel is $10.7\ \Omega$. The conductance of $R_1 = 15.2$ mmhos and $R_2 = 12.1$ mmhos. Determine the resistance of R_3.

10. The current flow in a circuit is 15.2 A. The circuit consists of $R_1 = 27.2\ \Omega$, $R_2 = 36.5\ \Omega$, and $R_3 = 65.2\ \Omega$. Determine the current flow in each branch.

11. What voltage would be required to cause a circuit current of 15.2 mA through a parallel circuit composed of $R_1 = 15.1\ k\Omega$, $R_2 = 2.2\ k\Omega$, and $R_3 = 0.51\ M\Omega$?

12. In a parallel circuit of R_1, R_2, and R_3, determine the current flow through R_3 if $R_1 = 16\ \Omega$, $R_2 = 22\ \Omega$, $R_T = 8.4\ \Omega$, and $I_T = 15$ A.

13. What resistance must be placed in parallel with $R_1 = 200\ \Omega$ and $R_2 = 500\ \Omega$ to increase the circuit current flow by 20 percent when placed across 200 V?

14. Calculate R_T, I_T, I_1, I_2, and I_3 in a parallel circuit composed of $R_1 = 300\ \Omega$, $R_2 = 600\ \Omega$, and $R_3 = 900\ \Omega$ when connected to 120 V.

15. If a fourth parallel resistance, $R_4 = 10\ \Omega$, were added to the circuit of problem 14, what would be the effect on the previously calculated values?

16. A circuit consists of R_1 and R_2 in parallel. If $I_T = 10$ A, $I_2 = 7$ A, and $R_1 = 20\ \Omega$, calculate E, I_1, R_2, and R_T.

9–4   SERIES–PARALLEL CIRCUIT

The series–parallel circuit, as the name indicates, is simply a combination of the series circuit and the parallel circuit. A simple series–parallel circuit is shown in Figure 9–7.

The solution of problems involving the series–parallel circuit are made easier through circuit simplification. This is shown in the following examples.

example 9–7   Determine the total circuit resistance of the circuit in Figure 9–7.

solution: The equivalent resistance of the parallel branch may be determined as

$$R_{eq} = \frac{R_2 \times R_3}{R_2 + R_3} = \frac{20 \times 30}{20 + 30} = \frac{600}{50} = 12\ \Omega$$

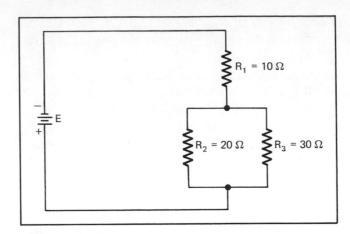

FIGURE 9-7
Circuit Diagram for Example 9-7

The circuit may then be redrawn in simplified form as shown in Figure 9–8. It should be observed that, in sim-

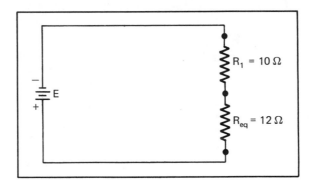

FIGURE 9-8
Simplification of Circuit of Figure 9-7

plified form, a simple series circuit results. This may be still further simplified as shown in Figure 9–9.

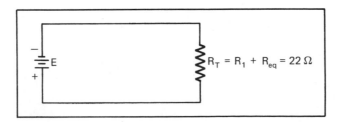

FIGURE 9-9
Simplification of Circuit of Figure 9-8

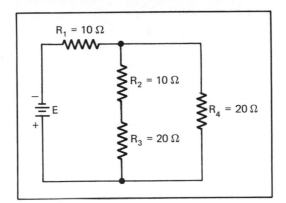

FIGURE 9-10
Circuit Diagram for Example 9-8

example 9-8 Determine the total resistance of the circuit of Figure
9-10.

solution: The series resistance of R_2 and R_3 may be calculated as
$R_2 + R_3 = 10 + 20 = 30 \ \Omega$. The simplified circuit then
appears as shown in Figure 9-11.

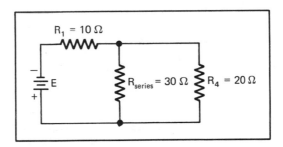

FIGURE 9-11
Simplification of Circuit of Figure 9-10

The equivalent resistance of the parallel branch is

$$R_{eq} = \frac{30 \times 20}{30 + 20} = \frac{600}{50} = 12 \ \Omega$$

The resultant simplified circuit is shown in Figure 9-12.
The total circuit resistance may now be found by simply
adding the series resistance of R_1 and R_{eq}:

$$R_T = R_1 + R_{eq} = 10 + 12 = 22 \ \Omega$$

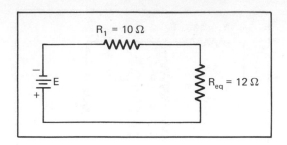

FIGURE 9–12
Simplification of Circuit of Figure 9–11

example 9–9 Determine the total resistance of the circuit of Figure 9–13.

solution: The equivalent resistance of R_2 and R_3 may be calculated as

$$R_{eq} = \frac{R_2 \times R_3}{R_2 + R_3} = \frac{20 \times 30}{20 + 30} = \frac{600}{50} = 12 \ \Omega$$

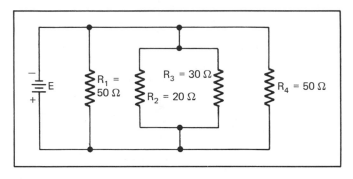

FIGURE 9–13
Circuit Diagram for Example 9–9

The simplified circuit appears as shown in Figure 9–14. The total circuit resistance may be calculated as

$$\frac{1}{R_T} = \frac{1}{R_1} + \frac{1}{R_{eq}} + \frac{1}{R_4} = \frac{1}{50} + \frac{1}{12} + \frac{1}{50}$$

$$= 0.02 + 0.083 + 0.02 = 0.123$$

$$R_T = 8.11 \ \Omega$$

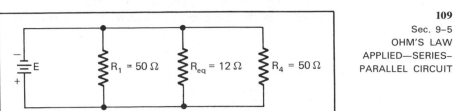

FIGURE 9–14
Simplification of Circuit of Figure 9–13

9–5 OHM'S LAW APPLIED—SERIES–PARALLEL CIRCUIT

The Ohm's law relationships that were applied in the series circuit, and in the parallel circuit, are also valid when used in circuits containing both series and parallel elements. That is, the current is common for series elements and the voltage is common for parallel elements.

A typical series–parallel circuit is shown in Figure 9–15. The direction of current flow is indicated by the arrows. It should be observed that the line current, I_T, flows through R_1. When point A is reached, I_T divides, with I_2 flowing through the R_2 branch and I_3 flowing through the R_3 branch. At point B, the currents I_2 and I_3 again combine to form the line current, I_T. The voltage that appears across the parallel combination of R_2 and R_3 is equal to the line voltage, E, minus the voltage drop in R_1.

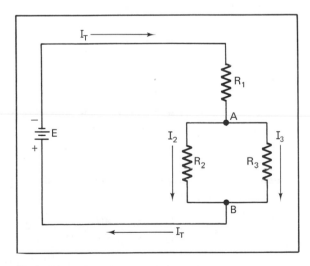

FIGURE 9–15
Series-Parallel Circuit

example 9-10 In the circuit of Figure 9–16, determine R_T, I_T, I_2, and I_3.

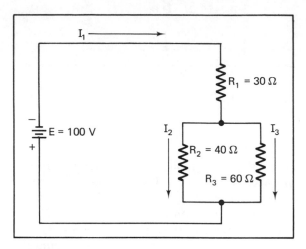

FIGURE 9–16
Circuit Diagram for Example 9–10

ANALYSIS:

The series–parallel circuit shows the following:

CIRCUIT KNOWN	SERIES BRANCH KNOWN	PARALLEL BRANCH KNOWN
E	R_1	R_2, R_3
UNKNOWN	**UNKNOWN**	**UNKNOWN**
I_T, R_T	E_1, I_1	I_2, I_3, E

Examination will show that R_1, R_2, and R_3 are known, and R_T may therefore be calculated. The line current, I_T, may then be determined.

solution: The equivalent resistance of the parallel branch of R_2 and R_3 is

$$R_{eq} = \frac{R_2 \times R_3}{R_2 + R_3} = \frac{40 \times 60}{40 + 60} = \frac{2,400}{100} = 24 \ \Omega$$

A simplified circuit may then be drawn, as shown in Figure 9–17. It is seen that the simplified circuit is a simple series circuit, from which R_T may be determined:

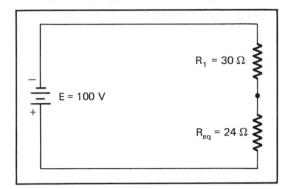

FIGURE 9–17
Simplified Circuit for Example 9–10

$R_T = R_1 + R_{\text{eq}} = 30 + 24 = 54 \ \Omega$

Then

$I_T = \dfrac{E}{R_T} = \dfrac{100}{54} = 1.85 \ \text{A}$

The voltage drops may now be found:

$E_{R_1} = I_T \times R_1 = 1.85 \times 30 = 55.5 \ \text{V}$

$E_{R_{\text{eq}}} = E - E_{R_1} = 100 - 55.5 = 44.5 \ \text{V}$

Or this may be calculated from

$E_{R_{\text{eq}}} = I_T \times R_{\text{eq}} = 1.85 \times 24 = 44.5 \ \text{V}$

The voltage of the parallel branch, $E_{R_{\text{eq}}} = 44.5$ V, may now be used in Figure 9–16 to determine I_2 and I_3:

$I_2 = \dfrac{E_{R_{\text{eq}}}}{R_2} = \dfrac{44.5}{40} = 1.11 \ \text{A}$

$I_3 = \dfrac{E_{R_{\text{eq}}}}{R_3} = \dfrac{44.5}{60} = 0.74 \ \text{A}$

As a check, $I_2 + I_3$ must equal $I_T = 1.85$ A:

$I_2 + I_3 = 1.11 + 0.74 = 1.85 \ \text{A}$

example 9-11 In the circuit in Figure 9–18, calculate R_T, I_T, I_1, I_2, I_3, I_4, and I_5.

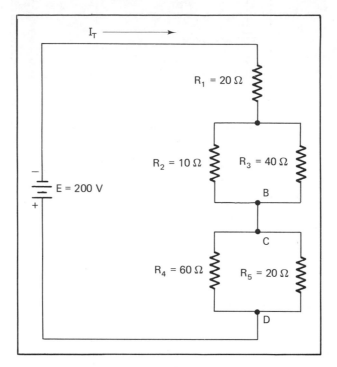

FIGURE 9–18
Circuit Diagram for Example 9–11

	ANALYSIS:			
	CIRCUIT KNOWN	SERIES BRANCH KNOWN	PARALLEL BRANCH 1 KNOWN	PARALLEL BRANCH 2 KNOWN
	E	R_1	R_2, R_3	R_4, R_5
	UNKNOWN	UNKNOWN	UNKNOWN	UNKNOWN
	I_T, R_T	I_1, E	I_2, I_3, E	I_4, I_5, E

It is observed that all the resistance values needed to calculate R_T are known.

solution:

$$R_{eq_1} = \frac{R_2 \times R_3}{R_2 + R_3} = \frac{10 \times 40}{10 + 40} = \frac{400}{50} = 8 \ \Omega$$

$$R_{eq_2} = \frac{R_3 \times R_4}{R_3 + R_4} = \frac{60 \times 20}{60 + 20} = \frac{1,200}{80} = 15 \ \Omega$$

Using the equivalent resistances of the parallel circuits, the simplified circuit shown in Figure 9–19 may be drawn.

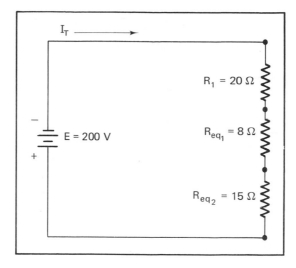

FIGURE 9–19
Simplified Circuit for Example 9–11

$$R_T = R_1 + R_{eq_1} + R_{eq_2} = 20 + 8 + 15 = 43 \ \Omega$$

$$I_T = \frac{E}{R_T} = \frac{200}{43} = 4.65 \ \text{A}$$

$$E_{R_1} = I_T \times R_1 = 4.65 \times 20 = 93 \ \text{V}$$

$$E_{Req_1} = I_T \times R_{eq_1} = 4.65 \times 8 = 37.2 \ \text{V}$$

$$E_{Req_2} = I_T \times R_{eq_2} = 4.65 \times 15 = 69.8 \ \text{V}$$

Returning to Figure 9–18, the currents in the parallel branches may now be calculated:

$$I_{R2} = \frac{E_{Req_1}}{R_2} = \frac{37.2}{10} = 3.72 \ \text{A}$$

$$I_{R3} = \frac{E_{Req_1}}{R_3} = \frac{37.2}{40} = 0.93 \ \text{A}$$

$$I_{R4.} = \frac{E_{Req_2}}{R_4} = \frac{69.8}{60} = 1.16 \text{A}$$

$$I_{R5} = \frac{E_{Req_2}}{R_5} = \frac{69.8}{20} = 3.49 \ \text{A}$$

Note that I_T passes through R_1, divides at point A of Figure 9–18, combines at point B, separates at point C, and again combines at point D. As a check, $I_{R_2} + I_{R_3}$ and $I_{R_4} + I_{R_5}$ must equal $I_T = 4.65$ A:

$$I_{R_2} + I_{R_3} = 3.72 + 0.93 = 4.65 \text{ A}$$

$$I_{R_4} + I_{R_5} = 1.16 + 3.49 = 4.65 \text{ A}$$

example 9–12 In the circuit shown in Figure 9–20, determine I_T, I_2, E_{R_1}, E_{R_2}, E_{R_3}, and R_T.

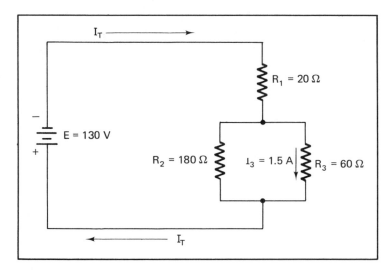

FIGURE 9–20
Circuit Diagram for Example 9–12

ANALYSIS:		
CIRCUIT KNOWN	**SERIES BRANCH KNOWN**	**PARALLEL BRANCH KNOWN**
E	R_1	R_2, R_3, I_3
UNKNOWN	**UNKNOWN**	**UNKNOWN**
R_T, I_T	$E_{R_1}, I_1 = I_T$	I_2, E_{R_2}, E_{R_3}

The analysis shows that the resistance of R_3 and the current through R_3 are both known. The voltage across the parallel branch, $E_{R_2} = E_{R_3}$, may be determined from these values.

solution:

$$E_{R_3} = I_3 \times R_3 = 1.5 \times 60 = 90 \text{ V}$$

$$E_{R_3} = E_{R_2} = 90 \text{ V}$$

Then

$$I_2 = \frac{E_{R_2}}{R_2} = \frac{90}{180} = 0.5 \text{ A}$$

$$I_T = I_2 + I_3 = 0.5 + 1.5 = 2 \text{ A}$$

$$R_T = \frac{E}{I_T} = \frac{130}{2} = 65 \text{ } \Omega$$

$$E_{R_1} = I_T \times R_1 = 2 \times 20 = 40 \text{ V}$$

As a check,

$$E_{R_1} = E - E_{R_2} = 130 - 90 = 40 \text{ V}$$

EXERCISE 9-2

1. Determine the circuit current flow when a resistance $R_1 = 100 \text{ } \Omega$ is placed in series with the parallel combination of $R_2 = 200 \text{ } \Omega$, $R_3 = 300 \text{ } \Omega$, and $R_4 = 400 \text{ } \Omega$. The circuit voltage is 1,500 V.

2. In the circuit shown in Figure 9–21, determine $I_T, I_3, I_4,$ and E_{R_4}.

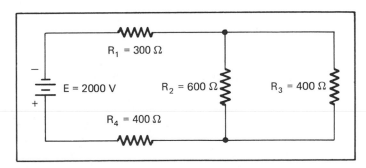

FIGURE 9–21
Circuit for Problems 2 and 3

3. In the circuit of problem 2, it is desired to limit the circuit current to 1.5 A. What value would R_1 have to be in order to limit this current?

4. In the circuit shown in Figure 9–22, the circuit current is 5 A. Calculate the value of $R_5, I_1, I_2, I_3, I_4, I_5, E_{R_3}, E_{R_2},$ and E_{R_5}.

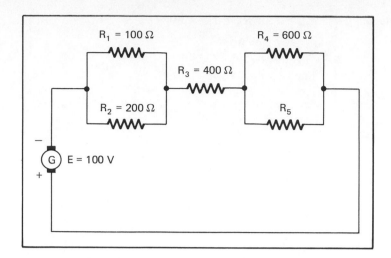

FIGURE 9–22
Circuit for Problems 4 and 5

5. In the circuit of problem 4, what effect would placing short circuits across both R_2 and R_5 have on the circuit current? What would be the effect if both R_2 and R_5 were open-circuited?

6. In the circuit of Figure 9–23, determine I_T, I_2, I_3, I_4, E_{R_1}, E_{R_2}, E_{R_3}, and E_{R_4}. The values of resistance are $R_1 = 300\ \Omega$, $R_2 = 400\ \Omega$, $R_3 = 200\ \Omega$, and $R_4 = 600\ \Omega$.

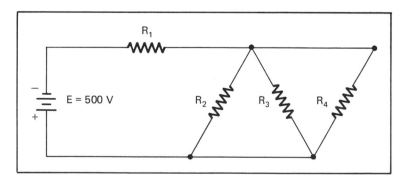

FIGURE 9–23
Circuit for Problem 6

7. In the circuit of Figure 9–24, calculate the line current.

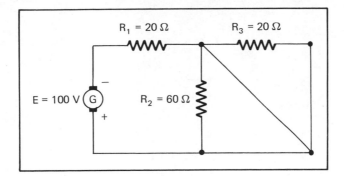

FIGURE 9–24
Circuit for Problem 7

8. In the circuit of Figure 9–25, determine E, R_2, I_T, E_{R_1}, and E_{R_4}.

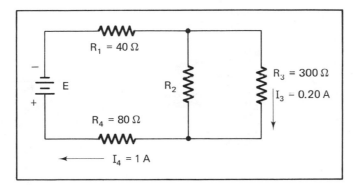

FIGURE 9–25
Circuit for Problem 8

10

ALGEBRAIC PRODUCTS AND FACTORING

In Chapter 2, a definition of a factor was provided. It was seen that when numbers were multiplied together to form a product, the numbers were considered factors of that product. In algebraic operations, products of a particular type and form frequently reoccur. It is necessary that a familiarity be established with these products and their factors.

10–1 FACTORING

Numbers when multiplied together are factors of the resulting product. The process of determining the factors of a product is called *factoring*.

A product is the result of the multiplication of factors. Factoring is the reverse of multiplication, a division procedure. For example, given the product, 42, factoring would establish what numbers, or factors, when multiplied together produce this product. Recall from the explanation of division in Chapter 3 that the division of 42 by 7 involved determining what number when multiplied by 7 would produce 42. The similiarity involved in factoring should be obvious.

10–2 PRIME FACTORS

Factoring involves obtaining the prime factors of a product, that is, factors that are divisible only by themselves and by 1.

Factors of the product 42 are 7 and 6. The factoring is incomplete, however, in that the factor 6 may again be factored as 3 and 2. Neither 7, 3, or 2 may be further divided by any number but itself or 1, and hence are prime factors of the product 42.

10–3 FREQUENTLY OCCURRING PRODUCT FORMS

In many algebraic operations, products of a particular type reoccur often. The factors and the resultant product form are shown in Table 10–1. In the table it is seen that when factors of the indicated type are multiplied, a general product form results. It follows, then, that when a particular product form occurs, the factors will be of the indicated type.

TABLE 10–1 Factors and Resultant Product Forms

TYPE FACTORS	RESULTANT PRODUCT FORM
1. $a(x + y)$	$ax + ay$
2. $(x + y)(x - y)$	$x^2 - y^2$
3. $(x + y)(x + y)$	$x^2 + 2xy + y^2$
4. $(x - y)(x - y)$	$x^2 - 2xy + y^2$
5. $(x + a)(x + b)$	$x^2 + (a + b)x + ab$
6. $(ax + b)(cx + d)$	$(ac)x^2 + (ad + bc)x + bd$

The procedures for factoring each of the above product forms will be examined in the following sections.

10–4 COMMON FACTORS

Frequently, a product has a common factor. This is represented by type 1 in Table 10–1.

Product Form: $ax + ay$

It is seen that the factor a occurs in both terms. Factoring would be performed by dividing each term by the common factor, a. The result would be written

$a(x + y)$

---

example 10–1 Factor: $3bc + 12db + 9be$.

---

solution: Examination shows a common factor, $3b$. Factoring as above results in

$3b(c + 4d + 3e)$

---

example 10–2 Factor: $16x^2z + 4x^3y + 12x^4w$.

---

solution: Inspection shows that $4x^2$ is a common factor. Factoring produces

$4x^2(4z + xy + 3x^2w)$

---

example 10–3 Factor: $15ax^3y^4 + 30a^2xy^2 + 45a^3x^2y^3$.

---

solution: The factor $15axy^2$ is seen to occur in each term. Factoring produces

$15axy^2(x^2y^2 + 2a + 3a^2xy)$

EXERCISE 10-1   Factor the following expressions.

121

Sec. 10-5
FACTORING THE
DIFFERENCE OF
TWO SQUARES

1. $ab + ac + ab^2$

2. $15x^2y^2 + 30x^3y^2$

3. $3a^2x + 12a^3y + 30a^5z$

4. $16bdc + 32bd^3c^4 + 2b^2d^2c^2$

5. $4xyz + xyz^2 + xy^2z^3$

6. $3w^2x^2y^2 + 33w^4x^3y^2 + \dfrac{15w^2x^3y^4}{5}$

7. $3.25a^2x^3 + 6.50a^3x^4 + 13a^5x^5$

8. $\dfrac{3x^2y}{4} + \dfrac{x^3y^2}{2} + \dfrac{2x^4y^3}{8}$

9. $\dfrac{12cd^2e}{3} + \dfrac{14c^2d^3e^5}{7} + \dfrac{20c^5d^4e^3}{5}$

10. $1.25g^2h^3 + 3.75g^4h^5 + 5g^6h^2$

10-5 FACTORING THE DIFFERENCE OF TWO SQUARES

The product form represented by type 2 in Table 10-1 is seen to be the difference of two perfect squares:

Product Form: $x^2 - y^2$

This product is found to be the result of the multiplication of the sum and difference of two quantities $(x + y)$ and $(x - y)$. The process of multiplication is shown as

$$
\begin{array}{l}
x + y \\
\underline{x - y} \\
x^2 + xy \\
\underline{\quad - xy - y^2} \\
x^2 \qquad - y^2
\end{array}
$$

The middle term in the expression is seen to cancel, as shown.

Factoring a product in the form $x^2 - y^2$ involves extracting the square root of each term. The first factor would be formed by adding the square root of the second to the square root of the first:

$(x + y)$

The second factor would be formed by subtracting the square root of the second from the square root of the first:

$(x - y)$

Combining the two factors produces

$$(x + y)(x - y)$$

example 10-4 Factor: $a^2 - 16$.

solution: Extracting the square root of each term produces a and 4. Forming factors results in

$$(a + 4)(a - 4)$$

example 10-5 Factor: $x^2 - y^4$.

solution: The square root of each term is x and y^2, which results in

$$(x + y^2)(x - y^2)$$

example 10-6 Factor: $16a^2y^6 - b^8$.

solution: The square roots are $4ay^3$ and b^4. Resulting factors are

$$(4ay^3 + b^4)(4ay^3 - b^4)$$

EXERCISE 10-2 Factor the following expressions.

1. $x^2 - 4y^2$ 2. $16x^4 - 16y^6$

3. $64a^2y^2 - 16b^4$ 4. $25w^{16} - 25$

5. $36a^2x^4 - 49b^4z^6$ 6. $16 - x^4$

7. $9w^4 - 4$ 8. $1 - x^2$

9. $36a^2b^4 - 1$ 10. $1 - c^4$

11. $1 - 64b^2e^4$ 12. $\dfrac{x^2}{y^2} - \dfrac{w^4}{z^2}$

10-6 FACTORING THE PERFECT TRINOMIAL SQUARE

In Section 10-5, the factoring of the product of the sum and difference of two factors, $(x + y)$ and $(x - y)$, was discussed. Let us now examine the products of the two factors, $(x + y)(x + y)$ and $(x - y)(x - y)$. The process of multiplication is shown as

$$
\begin{array}{ll}
\begin{array}{r}
x + y \\
\underline{x + y} \\
x^2 + xy \\
\underline{ + xy - y^2} \\
x^2 + 2xy + y^2
\end{array}
&
\begin{array}{r}
x - y \\
\underline{x - y} \\
x^2 - xy \\
\underline{ - xy + y^2} \\
x^2 - 2xy + y^2
\end{array}
\end{array}
$$

It should be observed that unlike the previous product type, the second term does not cancel.

The resultant products shown above are designated as *perfect trinomial squares*. A trinomial is considered a perfect square if the second term is twice the product of the square roots of the first and third term.

The factoring of perfect trinomial squares, of type 3 and type 4, merely involves extracting the square root of the first and last terms and connecting these factors with the sign of the middle term.

example 10–7 Factor: $4x^2 + 4xy + y^2$.

solution: Extracting the square root of the first and last terms produces

$2x$ and y

Affixing the sign of the second term results in factors of

$(2x + y)(2x + y)$ or $(2x + y)^2$

example 10–8 Factor: $9a^2 - 24ab + 16b^2$.

solution: The square roots of the first and third terms are $3a$ and $4b$. Using the sign of the second term,

$(3a - 4b)(3a - 4b)$ or $(3a - 4b)^2$

example 10–9 Determine the missing term, to form a perfect trinomial square.

$64w^4 - \underline{\hspace{1cm}} + 16z^2$

solution: The second term must be equal to twice the product of the square roots of the first and third terms:

$2 \times 8w^2 \times 4z$ or $64w^2z$

Then

$64w^4 - 64w^2z + 16z^2$

EXERCISE 10–3   Factor the following expressions.

1. $4x^2 - 4xy + y^2$ 2. $9x^6 + 36x^3y^3 + 36y^6$

3. $144a^2 + 24a + 1$ 4. $9w^2 - 36wz + 36z^2$

5. $0.25m^2 + 0.20mn + 0.04n^2$

Determine the missing term to form a perfect trinomial square.

6. $x^2 -$ _____ $+ 9y^4$

7. $144a^4 +$ _____ $+ 64b^2$

8. $+$ _____ $- 30wx^2 + 25x^4$

9. $81c^2 + 72cd +$ _____

10. $36w^2 -$ _____ $+ 144z^4$

11. $9x^2 - 6xy +$ _____

12. $+$ _____ $+ 112a^2c + 64c^2$

10–7 FACTORING OTHER TRINOMIALS

This section will deal with the factoring of trinomials other than the perfect-trinomial-square type.

Multiplication of the factors $(x + a)$ and $(x + b)$ will produce

$$
\begin{array}{l}
x + a \\
\underline{x + b} \\
x^2 + ax \\
\underline{ + bx + ab} \\
x^2 + ax + bx + ab
\end{array}
$$

As x is common in the second and third terms, the product may be written

$$x^2 + (a + b)x + ab$$

This is product form type 5 in Table 10–1.

A trinomial would not normally be found in this form. It would more likely be expressed as

$$x^2 + cx + d$$

where $c = (a + b)$ and $d = ab$. This relationship indicates that factoring a trinomial in this form involves a search for the coefficient of the second term, which is $(a + b)$, and the third term, which is ab. Simply stated, the solution requires integers whose product is ab and whose sum is $a + b$. This may often be obtained by inspection. At other times a trial-and-error procedure will be required.

solution: Factoring will involve obtaining factors whose product is 8 and whose sum is 6. Possible factors whose product is 8 are

$+8$ and $+1$

-8 and -1

$+4$ and $+2$

-4 and -2

Inspection shows that only the factors $+4$ and $+2$ will meet the above requirement, and the factors of $x^2 + 6x + 8$ are

$(x + 4)(x + 2)$

In the previous example, if the second term was $-6x$, as in $x^2 - 6x + 8$, only the factors of -4 and -2 would suffice. In other words,

$x^2 - 6x + 8 = (x - 4)(x - 2)$

example 10-11   Factor: $a^2 + 11a + 30$.

solution: The factors required must have a sum of 11 and a product of 30. Possible factors of 30 include $+30$ and $+1$, -30 and -1, $+6$ and $+5$, and -6 and -5. Inspection shows that factors of $a^2 + 11a + 30$ are $(a + 6)$ and $(a + 5)$.

Another trinomial product form results when $(ax + b)$ and $(cx + d)$ are multiplied:

$$ax + b$$
$$\underline{cx + d}$$
$$acx^2 + adx$$
$$\underline{\qquad\qquad + bcx + bd}$$
$$(ac)x^2 + (ad + bc)x + bd$$

As with the previous trinomial form, the trinomial would not usually be arranged in this manner. Normally, it would be expressed as

$mx^2 + nx + p$

Note that this is similar in form to the previous trinomial form except that the coefficient of the first term has a value other than 1. In this form

$$m = ac$$

$$n = ad + bc$$

$$p = bd$$

Factoring of a trinomial in this form involves determination of a, b, c, and d.

Examination of the multiplication process shows that the coefficient of the first term of the trinomial results from the multiplication of the first terms of the binomials $(ax + b)$ and $(cx + d)$. Likewise, the third term of the trinomial is the product of the second terms of the binomial factors.

Determination of the coefficient of the second term of the trinomial is more difficult. It involves obtaining the sum of the cross-multiplication products of the binomials. In other words, the *sum* of the first term of the first binomial, multiplied by the second term of the second binomial, and the first term of the second binomial, multiplied by the second term of the first binomial. As shown in the following examples, this is a trial-and-error procedure.

example 10–12 Factor: $3x^2 + 6x + 3$.

solution: Examination shows that possible factors include

$$(3x + 1)(x + 3)$$

$$(3x + 3)(x + 1)$$

Note that in the multiplication indicated below, both produce the correct coefficient of the first term and the correct third term.

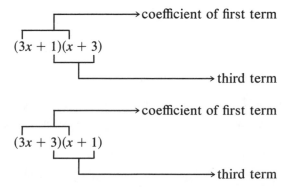

The sum of the cross multiplications indicated below produces only one that provides the correct second term.

$$(3x + 1)(x + 3) \quad \longrightarrow \text{product} \quad 9x$$
$$\longrightarrow \text{product} \quad x$$
$$\text{sum} \quad \overline{10x} \text{ (incorrect)}$$

$$(3x + 3)(x + 1) \quad \longrightarrow \text{product} \quad 3x$$
$$\longrightarrow \text{product} \quad 3x$$
$$\overline{6x} \text{ (correct)}$$

So the factors of

$$3x^2 + 6x + 3 = (3x + 3)(x + 1)$$

example 10–13 Factor: $8a^2 + 10a + 3$.

solution: Possible factors, all of which produce the correct coefficient for the first term and the correct third term, include

$$(8a + 1)(a + 3)$$
$$(8a + 3)(a + 1)$$
$$(4a + 1)(2a + 3)$$
$$(4a + 3)(2a + 1)$$

The sum of the cross multiplications for the second-term coefficient produces

Sum of Cross-Multiplication
Products

$(8a + 1)(a + 3)$	$25a$	(incorrect)
$(8a + 3)(a + 1)$	$11a$	(incorrect)
$(4a + 1)(2a + 3)$	$14a$	(incorrect)
$(4a + 3)(2a + 1)$	$10a$	(correct)

Therefore, factors of

$$8a^2 + 10a + 3 = (4a + 3)(2a + 1)$$

example 10-14 Factor: $6a^2 + 5a - 4$.

solution: Possible factors include

$$(6a + 4)(a - 1) \qquad (3a + 2)(2a - 2)$$

$$(6a - 4)(a + 1) \qquad (3a - 2)(2a + 2)$$

$$(6a + 2)(a - 2) \qquad (3a + 4)(2a - 1)$$

$$(6a - 2)(a + 2) \qquad (3a - 4)(2a + 1)$$

Examination will show that only the factors

$$(3a + 4)(2a - 1)$$

will produce the correct second term; hence

$$6a^2 + 5a - 4 = (3a + 4)(2a - 1)$$

EXERCISE 10-4 Factor the following expressions.

1. $x^2 + 7x + 12$ 2. $a^2 - 2a - 8$

3. $w^4 + 9w^2 + 18$ 4. $9s^2 - 18s + 8$

5. $b^2 - 7b + 12$ 6. $6t^2 + 7t + 2$

7. $6s^2 - 13s + 6$ 8. $-6x^2 + 16x - 8$

9. $36a^2 - 24a - 12$ 10. $12x^2 - 27x + 15$

10-8 HIGHEST COMMON FACTOR

A factor that is found in two or more algebraic relationships is said to be a common factor. For example, 4 is a common factor of 8, 12, 16, and 20. x is a common factor of x^4, $x^2 - x$, and $3x^2 + 3x$.

The *highest common factor*, *HCF*, of two or more expressions may be determined by obtaining the prime factors of each expression and combining the common factors as a product. Essentially this is a process which determines the largest numerical quantity and the highest-degree literal quantity, which will divide into each expression without leaving a remainder. For example, $5x^2$ is the HCF of the expression $5x^2$, $25x^3$, and $10x^4$, and $3ab^2$ is the HCF of $6a^3b^4$, $3a^4b^2$, and $12ab^6$.

10-9 LOWEST COMMON MULTIPLE

A number multiplied by a whole number produces a multiple of that number. Expressed another way, a number is a multiple of any of its factors. For example, 12 is a multiple of 2, 3, 4, or 6, and $x^2 + 6x + 9$ is a multiple of $x + 3$.

A number that is evenly divisible by two or more numbers is a common multiple of those numbers. Thus 18 is a common multiple of 2, 3, 6, and 9.

The *lowest common multiple*, *LCM*, is the smallest number that is evenly divisible by two or more numbers. Thus whereas 6, 9, and 18 are common multiples of 2 and 3, 6 is the smallest number evenly divisible by both and hence the LCM.

In other examples the LCM is not as easily discernible. In such situations the following procedure may be used:

The LCM may be determined by obtaining the product of the prime factors, using each factor the greatest number of times that it occurs in any one number.

----

example 10–15 Determine the LCM of 6, 9, and 12.

solution: The prime factors of

$$6 = 2, 3$$
$$9 = 3, 3$$
$$12 = 2, 2, 3$$

The greatest number of times each of the factors occurs is: 2 occurs twice in 12 and 3 occurs twice in 9. Hence the

$$LCM = 2 \cdot 2 \cdot 3 \cdot 3 = 36$$

example 10–16 Determine the LCM of 24, 16, and 9.

solution: The prime factors are

$$24 = 2 \cdot 2 \cdot 2 \cdot 3$$
$$16 = 2 \cdot 2 \cdot 2 \cdot 2$$
$$9 = 3 \cdot 3$$

The $LCM = 2 \cdot 2 \cdot 2 \cdot 2 \cdot 3 \cdot 3 = 144$.

example 10–17 Determine the LCM of $15x^2y$, $12xy^2$, and $6x^3y^3$.

solution: The prime factors are

$$15x^2y = 3 \cdot 5 \cdot x \cdot x \cdot y$$

$$12xy^2 = 2 \cdot 2 \cdot 3 \cdot x \cdot y \cdot y$$

$$6x^3y^3 = 2 \cdot 3 \cdot x \cdot x \cdot x \cdot y \cdot y \cdot y$$

Determining the product of the greatest number of times each factor occurs produces

$$\text{LCM} = 2 \cdot 2 \cdot 3 \cdot 5 \cdot x \cdot x \cdot x \cdot y \cdot y \cdot y$$

$$= 60x^3y^3$$

EXERCISE 10–5 Determine the LCM.

1. 16, 5, 18, 9   2. 21, 14, 13

3. $5a^2$, $4ay^3$, $7y^2$ 4. $(x + 3)$, $x^2 + 3x + 9$

5. $m^2 - 16$, $m + 4$, $m - 2$ 6. $4a^2 - b^4$, $2a - b^2$

7. $3t^2 - 3$, $t + 1$, t^3 8. $9w^2 - 24wx + 16x^2$, $3w - 4x$

11

FRACTIONS
AND FRACTIONAL
EQUATIONS

Fractions and fractional equations occur in electronics calculations. A working knowledge of this subject area is therefore required. This will not be a completely new topic, for it will be found that the definitions and procedures developed for fractions in arithmetic apply here also.

A very short review of basic fractions is provided where it is deemed necessary. If this is found to be inadequate, the reader is urged to undertake a thorough review of arithmetic fractions.

11-1 FRACTIONS

The reciprocal was defined in Chapter 2. It was seen that the *vinculum*, also called the *fraction bar*, indicated division of the numerator, 1, in the case of a reciprocal, by the denominator. Like the reciprocal, the division of the numerator by the denominator is indicated in all fractions. Several examples of fractions are as follows:

$$\frac{1}{6}, \quad \frac{3}{32}, \quad \frac{6a^2}{15a^4}, \quad \frac{5IR}{E}$$

11-2 EQUIVALENT FRACTIONS

In our previous work with equations it was found that multiplication or division of both sides of the equation by the same number did not change the equality. Similarly, multiplication or division of both the numerator and denominator by the same number will leave the value of the fraction unchanged. The result is a fraction, changed in form but of the same value, called an *equivalent fraction*. For example, multiplication of both the numerator and denominator by the same number results in an equivalent fraction of unchanged value:

$$\frac{12}{20} = \frac{12 \times 2}{20 \times 2} = \frac{24}{40}, \qquad \frac{25}{55} = \frac{25 \times 4}{55 \times 4} = \frac{100}{220}$$

$$\frac{3a^2}{5a^3} = \frac{3a^2 \times 2a}{5a^3 \times 2a} = \frac{6a^3}{10a^4}$$

Similarly, dividing both the numerator and denominator of the following fractions by the same number results in equivalent fractions of the same value:

$$\frac{12}{20} = \frac{12 \div 4}{20 \div 4} = \frac{3}{5}, \qquad \frac{25}{55} = \frac{25 \div 5}{55 \div 5} = \frac{5}{11}$$

132

$$\frac{3a^2}{15a^3} = \frac{3a^2 \div 3a}{15a^3 \div 3a} = \frac{a}{5a^2}$$

The discussion of fractions to this point has involved only fractions with positive signs. The absence of any sign has really meant that the sign before the fraction as well as the sign of both the numerator and denominator was understood to be positive. This may be represented as

$$\frac{a}{b} = +\frac{+a}{+b}$$

Actually, the sign before the fraction as well as the signs of the numerator or denominator may either be positive or negative. Some of these various combinations may be represented as

$$+\frac{+x}{+y}, \quad +\frac{-x}{-y}, \quad -\frac{+x}{-y}, \quad -\frac{-x}{+y}$$

The indicated division would follow the rules developed previously for the division of signed numbers. After division, the sign preceding the fraction would either change the sign of the result or leave it unchanged. For example, the result of the indicated division in the following fractions would produce

$$+\frac{+21}{+7} = +(+3) = +3 \quad \text{and} \quad +\frac{-21}{-7} = +(+3) = +3$$

while

$$-\frac{+21}{-7} = -(-3) = +3 \quad \text{and} \quad -\frac{-21}{+7} = -(-3) = +3$$

The divisions above, if examined closely, show that:

Changing any two of the signs will result in an unchanged value of the fraction.

In effect, this procedure is the result of multiplying twice by -1; and $-1 \times -1 = +1$. This really means that the value of the fraction has been multiplied by $+1$; hence its value is unchanged.

If only one of the signs of the fraction

$$-\frac{+21}{-7} = +3$$

were changed, this would produce the following results:

$$-\left(\frac{+21 \times -1}{-7}\right) \quad \text{or} \quad -\left(\frac{-21}{-7}\right) \quad \text{or} \quad -(+3) \quad \text{or} \quad -3$$

or

$$-\left(\frac{+21}{-7 \times -1}\right) \quad \text{or} \quad -\left(\frac{+21}{+7}\right) \quad \text{or} \quad -(+3) \quad \text{or} \quad -3$$

or

$$\left(-\frac{+21}{-7}\right) \times -1 \quad \text{or} \quad (+3) \times -1 \quad \text{or} \quad -3$$

The value of the original fraction was $+3$ and not the -3 indicated. Hence when only one sign of the fraction is changed, in effect multiplied by -1, the sign of the result must be changed.

It should be remembered that when the numerator or denominator contains more than one term, the sign of *each* term must be changed, if multiplied by -1. Hence

$$+\frac{3a - 4b}{6a + 3b} = +\frac{(3a - 4b) \times -1}{(6a + 3b) \times -1} = +\frac{-3a + 4b}{-6a - 3b}$$

The purpose of the preceding discussions is to develop an understanding of the meaning of the signs of fractions. This will permit us, through manipulation of the signs, to change the original fraction to an equivalent one with a more convenient or workable form.

11-4 SIMPLIFICATION OF FRACTIONS

With the background of the previous sections, we are now in a position to examine procedures to simplify fractions. This is of course for the purpose of reducing the fraction to its simplest form. In this form it is obviously the easiest to handle or evaluate.

Simplification involves reducing the fraction to its lowest terms. In this form, no common factor other than 1 would occur in either the numerator or denominator.

The fractions

$$\frac{1}{2}, \quad \frac{13}{15}, \quad \frac{1}{a}, \quad \frac{a + 1}{3}, \quad \frac{a - b}{a + b}$$

have no common factors other than 1 and are expressed in their lowest terms. The fractions

$$\frac{2}{4}, \quad \frac{12}{30}, \quad \frac{6a^2}{2a}, \quad \frac{a^2 - b^2}{a + b}$$

have common factors and are not in their lowest terms. The procedure for reducing a fraction to its lowest terms is as follows:

----

1. Factor the numerator and denominator into prime factors.
2. Cancel common factors.

The reduction of the above fractions to their lowest terms would be as follows:

$$\frac{2}{4} = \frac{\not{2}}{2 \cdot \not{2}} = \frac{1}{2}$$

$$\frac{12}{30} = \frac{\not{2} \cdot 2 \cdot \not{3}}{\not{2} \cdot \not{3} \cdot 5} = \frac{2}{5}$$

$$\frac{6a^2}{2a} = \frac{\not{2} \cdot 3 \cdot \not{a} \cdot a}{\not{2} \cdot \not{a}} = 3a$$

$$\frac{a^2 - b^2}{a + b} = \frac{(a + b)(a - b)}{(a + b)} = a - b$$

In each of the above examples, we have, in effect, found the highest common factor, HCF. The simplification is the result of dividing both the numerator and denominator by the HCF, and the resultant cancellation of factors.

example 11–1   Reduce to lowest terms, $\dfrac{15x^3y^2z}{33x^4y}$.

----

solution: $\dfrac{15x^3y^2z}{33x^4y} = \dfrac{3 \cdot 5 \cdot x \cdot x \cdot x \cdot y \cdot y \cdot z}{3 \cdot 11 \cdot x \cdot x \cdot x \cdot x \cdot y}$

The HCF is seen to be $3x^3y$. Dividing both the numerator and denominator produces the following cancellation:

$$\frac{\not{3} \cdot 5 \cdot \not{x} \cdot \not{x} \cdot \not{x} \cdot \not{y} \cdot y \cdot z}{\not{3} \cdot 11 \cdot \not{x} \cdot \not{x} \cdot \not{x} \cdot x \cdot \not{y}} = \frac{5yz}{11x}$$

example 11–2   Reduce to lowest terms: $\dfrac{16 - a^2}{(4 - a)(a + 6)}$.

----

solution: Factoring the numerator produces

$$\frac{(4 - a)(4 + a)}{(4 - a)(a + 6)}$$

which results in

$$\frac{4 + a}{a + 6}$$

example 11-3 Reduce to lowest terms:

$$\frac{xz - yz}{2x^2 - 2y^2}$$

solution: A z is common to both terms in the numerator and a 2 is a common factor in the denominator. This results in

$$\frac{z(x - y)}{2(x^2 - y^2)}$$

The denominator may be further factored and results in the fraction appearing as

$$\frac{z(\cancel{x - y})}{2(x + y)(\cancel{x - y})}$$

Canceling the $(x - y)$ terms gives the answer as

$$\frac{z}{2(x + y)}$$

example 11-4 Reduce to lowest terms:

$$\frac{3b + 2a}{4a^2 + 12ab + 9b^2}$$

solution: The denominator factors to

$$(2a + 3b)^2 \quad \text{or} \quad (2a + 3b)(2a + 3b)$$

and the fraction appears as

$$\frac{3b + 2a}{(2a + 3b)(2a + 3b)}$$

Rearranging the numerator, the fraction appears as

$$\frac{\cancel{(2a + 3b)}}{\cancel{(2a + 3b)}(2a + 3b)} \quad \text{or} \quad \frac{1}{2a + 3b}$$

1. $\dfrac{15}{16} = \dfrac{?}{32}$

2. $\dfrac{12}{144} = \dfrac{?}{1,728}$

3. $\dfrac{4}{a} = \dfrac{?}{a^2}$

4. $\dfrac{w}{w - x} = \dfrac{?}{(w - x)^2}$

Reduce to the lowest terms.

5. $\dfrac{27}{60}$

6. $\dfrac{352}{616}$

7. $\dfrac{162}{180}$

8. $\dfrac{x^3 y^2}{x^4 y}$

9. $\dfrac{10a^2 b^2 c^3}{88 a^3 b^4 c}$

10. $\dfrac{22 wzt}{68 w 5 t^4}$

11. $\dfrac{2x - 2y}{x^2 - 2xy + y^2}$

12. $\dfrac{2a - 4b}{a^2 - 4ab + 4b^2}$

13. $\dfrac{(x - 6)^2}{x^2 - 12x + 36}$

14. $\dfrac{4w + 6v}{4w^2 + 12vw + 9v^2}$

15. $\dfrac{18s + 21t}{30s^2 + 59st + 28t^2}$

16. $\dfrac{6a + 3b}{4a^2 - b^2}$

11–5 SIMPLIFICATION PITFALLS

There are several pitfalls to avoid in simplifying fractional expressions. These are common student mistakes that are made in reducing fractions to their lowest terms.

It has been established that multiplication or division of both the numerator and denominator by the same number does not change the value of the fraction. This often leads to the mistaken impression that this is also true for addition and subtraction. For example, in the fraction

$$\frac{1 + 4}{3 + 4}$$

canceling the 4's by subtraction is incorrect.

$$\frac{1 + \cancel{4}}{3 + \cancel{4}} \neq \frac{1}{3}$$

$$\frac{1 + 4}{3 + 4} = \frac{5}{7}$$

Remember that the vinculum, or fraction bar, is a sign of grouping. This groups the terms above and below the bar. This in effect directs that while common factors may be canceled, common terms may not. For example, in the fraction

$$\frac{2a + 4}{4a + 4}$$

2 is seen to be a common factor and may be factored and canceled as

$$\frac{2a + 4}{4a + 4} = \frac{\cancel{2}(a + 2)}{\cancel{2}(2a + 2)} = \frac{a + 2}{2a + 2}$$

while the common term 4 in the original expression or the common term 2 in the factored expression may not be canceled.

Another error is that of squaring, or taking the square root of, the numerator or denominator of a fraction. This is done in the belief that this is the same as multiplying or dividing both by the same number. This is not correct. For example,

$$\frac{4}{5} \neq \frac{(4)^2}{(5)^2}$$

The reason is that squaring the numerator requires multiplication by 4, while multiplication by 5 is required in the denominator.

In a similar manner, extracting a common root from numerator and denominator is not correct. For example,

$$\frac{4}{9} \neq \frac{\sqrt{4}}{\sqrt{9}} \quad \text{because} \quad \frac{\sqrt{4}}{\sqrt{9}} = \frac{2}{3}$$

and of course

$$\frac{4}{9} \neq \frac{2}{3}$$

11–6 ADDITION AND SUBTRACTION OF FRACTIONS

From arithmetic we know that the addition or subtraction of fractions with the same denominator is a simple task. For we are adding or subtracting fractional parts of similar units. For example,

$$\frac{1}{2} + \frac{1}{2} = \frac{2}{2} = 1 \quad \text{or} \quad \frac{5}{6} - \frac{3}{6} = \frac{2}{6} = \frac{1}{3}$$

In effect, these processes involve the addition or subtraction of so many of the common units represented in the denominator.

More often than not the denominators are not the same. This means that the units represented by the denominator are not the same. As a result they cannot be added or subtracted, any more than we can add or subtract dollars and francs. In the example

$$\frac{3}{5} + \frac{4}{7}$$

the addition cannot be performed with the fraction in this form. Each fraction must be reduced to equivalent fractions with the same denominators before the indicated addition can be carried out.

The process of obtaining fractions with the same denominator requires determining the lowest common multiple, LCM, of the denominators. Refer to Section 10–9 for review. When used with fractions the LCM is referred to as the lowest common denominator, LCD. In the example above,

$$\frac{3}{5} + \frac{4}{7}$$

the LCM = LCD would be found by $5 \cdot 7 = 35$. This would now require determining equivalent fractions, each with a denominator of 35. This results in

$$\frac{3}{5} + \frac{4}{7} = \frac{7 \cdot 3}{35} + \frac{5 \cdot 4}{35}$$

$$= \frac{21}{35} + \frac{20}{35} = \frac{41}{35}$$

or, expressed as a mixed number, $\frac{41}{35} = 1\frac{6}{35}$.

example 11–5 Perform the indicated operation:

$$\frac{3}{6a} + \frac{5}{3a^2}$$

solution: The LCM or LCD is found:

$$6a = 2 \cdot 3 \cdot a, \qquad 3a^2 = 3 \cdot a \cdot a$$

$$\text{LCD} = 2 \cdot 3 \cdot a \cdot a = 6a^2$$

Reducing to equivalent fractions,

$$\frac{3}{6a} + \frac{5}{3a^2} = \frac{3a}{6a^2} + \frac{10}{6a^2}$$

Combining,

$$\frac{3a + 10}{6a^2}$$

example 11–6 Perform the indicated operation.

$$\frac{5}{2x^2} - \frac{1}{3x} + \frac{2}{5x^3}$$

solution: The LCM or LCD is found by

$$2x^2 = 2 \cdot x \cdot x, \qquad 3x = 3 \cdot x, \qquad 5x^3 = 5 \cdot x \cdot x \cdot x$$

$$LCD = 2 \cdot 3 \cdot 5 \cdot x \cdot x \cdot x = 30x^3$$

Then, reducing to equivalent fractions,

$$\frac{5}{2x^2} = \frac{75x}{30x^3}, \qquad \frac{1}{3x} = \frac{10x^2}{30x^3}, \qquad \frac{2}{5x^3} = \frac{12}{30x^3}$$

Then

$$\frac{75x}{30x^3} - \frac{10x^2}{30x^3} + \frac{12}{30x^3} = \frac{-10x^2 + 75x + 12}{30x^3}$$

E X E R C I S E   11–2   Perform the indicated operations.

1. $\dfrac{3}{5} + \dfrac{4}{6}$

2. $\dfrac{6}{7} + \dfrac{5}{6} - \dfrac{8}{12}$

3. $\dfrac{7}{8} - \dfrac{1}{5} - \dfrac{3}{32}$

4. $\dfrac{3}{a} + \dfrac{4}{a} - \dfrac{1}{a}$

5. $\dfrac{1}{x} + \dfrac{1}{x} - \dfrac{4}{x}$

6. $\dfrac{5}{b} - \dfrac{1}{b^2}$

7. $\dfrac{1}{a} + \dfrac{4}{b}$

8. $\dfrac{3}{ab} + \dfrac{1}{a^2b}$

9. $\dfrac{6}{s} + \dfrac{5}{2s} - \dfrac{1}{3s}$

10. $\dfrac{8}{2(x + 1)} + \dfrac{3}{3x + 3}$

11. $\dfrac{5}{3a^2 - 3} - \dfrac{4}{5a^2 - 5}$

12. $\dfrac{5}{t + 2} - \dfrac{3}{t - 2}$

13. $\dfrac{16}{s^2 + 6s + 9} + \dfrac{3}{s + 3}$

14. $\dfrac{7a}{3} + \dfrac{5b}{2}$

15. $\dfrac{8c}{5d} + \dfrac{4e}{6f} + \dfrac{g}{2h}$

16. $\dfrac{5}{9w^2 + 12w + 4} - \dfrac{3}{(3w + 2)^2}$

The multiplication and division of fractions is normally an easier process than addition and subtraction. From arithmetic,

$$\frac{1}{2} \times \frac{3}{5} = \frac{3}{10}$$

$$\frac{3}{7} \div \frac{4}{5} = \frac{3}{7} \times \frac{5}{4} = \frac{15}{28}$$

Algebraic fractions would be handled in the same manner. For example,

$$\frac{3a}{4b} \times \frac{5a}{6c} = \frac{15a^2}{24bc}$$

$$\frac{5s}{6t} \div \frac{3t}{5v} = \frac{5s}{6t} \times \frac{5v}{3t} = \frac{25sv}{18t^2}$$

A review of several basic concepts involving fractions will be helpful at this point. The reciprocal of the fraction $\frac{3}{16}$ may be expressed as

$$\frac{1}{\frac{3}{16}}$$

This means, of course, that the fraction $\frac{3}{16}$ is to be divided into 1. Inverting the fraction and multiplying produces

$$1 \cdot \frac{16}{3} = \frac{16}{3} = 5\frac{1}{3}$$

Another process for review involves raising a fraction to a particular power. For example,

$$\left(\frac{5}{6}\right)^2$$

would involve squaring both the numerator and denominator:

$$\left(\frac{5}{6}\right)^2 = \frac{5^2}{6^2} = \frac{25}{36}$$

Refer to Section 11–5 if a question arises regarding simplification procedures. Remember that raising a fraction to a power or extracting a root is not the same as multiplication or division of the numerator and the denominator by the same number.

If a review of more involved multiplication and division procedures is desired, the reader is referred to Chapter 3.

The simplification of the results of the multiplication or division is performed in the following manner:

$$\frac{3xy^2z}{wv} \cdot \frac{4w^2v}{6x^3z^2} = \frac{12xy^2zw^2v}{6wvx^3z^2}$$

The cancellation of common factors results in

$$\frac{12xy^2zw^2v}{6wvx^3z^2} = \frac{2y^2w}{x^2z}$$

It should again be pointed out that this process involves the cancellation of factors and not terms. The cancellation of common individual terms in the numerator and the denominator may not, as noted previously, be performed.

EXERCISE 11–3 Perform the indicated operation and simplify the answers.

1. $\dfrac{4}{5} \cdot \dfrac{3}{9} \cdot \dfrac{6}{7}$

2. $\dfrac{15}{16} \cdot \dfrac{12}{14} \cdot \dfrac{5}{25}$

3. $\dfrac{3}{5} \div \dfrac{1}{6}$

4. $\dfrac{13}{15} \div \dfrac{3}{7}$

5. $\dfrac{3w}{4} \div \dfrac{5}{6w}$

6. $\dfrac{6x^2}{3xy} \div \dfrac{5x^2y}{5y^2}$

7. $\dfrac{12wv^2}{15xy} \div \dfrac{13w^2v}{5x^2y^2}$

8. $\dfrac{3a^2b^3}{14cd^4} \div \dfrac{2c^3d^5}{15a^3b^4}$

9. $\dfrac{a+b}{a-b} \div \dfrac{a-b}{a+b}$

10. $\dfrac{3}{w+z} \div \dfrac{w+z}{w^2+2wz+z^2}$

11. $\dfrac{(c-d)^2}{2} \div \dfrac{c-d}{2}$

12. $\dfrac{3e+4}{5} \div \dfrac{4e+2}{5}$

13. $\dfrac{2x^2-2y^2}{15} \cdot \dfrac{5}{x-y}$

14. $\dfrac{2(a+2)}{3} \cdot \dfrac{3(a+3)}{4}$

15. $\dfrac{x^2+4x+4}{2x+4} \cdot \dfrac{4}{2x+4}$

16. $\dfrac{9a^2-6ay-8y^2}{2} \div \dfrac{(3a+2y)(3a-4y)}{2}$

A *complex fraction* is one in which its numerator, denominator, or both, contain fractions. Examples of complex fractions are

$$\frac{\dfrac{3}{5}}{\dfrac{4}{9}} \qquad \frac{3 + \dfrac{1}{s}}{\dfrac{4}{5}} \qquad \frac{\dfrac{3a}{b} + 1}{\dfrac{4a}{b^2}}$$

The simplification of a complex fraction requires a reduction of both the numerator and denominator to its simplest form. This is then followed by the required division.

Let us examine the simplification of the three examples given above.

example 11–7   Simplify $\dfrac{\dfrac{3}{5}}{\dfrac{4}{9}}$.

solution: This complex fraction may be written

$$\frac{3}{5} \div \frac{4}{9}$$

In this form, it is seen that there is nothing about it which is complex. It is simply the division of one fraction by another.

$$\frac{3}{5} \div \frac{4}{9} = \frac{3}{5} \cdot \frac{9}{4} = \frac{27}{20} \quad \text{or} \quad 1\frac{7}{20}$$

example 11–8   Simplify:

$$\frac{3 + \dfrac{1}{5}}{\dfrac{4}{5}}$$

solution: First, the numerator must be simplified as

$$\frac{3 + \dfrac{1}{5}}{\dfrac{4}{5}} = \frac{\dfrac{15}{5} + \dfrac{1}{5}}{\dfrac{4}{5}} = \frac{\dfrac{16}{5}}{\dfrac{4}{5}}$$

143

Performing the indicated division,

$$\frac{16}{5} \div \frac{4}{5} = \frac{16}{5} \cdot \frac{5}{4} = \frac{80}{20} = 4$$

example 11-9   Simplify: $\dfrac{\dfrac{3a}{b}+1}{\dfrac{4a}{b^2}}$.

solution: The numerator may be simplified to form a simple fraction.

$$\frac{\dfrac{3a}{b}+1}{\dfrac{4a^2}{b^2}} = \frac{\dfrac{3a}{b}+\dfrac{b}{b}}{\dfrac{4a^2}{b^2}} = \frac{\dfrac{3a+b}{b}}{\dfrac{4a^2}{b^2}}$$

Performing the indicated division,

$$\frac{3a+b}{b} \div \frac{4a^2}{b^2} = \frac{3a+b}{b} \cdot \frac{b^2}{4a^2} = \frac{3ab^2+b^3}{4a^2b}$$

EXERCISE   11-4   Simplify the following complex fractions.

1. $\dfrac{\dfrac{4}{5}}{\dfrac{1}{4}}$

2. $\dfrac{1}{\dfrac{3}{5}+\dfrac{4}{6}}$

3. $\dfrac{\dfrac{1}{3}+3}{\dfrac{4}{5}+2}$

4. $\dfrac{\dfrac{5a+1}{2}}{\dfrac{2}{5}}$

5. $\dfrac{\dfrac{1}{a}+b}{\dfrac{5a}{2}}$

6. $\dfrac{\dfrac{3w}{2}+\dfrac{4w}{5}}{\dfrac{w^2}{4}}$

7. $\dfrac{\dfrac{1}{x+y}}{\dfrac{2}{x^2+2xy+y^2}}$

8. $\dfrac{\dfrac{3}{x}+\dfrac{1}{2x}+\dfrac{5}{3x}}{\dfrac{1}{6x}}$

11-9   FRACTIONAL EQUATIONS

A *fractional equation*, as the name indicates, is one that contains a fraction. Examples of fractional equations are

$$\frac{25}{a} = \frac{15}{3a} + 5 \quad \text{and} \quad \frac{w}{5} + \frac{w+5}{6} = 6$$

Our previous experience with equations involved rearranging the terms so that the unknown was on one side and all the remaining terms were on the other side. The solution of fractional equations requires one preliminary step. That is the procedure of eliminating all fractions from the equation. The solution of the equation may then be completed in the conventional manner.

Clearing the equation of fractions is usually a simple procedure. It requires obtaining the lowest common multiple of the denominators of each fraction. Multiplication of each term in the equation by the LCM will result in the cancellation of all denominators, which eliminates all fractions.

example 11–10 Solve for a.

$$\frac{25}{a} = \frac{15}{3a} + 5$$

solution: The LCM is found to be $3a$. Multiplying each term by $3a$,

$$(3a)\frac{25}{a} = \frac{(3a)15}{3a} + (3a)5$$

$$75 = 15 + 15a$$

$$75 - 15 = 15a$$

$$15a = 60$$

$$a = 4$$

example 11–11 Solve for w:

$$\frac{w}{5} + \frac{w+5}{6} = 6$$

solution: The LCM is found to be 30. Multiplying each term by 30,

$$6(30)\frac{w}{5} + 5(30)\frac{w+5}{6} = (30)6$$

$$6w + 5(w + 5) = 180$$

$$6w + 5w + 25 = 180$$

$$11w = 180 - 25$$
$$= 155$$
$$w = 14\tfrac{1}{11}$$

EXERCISE 11–5 Solve the following fractional equations.

1. $\dfrac{6}{b} + 8 = \dfrac{5}{2b}$

2. $\dfrac{3x}{2} + \dfrac{x-5}{4} = 12$

3. $\dfrac{4}{y} + \dfrac{3}{2y} = 16$

4. $\dfrac{2}{z} - \dfrac{1}{z} + 5 = 10$

5. $\dfrac{38}{w} - \dfrac{12}{6w} = 15$

6. $5 = \dfrac{6}{a} - \dfrac{2}{3a}$

7. $\dfrac{1}{3d} + \dfrac{16}{5} = 5$

8. $\dfrac{c+4}{5} = 15 - \dfrac{c}{7}$

12

VOLTAGE DIVIDERS

In Chapter 3, a series circuit was shown as a method of obtaining various circuit voltages. The device for "dividing" a supply voltage to obtain the desired circuit voltages was called a voltage divider. The operation of voltage dividers will be more thoroughly explored in this chapter.

12–1 VOLTAGE DIVIDER

A simple voltage divider is shown in Figure 12–1. Often dc voltages are obtained from an alternating current source using power-supply rectifiers. The output of the rectifier is usually filtered. The filter often consists of filter chokes and capacitors. This filtered output is then used to supply the voltage divider. In addition to "dividing" this voltage, the voltage divider serves to "drain" or "bleed" the voltage charge from the filter capacitors when the power supply is turned off. For this reason, the current flow through a voltage divider is called the *bleeder current*. This will frequently be used in the design of voltage dividers with a value of bleeder current equal to 10 percent of the line current often used.

The design of a simple voltage divider will be shown in the following example.

FIGURE 12–1
Simple Voltage Divider

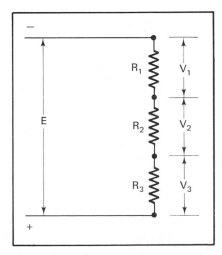

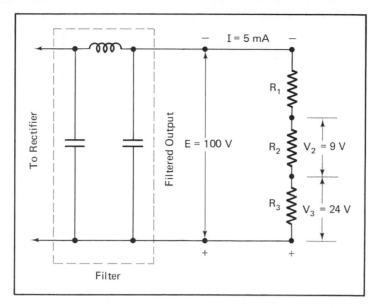

FIGURE 12–2
Circuit for Example 12–1

example 12–1 Design a voltage divider that will obtain voltages of 9 V and 24 V from a 100-V supply. The bleeder current must not exceed 5 mA.

solution: The voltage divider indicating the desired voltage is shown in Figure 12–2. The total circuit resistance required to limit the current to 5 mA is found as

$$R_T = \frac{E}{I} = \frac{100}{5 \times 10^{-3}} = 20 \times 10^3 \ \Omega$$

If a drop of 100 V occurs across the divider and 9 V and 24 V drops occur across R_2 and R_3, the voltage drop across R_1 must be

$$V_1 = 100 - V_2 - V_3 = 100 - 9 - 24 = 67 \text{ V}$$

Then

$$R_1 = \frac{V_1}{I} = \frac{67}{5 \times 10^{-3}} = 13.4 \times 10^3 \ \Omega$$

$$R_2 = \frac{V_2}{I} = \frac{9}{5 \times 10^{-3}} = 1.8 \times 10^3 \ \Omega$$

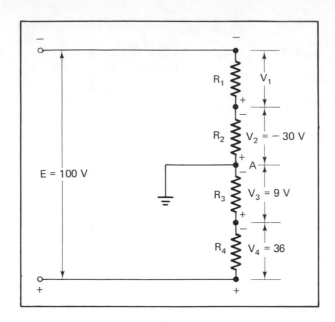

FIGURE 12–3
Circuit for Example 12–2

$$R_3 = \frac{V_3}{I} = \frac{24}{5 \times 10^{-3}} = 4.8 \times 10^3 \ \Omega$$

In our previous work with signed numbers, we saw that the choice or reference point determined whether a voltage was considered positive or negative. This may be applied to voltage dividers.

example 12-2 Design a voltage divider to obtain −30 V, +9 V, and +36 V from a 100-V supply. The divider current must not exceed 10 mA.

solution: A voltage divider indicating the desired voltages is shown in Figure 12–3. Note that placing the ground connection at point A establishes the reference point. The 30 V above this reference will be negative while the 9 V and 36 V below this point will be positive.

As in the previous example, a drop of 100 V occurs across the divider. To limit I to 10 mA,

$$R_T = \frac{E}{I} = \frac{100}{10 \times 10^{-3}} = 10 \times 10^3 \ \Omega$$

The voltage drop across V_1 must first be determined. From the reference point A, voltage drop of 9 V and 36 V occurs in the positive direction. A voltage drop of 30 V occurs in the negative direction. In terms of absolute values,

$$E = V_3 + V_4 - (V_1 - V_2)$$

$$100 = +9 + 36 - (-V - 30)$$

$$V_1 = -25 \text{ V}$$

Figure 12–4 shows the divider voltage with reference to ground point A. In Figure 12–4 point B is -30 V below point A and point C is -55 V below point A. Point D is $+9$ V above point A, and point E is $+45$ V above point A. It should be obvious that with point C -55 and point E $+45$ with reference to point A, the total voltage drop across the divider, or the voltage difference between points C and E, is

$$+45 - (-55) = 100 \text{ V}$$

See Section 3–4 for review. The value of resistances required are found as

$$R_1 = \frac{V_1}{I} = \frac{25}{10 \times 10^{-3}} = 2.5 \times 10^3 \ \Omega$$

FIGURE 12–4
Voltages for Example 12–2

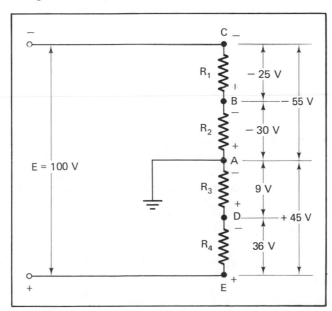

$$R_2 = \frac{V_2}{I} = \frac{30}{10 \times 10^{-3}} = 3 \times 10^3 \ \Omega$$

$$R_3 = \frac{V_3}{I} = \frac{9}{10 \times 10^{-3}} = 0.9 \times 10^3 \ \Omega$$

$$R_4 = \frac{V_4}{I} = \frac{36}{10 \times 10^{-3}} = 3.6 \times 10^3 \ \Omega$$

12-2 VOLTAGE DIVIDER UNDER LOAD

The voltage dividers in the previous sections had no loads connected to their terminals. Under normal circumstances, the individual voltages would be applied to a load. Let us examine what effect the application of load will have on the operation of the voltage divider.

First, let us look into what effect a changing load would have on a somewhat simpler circuit. Figure 12–5 shows a series dropping resistor used to reduce the voltage applied to the load resistor R_L.

In the following example, the changes in circuit conditions with changes in load will be examined.

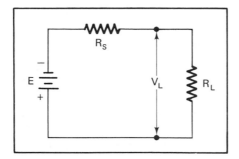

FIGURE 12–5
Series Resistor Used to
Reduce Voltage

example 12–3 Determine the size of the series resistor required to obtain a load voltage 200 V from a 300-V supply. The load current is to be 1 mA. What would be the effect on the load voltage if the load current is reduced to 0.5 mA?

solution: The voltage drop across R_s may be found as

$$V_{R_s} = E - V_L = 300 - 200 = 100 \ \text{V}$$

$$R_s = \frac{V_{R_s}}{I} = \frac{100}{1 \times 10^{-3}} = 100 \times 10^3 \ \Omega$$

The load resistance R_L would have a value of

$$R_L = \frac{V_L}{I} = \frac{200}{1 \times 10^{-3}} = 200 \times 10^3 \ \Omega$$

If the load current was reduced to 0.5 mA, the voltage drop across R_s would be

$$V_{Rs} = I_{Rs} = 0.5 \times 10^{-3} \times 100 \times 10^3 = 50 \ \text{V}$$

The voltage across the load would then be

$$V_L = E - V_{Rs} = 300 - 50 = 250 \ \text{V}$$

The advantage of this type of device is that the current flow is only that required by the load. To more than offset this is the substantial variation in load voltage with changes in load current, as shown in this example. Most electronic applications could not tolerate this voltage variations, and as a result such a device is very infrequently used.

Let us now examine the effect of placing a load of 100 Ω across R_3 in Figure 12–2. This would appear as shown in Figure 12–6. The parallel resistance of R_3 and R_L is found as

$$R_{\text{par}} = \frac{(4,800)(100,000)}{4,800 + 100,000} = 4,580 \ \Omega = 4.58 \ \text{k}\Omega$$

FIGURE 12–6
Circuit of Example 12–1, Load Connected to R₃

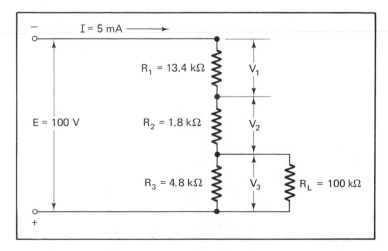

The total resistance of the divider is now

$$R_T = R_1 + R_2 + R_{par}$$

$$= 13.4 \text{ k}\Omega + 1.8 \text{ k}\Omega + 4.58 \text{ k}\Omega = 19.78 \text{ k}\Omega$$

The total current is now found as

$$I = \frac{E}{R_T} = \frac{100}{19.78 \times 10^3} = 5.056 \times 10^{-3} \text{ A} = 5.06 \text{ mA}$$

The circuit voltage may now be found:

$$V_1 = IR_1 = 5.06 \times 10^{-3} \times 13.4 \times 10^3 = 67.8 \text{ V } (67 \text{ V})$$

$$V_2 = IR_2 = 5.06 \times 10^{-3} \times 1.8 \times 10^3 = 9.11 \text{ V } (9 \text{ V})$$

$$V_3 = IR_{par} = 5.06 \times 10^{-3} \times 4.58 \times 10^3 = 23.2 \text{ V } (24 \text{ V})$$

The voltages without load from Example 12–1 are shown in parentheses. Note that the large voltage variation that occurs when the series dropping resistor was used does not occur.

example 12–4 A voltage divider is to be designed to provide 9 V at 30 mA with a bleeder current of 3 mA from a 100-V supply.

solution: The circuit with the known voltages and current flow indicated is shown in Figure 12–7. From the figure it is

FIGURE 12–7
Circuit for Example 12–4

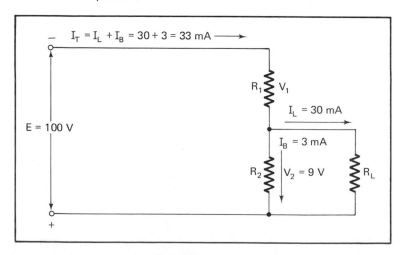

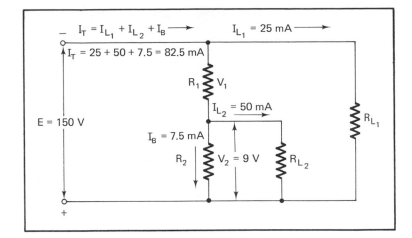

FIGURE 12-8
Circuit for Example 12-5

seen that $V_2 = 9$ V and the current flow through R_2 is $I_B = 3$ mA, then

$$R_2 = \frac{V_2}{I_B} = \frac{9}{3 \times 10^{-3}} = 3 \times 10^3 = 3{,}000 \ \Omega$$

$$V_1 = E - V_2 = 100 - 9 = 91 \ \text{V}$$

$$R_1 = \frac{V_1}{I_T} = \frac{91}{33 \times 10^{-3}} = 2.757 \times 10^3 = 2{,}757 \ \Omega$$

example 12-5 A voltage divider is to be designed to provide 25 mA at 150 V and 50 mA at 9 V from a 150-V supply. The bleeder current is to be 10 percent of the load current.

solution: The total load current is found to be

$$I_L = I_{L_1} + I_{L_2} = 25 + 50 = 75 \ \text{mA}$$

The bleeder current is to be 10 percent of I_L, or

$$I_B = 0.10 \times I_L = 0.10 \times 75 = 7.5 \ \text{mA}$$

The known voltages and current flow is shown in Figure 12-8. From the figure it is seen that the voltage V_1 across R_1 is

$$V_1 = E - V_2 = 150 - 9 = 141 \ \text{V}$$

$$I_{R_1} = I_{L_2} + I_B = 50 + 7.5 = 57.5 \ \text{mA}$$

With V_1 and I_{R_1} known, R_1 may be calculated as

$$R_1 = \frac{V_1}{I_{R_1}} = \frac{141}{57.5 \times 10^{-3}} = 2.452 \times 10^3 = 2,452 \ \Omega$$

Similarly, R_2 may be calculated as

$$R_2 = \frac{V_2}{I_B} = \frac{9}{7.5 \times 10^{-3}} = 1.2 \times 10^3 \ \Omega = 1,200 \ \Omega$$

example 12-6 Design a voltage divider to provide 150 V at 0 mA, 30 mA at 90 V, 20 mA at 60 V, and 40 mA at 50 V from a 150-V supply. The bleeder current is to be 10 percent of the load current.

solution: The load current is found to be

$$I_L = 30 + 20 + 40 = 90 \ \text{mA}$$

and

$$I_B = 10\% \ I_L$$

$$I_B = 0.10 \times 90 \ \text{mA} = 9 \ \text{mA}$$

$$I_T = I_L + I_B = 90 \ \text{mA} + 9 \ \text{mA} = 99 \ \text{mA}$$

The known currents and voltages are shown in Figure 12–9. At point B, 90 V must exist to supply R_{L_1}. The voltage drop through R_1 must then be

$$V_{R_1} = 150 - 90 = 60 \ \text{V}$$

As the total load current, 99 mA, flows through R_1, then

$$R_1 = \frac{V_{R_1}}{I_T} = \frac{60}{99 \times 10^{-3}} = 0.606 \times 10^3 \ \Omega = 606 \ \Omega$$

At point C, 60 V must exist, which means that the voltage drop through R_2 must be $V_B - V_C$:

$$V_{R2} = V_B - V_C = 90 - 60 = 30 \ \text{V}$$

The current flow through R_2 is $I_{R_2} = I_T - I_{RL_1}$:

$$I_{R_2} = 99 - 30 = 69 \ \text{mA}$$

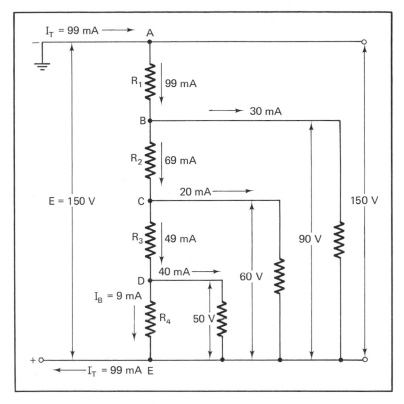

FIGURE   12–9
Circuit for Example 12–6

Then

$$R_2 = \frac{V_{R2}}{I_{R2}} = \frac{30}{69 \times 10^{-3}} = 0.435 \times 10^3 \ \Omega = 435 \ \Omega$$

Similarly,

$$V_{R3} = V_C - V_D = 60 - 50 = 10 \text{ V}$$
$$I_{R3} = 69 - 20 = 49 \text{ mA}$$

Then

$$R_3 = \frac{V_{R3}}{I_{R3}} = \frac{10}{49 \times 10^{-3}} = 0.204 \times 10^3 \ \Omega = 204 \ \Omega$$

$$V_{R4} = V_D - V_E = 50 - 0 = 50 \text{ V}$$
$$I_{R4} = I_B = 49 - 40 = 9 \text{ mA}$$
$$R_4 = \frac{V_{R4}}{I_{R4}} = \frac{50}{9 \times 10^{-3}} = 5.555 \times 10^3 \ \Omega = 5,555 \ \Omega$$

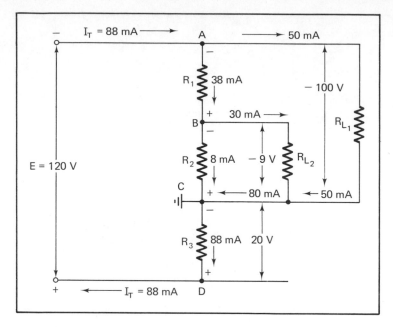

FIGURE 12–10
Circuit for Example 12–7

example 12–7 A voltage divider is to be designed to supply 50 mA at −100 V, 30 mA at −9 V, and 0 mA at +20 V, all from a 120-V supply (Figure 12–10). The bleeder current is 10 percent of the load current.

solution: The load current is found to be

$$I_L = 50 + 30 = 80 \text{ mA}$$

Then

$$I_B = 10\% \ I_L = 0.10 \times 80 = 8 \text{ mA}$$

$$I_T = I_L + I_B = 80 + 8 = 88 \text{ mA}$$

$$V_{R_1} = 100 - 9 = 91 \text{ V} \quad \text{and} \quad I_{R_1} = 38 \text{ mA}$$

$$R_1 = \frac{V_{R_1}}{I_{R_1}} = \frac{91}{38 \times 10^{-3}} = 2.39 \times 10^3 \ \Omega = 2,390 \ \Omega$$

$$V_{R_2} = 9 \text{ V} \qquad I_{R_2} = 8 \text{ mA}$$

$$R_2 = \frac{V_{R_2}}{I_{R_2}} = \frac{9}{8 \times 10^{-3}} = 1.125 \times 10^3 \ \Omega = 1,125 \ \Omega$$

$$V_{R_3} = 20 \text{ V},$$

$$I_T = I_B + I_{RL_1} + I_{RL_2} = 8 + 50 + 30 = 88 \text{ mA}$$

$$R_3 = \frac{V_{R_3}}{I_{R_3}} = \frac{20}{88 \times 10^{-3}} = 0.227 \times 10^3 \ \Omega = 227 \ \Omega$$

EXERCISE 12–1

1. Design an unloaded voltage divider to provide 300 V, 150 V, 75 V, and 30 V from a 300-V filtered source. The bleeder current is 10 mA.

2. What effect would doubling the bleeder current have on the circuit design of problem 1?

3. Design an unloaded voltage divider to develop −25 V, +50 V, +10 V, and +5 V from a 100-V source. The bleeder current is 5 mA.

4. Design a voltage divider to provide 300 V at 0 mA and 150 V at 50 mA from a 300-V source. The bleeder current is to be 10 percent of the total load current.

5. Redesign the voltage divider of problem 4 to provide the same voltages from a 400-V source.

6. Design a voltage divider to provide 250 V at 0 mA, 150 V at 100 mA, 100 V at 50 mA, and −50 V at 0 mA from a 300-V source. The bleeder current is to be 10 percent of the total load current.

7. Determine the power rating of the resistors of the voltage divider of problem 6.

8. If the resistors used in problem 1 had a ±10 percent resistance tolerance, what effect would using resistors all with a value 10 percent over the design value have on the voltage-divider output?

13

MEASUREMENT OF CURRENT

This chapter will deal with the measurement of the basic electrical quantity, current. The measurement of voltage and resistance will be presented in the following chapters.

One of the primary functions of an electronic technician is the measurement of these quantities. The importance of these measurements cannot be overemphasized. It is therefore absolutely essential for the reader to become thoroughly familiar with these procedures.

13–1 BASIC DIRECT-CURRENT METER MOVEMENT

Most of the meters used for dc measurements use a *D'Arsonval meter movement*. This type of meter is a permanent magnet moving-coil type of movement. It consists of a wire-wound moving coil supported by jeweled bearings and mounted between the poles of a permanent magnet. Current flow through the moving-coil winding develops an electromagnetic field. This reacts with the magnetic field of the permanent magnet and causes the moving coil to turn. The amount the coil turns is proportional to the amount of current flow. A pointer mounted on the moving coil indicates the magnitude of the current on a calibrated scale. A D'Arsonval moving-coil meter movement is shown in Figure 13–1.

13–2 GALVANOMETERS

The *galvanometer* is a device for detecting the amount and direction of very small levels of current. It has a moving-coil D'Arsonval type

FIGURE 13–1
D'Arsonval Moving-Coil Meter
(Courtesy of Weston Instruments)

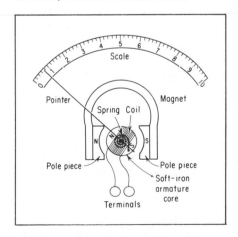

of meter movement. The basic structure of the galvanometer is similar to that shown in Figure 13–1. The basic difference is that it is a zero-center type of meter. That is, the pointer is mounted, and the scale is calibrated, so that the zero-current-flow position is in the center of the scale. The level of current flow and its direction may then be indicated on the meter. The typical construction of a zero-center galvanometer is shown in Figure 13–2.

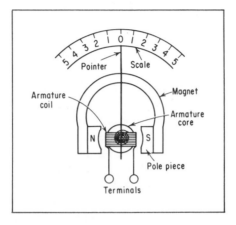

FIGURE 13–2
Zero-Center Galvanometer
(Courtesy of Weston Instruments)

The numerical values indicated on the scale of a galvanometer do not represent actual values. That is, a galvanometer normally indicates only the *relative* magnitude, as well as the direction, of the current.

Certain specialized types of galvanometers are calibrated to read absolute values. That is, the scale reading may be used to determine the actual value of the current flow.

The galvanometer is often used in bridge circuits. Several of these will be discussed in Chapter 15. When used for this purpose the bridge is "balanced," to obtain a zero galvanometer reading. For this reason, only a relative indication of the magnitude of current flow is required.

13–3 AMMETERS

The physical arrangement of the D'Arsonval meter limits the current-carrying capacity of the moving-coil movement. Commercially available ammeters normally have movements that require from 0–10 μA to 0–5 mA to produce full-scale deflection. The amount of current that is required to produce full-scale deflection is a measure of the meter sensitivity.

If the measurement of current were restricted to the above

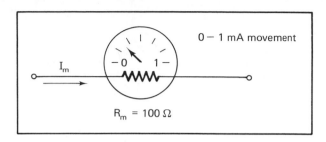

FIGURE 13–3
Schematic Representation of Meter Movement

ranges, the usefulness of these meters would be very limited. The use of parallel resistance, which bypasses a portion of the circuit current around the meter, results in an extension of the meter range. These bypass resistances are called *shunts*.

13–4 EXTENDING THE RANGE OF AN AMMETER

The use of resistance shunts permits the range of the meter movement to be extended. This procedure involves the use of a parallel resistance, the shunt, to bypass a specific proportion of the circuit current around the ammeter.

In practice, a meter movement is selected with appropriate sensitivity for the type of application involved. A shunt of suitable size is then chosen in order that current of the desired level may be measured. To understand the shunting procedure, a more detailed examination of the meter movement is necessary.

The moving coil of the meter is wound with a number of turns of wire of appropriate size. The amount of rotation of the moving coil is a function of the number of turns and the amount of current flow. The size of the wire and the number of turns result in a certain amount of meter resistance.

For example, a typical meter movement of 0–1 mA may have a meter resistance of 100 Ω. A schematic representation of this movement is shown in Figure 13–3. Ohm's law may be used to determine what voltage is required to produce full-scale deflection. A current flow of 1 mA is required with this movement for full-scale deflection. Hence

$$E_m = I_m R_m = 0.001 \times 100 = 0.1 \text{ V}$$

This of course means that a voltage of 0.1 V is required to produce full-scale deflection of the meter.

A schematic of this meter movement with a shunting resistor is shown in Figure 13–4. It is seen that when the total circuit current reaches point A, part flows through the meter and part flows through

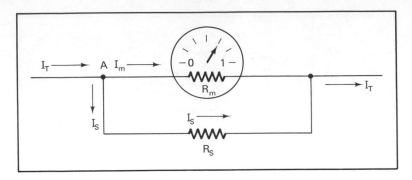

FIGURE 13–4
Meter Movement with Shunt

the shunt. For this meter movement it was found that a voltage of 0.1 V resulted in full-scale deflection. Inasmuch as the shunt resistor is in parallel with the meter, the same voltage also appears across R_s. Using Ohm's law, the resistance of a shunt to bypass any amount of current may be calculated.

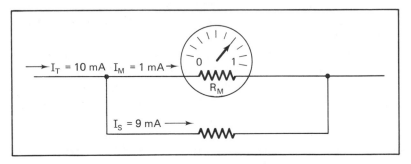

FIGURE 13–5
Circuit for Example 13–1

example 13–1 Design a circuit that will permit a meter movement of 0–1 mA to be used to measure 0–10 mA. The meter resistance $R_m = 100\ \Omega$.

solution: The circuit schematic is first drawn as shown in Figure 13–5. Full-scale deflection occurs when $I_m = 1$ mA and $E_m = 0.1$ V, which means that

$$I_s = I_T - I_m \quad \text{or} \quad I_s = 10 - 1 = 9 \text{ mA}$$

and

$$E_m = E_s = 0.1 \text{ V}$$

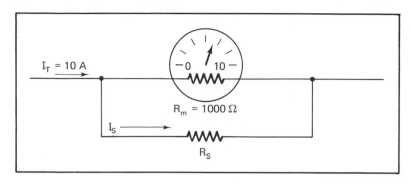

FIGURE 13–6
Circuit for Example 13–2

With V_s and I_s known,

$$R_s = \frac{V_s}{I_s} = \frac{0.1}{9 \times 10^{-3}} = 0.011 \times 10^3 \ \Omega = 11 \ \Omega$$

In a similar manner, as in the above example, a shunt of suitable size may be selected to measure any level of current. The choice of a suitable meter movement will permit a meter with the desired degree of sensitivity to be used.

example 13–2   Design a circuit (Figure 13–6) to measure 0–10 A with a meter rated at 0–100 μA. The meter resistance $R_m = 1,000 \ \Omega$.

solution: Full-scale deflection occurs with $I_m = 100 \ \mu$A. Then

$$V_m = I_m R_m = 100 \times 10^{-6} \times 1,000 = 0.1 \text{ V}$$

$$I_s = I_T - I_m = 10 - 100 \times 10^{-6}$$

$$= 10 - 0.0001 = 9.9999 \text{ A}$$

$$R_s = \frac{V_s - V_m}{I_s} = \frac{0.1}{9.9999} = 0.010 \ \Omega$$

A variation of the above method for calculation of R_s follows. For full-scale deflection, $E_s = E_m$; then

$$I_s R_s = I_m R_m$$

Solving for R_s produces

$$R_s = \frac{I_m}{I_s} R_m$$

As $I_s = I_T - I_m,$

$$R_s = \frac{I_m}{I_T - I_m} R_m$$

example 13-3 Using the 0–100-μA meter movement of Example 13–2 with $R_m = 1,000\ \Omega$, determine the value of R_s to measure 0–1 A, 0–100 mA, 0–1 mA, and 0–100 μA.

solution: For 0–1 A,

$$R_s = \frac{I_m}{I_T - I_m} R_m = \frac{100 \times 10^{-6}}{1 - 100 \times 10^{-6}} \times 1,000$$

$$= \frac{100 \times 10^{-6}}{0.9999} \times 1,000 = 100.01 \times 10^{-6} \times 1,000$$

$$= 0.10001\ \Omega$$

For 0–100 mA,

$$R_s = \frac{100 \times 10^{-6}}{100 \times 10^{-3} - 100 \times 10^{-6}} \times 1,000$$

$$= \frac{100 \times 10^{-6}}{0.0999} \times 1,000 = 1.001\ \Omega$$

For 0–1 mA,

$$R_s = \frac{100 \times 10^{-6}}{1 \times 10^{-3} - 100 \times 10^{-6}} \times 1,000$$

$$= \frac{100 \times 10^{-6}}{0.0009} \times 1,000 = 111.11\ \Omega$$

For 0–100 μA, no shunt would be required.

In the above three examples the calculated value of R_s is relatively small. With larger current measurements R_s would further decrease in value because of the need for a larger amount of current to bypass the meter. The accuracy of the current measurement depends on the accuracy with which R_s is determined. It also should be emphasized that a precision resistor is required for R_s. A commercially available resistor, with a ±10 percent resistance tolerance, obviously would be unsuitable.

It was demonstrated in Section 13–4 that a wide range of current measurements may be made with a single meter movement and appropriate size shunts. When enclosed in a single instrument, the device is referred to as a *multirange ammeter*. A schematic representation of a multirange ammeter is shown in Figure 13–7. This diagram shows the meter and shunt values calculated in Examples 13–2 and 13–3.

The switch-arm contact in Figure 13–7 is arranged so as to make contact with the next shunt terminal before the connection with the previous shunt is broken. The reason for this is that without a shunt in the circuit the full circuit current, I_T, would pass through the meter. The result of 10 A passing through a 0–100-μA meter, even for an instant, should be obvious.

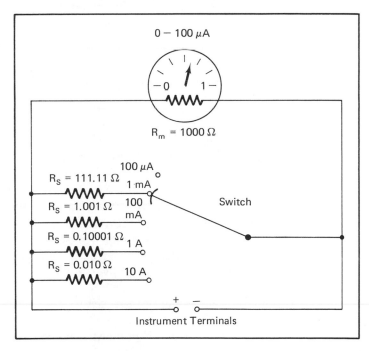

FIGURE 13–7
Multirange Ammeter

An electrical shunting method called the *Ayrton* or *universal shunt* eliminates the switching problems noted above. In this circuit, the total shunt resistance is across the meter at all times. The universal shunt is shown in Figure 13–8.

The operation of this type of shunting method is described as follows:

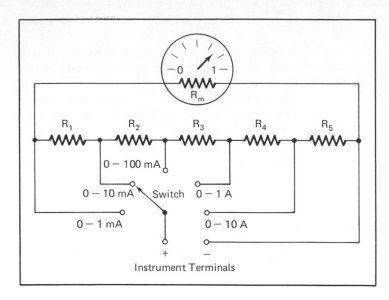

FIGURE 13–8
Multirange Ammeter Using Universal or Ayrton Shunt

1. With the switch in the 0–1-mA connection, the entire resistance of the shunt is across the meter.
2. With the switch in the 0–10-mA position, R_1 is placed in series with the meter and the shunting resistance is decreased, as it now includes only R_2, R_3, R_4, and R_5. This, of course, permits more current to bypass or shunt the meter.
3. Moving the switch to higher current positions increases the resistance in series with the meter while decreasing the shunt resistance. Moving the switch from a higher to a lower current position would have a reverse effect.

The calculation of the values of the resistors used in the universal shunt is most easily solved using simultaneous equations. This subject will not be presented until a later chapter. At that time, an example of this type of calculation will be provided.

The following example will show the operation of the universal shunt. This solution will not require the use of simultaneous equations.

example 13-4   Determine the values of R_1, R_2, and R_3 in the universal shunt shown in Figure 13–9 if $R_m = R_s = R_1 + R_2 + R_3 = 1{,}000\ \Omega$.

solution: For a simple shunt,

$$E_s = E_m \quad \text{or} \quad I_s R_s = I_m R_m$$

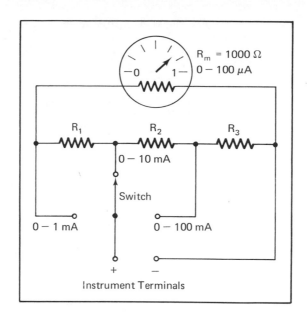

FIGURE 13–9
Circuit for Example 13–4

from which

$$R_s = \frac{I_m}{I_s} = R_m$$

For the 0–10 mA position,

$$R_{s_1} = 1,000 - R_1 \quad \text{and} \quad I_{s_1} = 10 \text{ mA} - I_m$$

and as R_1 is now in series with meter $R_{m_1} = R_m + R_1$, then

$$R_{s_1} = \frac{I_m}{I_{s_1}} R_{m_1}$$

We have

$$1,000 - R_1 = \frac{0.0001}{0.010 - 0.0001}(1,000 + R_1)$$

$$1,000 - R_1 = 0.01010(1,000 + R_1)$$

$$= 10.10 + 0.0101R_1$$

$$1,000 - 10.10 = R_1 + 0.0101R_1$$

$$989.9 = 1.0101R_1$$

$$R_1 = 980 \ \Omega$$

For the 0–100 mA scale,

$$R_{s2} = R_s - (R_1 + R_2) \quad \text{and}$$

$$R_{m2} = R_m + R_1 + R_2$$

$$I_{s2} = 100 \text{ mA} - I_m$$

$$R_{s2} = \frac{I_m}{I_{s2}} R_{m2}$$

$$1{,}000 - (R_1 + R_2) = \frac{0.0001}{0.10 - 0.0001} (1{,}000 + R_1 + R_2)$$

and as $R_1 = 980 \ \Omega$,

$$1{,}000 - 980 - R_2 = \frac{0.001}{} (1{,}000 + 980 + R_2)$$

$$20 - R_2 = 0.001(1{,}980 + R_2)$$

$$= 1.98 + 0.001 R_2$$

$$20 - 1.98 = R_2 + 0.001 R_2$$

$$R_2 = 18 \ \Omega$$

and as $R_s = R_1 + R_2 + R_3 = 1{,}000$,

$$980 + 18 + R_3 = 1{,}000$$

$$R_3 = 2 \ \Omega$$

The reader will have to make certain that in using any multirange meter that the proper interpretation of the meter scales are made. For example, in Example 13–4 the meter may be a single scale divided between 0 and 1. For the 0–1-mA range, this would be direct-reading. If the selection switch were in the 0–10-mA range, a full-scale meter indication would represent 10 mA. For this range, then, each reading would have to be multiplied by 10. For the 0–100-mA range, each scale reading would require multiplication by a factor of 100.

EXERCISE 13–1

1. Design a circuit that will permit a 0–100-μA meter with $R_m = 1{,}000 \ \Omega$ to be used to measure 0–10 mA.

2. Modify the circuit of problem 1 so that the meter could be used to measure 0–1 A.

3. If the meter used in problems 1 and 2 had a scale calibrated from 0 to 1, what would the meter reading have to be multiplied by?

4. Design a circuit to measure 0–50 mA using a 0–50-μA meter with $R_m = 600 \ \Omega$.

5. Design appropriate shunts so that the meter of problem 4 may be extended to measure 0–100 mA and 0–250 mA.

6. How could the sensitivity of the measurement procedures of problem 4 be increased?

7. If only a 10-Ω resistor were available for a shunt, what would be tha range that the meter of problem 1 could be used to measure?

8. Design a universal shunt to measure 0–1 mA, 0–100 mA, and 0–500 mA, using a 50-μA meter with $R_m = R_s = R_1 + R_2 + R_3 = 500 \ \Omega$.

14

MEASUREMENT OF VOLTAGE

In previous sections it was seen that an ammeter and its shunt were in parallel. As a result, the voltage developed across the shunt was equal to the voltage drop across the meter, or $E_s = E_m$. In effect, then, if the meter scale had been calibrated in volts, the meter would have been a voltmeter. So we see that a voltmeter is essentially an ammeter with a scale calibrated in volts.

The meter that was used in Figure 13–3 to explain ammeter operation had a 0–1-mA movement with $R_m = 100\ \Omega$. When reading full scale,

$$E_m = I_m R_m = 0.001 \times 100 = 0.1\ \text{V}$$

If we were to add a resistor in series with this movement, the same current, 1 mA, would still be required to obtain full-scale deflection. To measure a voltage of 10 V with 1 mA flowing, a circuit resistance of

$$R = \frac{E}{I} = \frac{10}{0.001} = 10,000\ \Omega$$

would be required. As the meter $R_m = 100\ \Omega$, a series resistance, $R_s = 10,000 - 100 = 9,900\ \Omega$, would be necessary. This circuit is shown in Figure 14–1.

The series resistance that is added in this manner is called a *multiplier*. Using the appropriate multiplier will permit such a meter movement to be used to measure various voltage levels.

FIGURE   14–1
Circuit Using 0–1-mA Meter to Measure 0–10 V

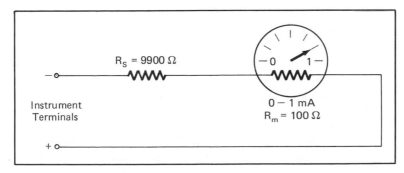

example 14-1 Determine the multipliers required to measure 0–100 V and 0–1,000 V using the meter movement shown in Figure 14–1.

solution: For either range, 0–100 V or 0–1,000 V, $I_m = 1$ mA is required for full-scale deflection. For 0–100 V, the circuit resistance would be

$$R = \frac{E}{I} = \frac{100}{0.001} = 100,000 \ \Omega$$

$$R_s = R - R_m = 100,000 - 100 = 99,900 \ \Omega$$

For 0–1,000 V,

$$R = \frac{E}{I} = \frac{1,000}{0.001} = 1,000,000 \ \Omega$$

$$R_s = R - R_m = 1,000,000 - 100 = 999,900 \ \Omega$$

14-2 VOLTMETER SENSITIVITY

The sensitivity of a voltmeter is a measure of the number of ohms per volt of meter range. In Example 14–1, the sensitivity would be found by dividing the total meter circuit resistance by the voltage range involved. For the 0–100-V range, $R = 100,000 \ \Omega$ and

$$\text{voltmeter sensitivity} = \frac{100,000}{100} = 1,000 \ \Omega/V$$

For the 0–1,000-V range, $R = 1,000,000$

$$\text{voltage sensitivity} = \frac{1,000,000}{1,000} = 1,000 \ \Omega/V$$

The sensitivity of this 0–1-mA meter when used on any voltage range is 1,000 Ω/V.

14-3 EFFECT OF VOLTMETER SENSITIVITY

A certain amount of resistance is introduced into a circuit when a voltmeter is used. Let us examine what effect this has on the accuracy of the voltage measurements.

example 14-2 Using the meter of Example 13–5 with a 1,000 Ω/V sensitivity, determine how the actual voltage drop across R_1 compares with the meter reading (Figure 14–2).

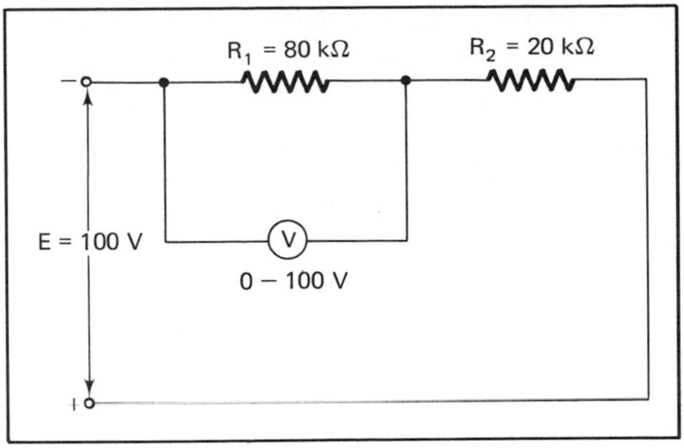

FIGURE 14–2
Circuit for Example 14–2

solution: The total circuit resistance, without the voltmeter connected, is

$$R_T = R_1 + R_2 = 80,000 + 20,000 = 1 \times 10^5$$

$$I = \frac{E}{R_T} = \frac{100}{1 \times 10^5} = 100 \times 10^{-5} = 0.001 \text{ A}$$

The actual voltage drop across R_1 is found as

$$V_{R_1} = IR_1 = 1 \times 10^{-3} \times 8 \times 10^4 = 8 \times 10^1 \text{ V} = 80 \text{ V}$$

The voltmeter when placed across R_1, with its resistance of $R_{mT} = 100,000 \ \Omega$ (R_m + multiplier), results in the parallel resistance of

$$R_{\text{par}} = \frac{80,000 \times 100,000}{80,000 + 100,000} = 44,444 \ \Omega$$

The total circuit resistance is now

$$R_{T_1} = R_{\text{par}} + R_2 = 44,444 + 20,000 = 64,444 \ \Omega$$

$$I_1 = \frac{E}{R_{T_1}} = \frac{100}{64,444} = 0.00155 \text{ A}$$

The meter reading measured across R_1 will be

$$V_{\text{par}} = I_1 R_{\text{par}} = 0.00155 \times 44,444 = 68.88 \text{ V}$$

This compares with an actual voltage drop of 80 V.

example 14-3 In place of the voltmeter in Example 14-2, a voltmeter with a sensitivity of 20,000 Ω/V is used. How does the use of this meter affect the circuit?

solution: On the 100-V scale this meter has a total resistance of $R_{mT} = 100 \times 20,000 = 2,000,000 \ \Omega$. The parallel resistance of R_1 and R_{mT} is

$$R_{\text{par}} = \frac{80,000 \times 2,000,000}{80,000 + 2,000,000} = 76,920 \ \Omega$$

The total circuit resistance now is

$$R_{T_2} = R_{\text{par}} + R_2 = 76,920 + 20,000 = 96,920 \ \Omega$$

$$I_2 = \frac{E}{R_{T_2}} = \frac{100}{96,920} = 0.00103 \ \text{A}$$

The voltmeter across R_1 would read

$$V_{\text{par}} = I_2 R_{\text{par}} = 0.00103 \times 76,920 = 79.36 \ \text{V}$$

These two examples should point out the necessity of using an appropriate meter for the measurement involved. Using the 1,000-Ω/V meter in the first example resulted in a voltage measurement of 68.88 V when the actual voltage was 80 V. In the second example the measurement was 79.36 V, compared to 80 V.

The first meter would have been suitable for many applications, such as power circuits with their relatively low resistance. The voltmeter circuit resistance would have only a minor effect on measurements in such circuit applications.

The voltmeter with the 20,000-Ω/V sensitivity proved to be suitable for the circuit of Figure 14-2. This type of circuit, with its relatively high resistance, is typical of those found in electronics and requires a voltmeter with a high sensitivity. This minimizes the effect of the voltmeter circuit resistance "loading" the measured circuit and the measurement effect noted above.

14-4 MULTIRANGE VOLTMETER

Including a number of multipliers within a single instrument provides a number of voltage ranges. This increases the versatility of the instrument, which is called a *multirange voltmeter*. A typical circuit is shown in Figure 14-3. In this circuit, individual multipliers are not used. An add-on arrangement is utilized. For example, the multiplier for the 0-50-V range consists of a value of resistance R_2 added to the R_1 multiplier for the 0-10-V range.

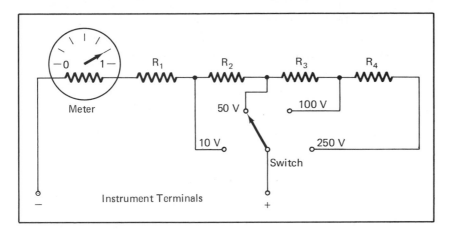

FIGURE 14–3
Typical Circuit Arrangement for
Multirange Voltmeter

example 14–4 Using the circuit of Figure 14–3, calculate the multipliers for the ranges indicated. The meter used is a 50-
μA movement with $R_m = 1,500$ Ω and a sensitivity of
20,000 Ω/V.

solution: On the 10-V scale, the total circuit resistance required is

$$R_{T_1} = 20,000 \ \Omega/V \times 10 \ V = 200 \ k\Omega$$

With a meter resistance of 1,500 Ω, R_1 is found as

$$R_1 = R_{T_1} - R_m = 200 \ k\Omega - 1.5 \ k\Omega = 198.5 \ k\Omega$$

In a similar manner, for the 50-V range,

$$R_{T_2} = 20,000 \times 50 = 1,000 \ k\Omega$$

Note that R_m has been included in the calculation of the
0–10-V multiplier, so $R_2 = R_{T_2} - R_{T_1}$ or
$R_2 = 1,000 \ k\Omega - 200 \ k\Omega = 800 \ k\Omega$.

For the 100-V range,

$$R_{T_3} = 20,000 \times 100 = 2,000 \ k\Omega$$
$$R_3 = 2,000 \ k\Omega - 1,000 \ k\Omega = 1,000 \ k\Omega$$

For the 250-V range,

$$R_{T_4} = 20,000 \times 250 = 5,000 \ k\Omega$$
$$R_4 = 5,000 \ k\Omega - 2,000 \ k\Omega = 3,000 \ k\Omega$$

EXERCISE 14-1

1. A multiplier of what size would be required to measure 0–10 V using a 0–100-μA meter with $R_m = 1,000\ \Omega$?

2. Determine the size of the multipliers required for the meter of problem 1 to be used to measure 0–250 V and 0–0.1 V.

3. What is the sensitivity of the meter used in problem 1?

4. Using the meter of problem 1, what effect would this have on measuring the voltage of each of two 500-kΩ resistors in series? How does the measured voltage compare with the actual voltage drop without the meter in the circuit?

5. Complete problem 4 using a meter with twice the sensitivity.

6. Complete problem 4 using a meter with a 20,000-Ω/V sensitivity.

7. Determine the multipliers required to make a multirange voltmeter using a 0–100-μA meter with $R_m = 2,000$. The ranges desired are 0–1 V, 0–10 V and 0–25 V.

8. Design the circuit for problem 7 using a 0–1-mA meter with $R_m = 100\ \Omega$.

15

MEASUREMENT OF RESISTANCE

The resistance of an unknown resistor could be determined using Ohm's law as

$$R_x = \frac{E}{I}$$

This would require a voltmeter and an ammeter to determine E and I.

To eliminate the need for two meters, the ohmmeter was developed. An ohmmeter basically consists of a meter movement and a known source of voltage. With a few circuit refinements the meter scale may be calibrated to indicate resistance.

15–1 OHMMETERS

The basic circuit used in many commercial ohmmeters is shown in Figure 15–1. The elements of this circuit are in addition to the basic meter movement:

E known source of voltage

R_L resistor to limit the circuit current flow

FIGURE   15–1
Basic Ohmmeter Circuit

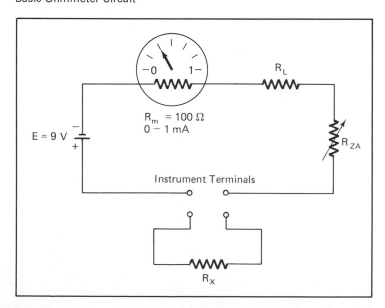

R_{ZA} variable resistor to provide a zero-adjust of the meter to compensate for voltage variations

R_x unknown resistor

If the instrument terminals of Figure 15–1 are shorted and R_{ZA} adjusted to have the meter read full scale, 1 mA,

$$R_T = R_m + R_L + R_{ZA} = \frac{E}{I_m} = \frac{9}{0.001} = 9 \text{ k}\Omega$$

This full-scale point on the dial would be marked 0 Ω.
If a $R_x = 9$ kΩ were added to the circuit,

$$I_m = \frac{E}{R_T + R_x} = \frac{9}{9,000 + 9,000} = 0.0005 \text{ A}$$

This would be one-half scale on the meter and represent a resistance of 9 kΩ.

At $\frac{3}{4}$ scale, the current flow would be

$$I_{3/4} = 0.75 \times 0.001 = 0.00075 \text{ A}$$

$$I_m = \frac{E}{R_T + R_x}$$

and solving for R_x,

$$R_T + R_x = \frac{E}{I_m} \quad \text{and} \quad R_x = \frac{E}{I_m} - R_T$$

$$R_x = \frac{9}{0.00075} - R_T = 12 \text{ k}\Omega - 9 \text{ k}\Omega = 3 \text{ k}\Omega$$

At $\frac{1}{4}$ scale,

$$I_{1/4} = 0.25 \times 0.001 = 0.00025 \, A$$

$$R_x = \frac{9}{0.00025} - 9,000 = 36 \text{ k}\Omega - 9 \text{ k}\Omega = 27 \text{ k}\Omega$$

At $\frac{1}{8}$ scale,

$$I_{1/8} = 0.125 \times 0.001 = 0.000125 \text{ A}$$

$$R_x = \frac{9}{0.000125} - 9,000 = 72 \text{ k}\Omega - 9 \text{ k}\Omega = 63 \text{ k}\Omega$$

At zero scale, $I = 0$ and $R_x = \infty$.

These values would provide a basis for calibrating this meter scale in ohms. This would appear as shown in Figure 15–2. On an actual dial there would, of course, be many more points than those indicated. The points shown do, however, indicate the nonlinear characteristic of the calibration points. For example, the last one eighth of the scale involves a range between 63 kΩ and ∞, while the first one fourth of the scale covers only 0–3,000 Ω. This points out the great difficulty of obtaining accurate readings, particularly at the high end of an ohmmeter scale.

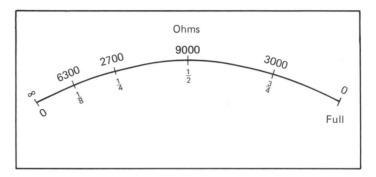

FIGURE 15–2
Calibration Points on Ohmmeter Dial

Other ohmmeter circuits are used in an attempt to overcome the measurement difficulties noted above. These circuits include the use of such elements as high-sensitivity meter movements and a separate high voltage supply for high-resistance measurements. Shunt types of meter circuits as well as series–shunt combinations are used also. Each method has some shortcomings, and very accurate resistance measurements are a problem.

15–2 BRIDGES

The difficulties in obtaining accurate resistance measurements were observed in Section 15–1. A device for the precise measurement of resistance is the *Wheatstone bridge*. The basic circuit of such a bridge is shown in Figure 15–3.

The Wheatstone bridge consists of the unknown resistance, R_x; two known resistances, R_1 and R_2; and a variable resistance, R_3, whose value is also known. A zero-center galvanometer is used to obtain a bridge balance. The bridge is balanced when the zero or null point is obtained on the galvanometer.

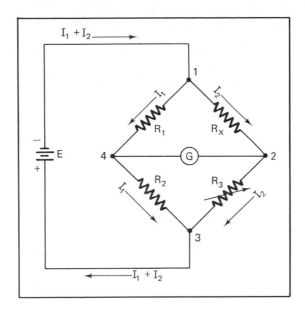

FIGURE 15–3
Wheatstone Bridge

In operation, current flowing from the battery divides at point 1, with I_1 flowing through R_1 and R_2 and I_2 flowing through R_x and R_3. At point 3, I_1 and I_2 join and return to the battery.

If points 2 and 4 are at different potentials, as indicated by the direction and level of the galvanometer reading, the bridge is said to be *unbalanced*. However, if no voltage exists between these points, a zero reading on the galvanometer, the bridge is *balanced*. When balanced,

$$V_{R_1} = V_{R_x} \quad \text{and} \quad V_{R_2} = V_{R_3} \quad \text{or}$$
$$I_1 R_1 = I_2 R_x \quad \text{and} \quad I_1 R_2 = I_2 R_3$$

If the second equation is solved for I_1, $I_1 = \dfrac{I_2 R_3}{R_2}$, and substituted in the first,

$$\frac{I_2 R_3}{R_2} R_1 = I_2 R_x$$

If both sides are now divided by I_2 and rearranged, the following equation results:

$$R_x = \frac{R_1}{R_2} R_3$$

The value of R_x may now be determined.

A more conventional arrangement for the Wheatstone bridge is shown in Figure 15–4. This is the same basic circuit as Figure 15–3 except that a potentiometer provides a means of adjusting R_1 and R_2 to obtain a balance. In addition, R_3 has been replaced by three range-extending resistors, which, depending on the position of the switch, introduce the multiplier shown.

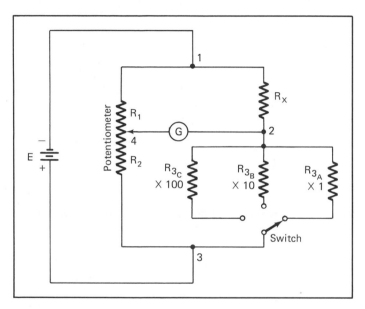

FIGURE   15–4
Conventional Wheatstone-Bridge Arrangement

A laboratory modification of the Wheatstone bridge, the *slide-wire bridge*, is shown in Figure 15–5. Note its similarity with the previous figures.

A practical application of the Wheatstone bridge, called the *Murray loop*, is shown in Figure 15–6. It is used to determine the location of a ground. For example, when a ground occurs on a power line, a connection is made with an unused line at a distant power station. This forms the Wheatstone-bridge circuit arrangement shown in the figure. The resistance of the entire line, R_T, is known. When the bridge is balanced,

$$\frac{R_1}{R_2} = \frac{R_x}{R_T - R_x}$$

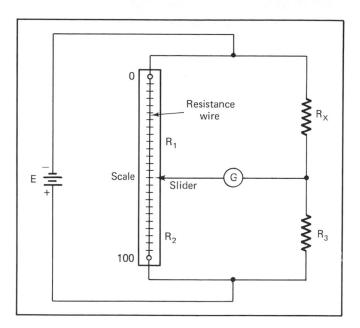

FIGURE 15–5
Slide-Wire Bridge

Solving for R_x,

$$R_1(R_T - R_x) = R_2R_x \quad \text{or} \quad R_1R_T - R_1R_x = R_2R_x$$

$$R_1R_T = R_1R_x + R_2R_x$$

FIGURE 15–6
Murray Loop

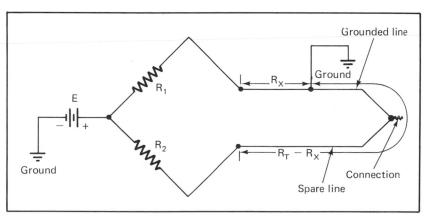

Factoring R_x from right-hand side,

$$R_1 R_T = R_x(R_1 + R_2)$$

Then

$$R_x = \frac{R_1}{R_1 + R_2} R_T$$

example 15–1 A ground occurs on a power line between stations A and B. An unused line of different size is joined to the grounded line at station B. The total resistance of these two lines without a short is known to be 5.320 Ω. When balanced, $R_1 = 37.367$ Ω and $R_2 = 63.854$ Ω. The line with a fault is of 0000 size with a resistance of 0.259 Ω/mi. Determine the location of the ground from station A.

solution:

$$R_x = \frac{R_1}{R_1 + R_2} R_T = \frac{37.367}{37.367 + 63.854}(5.320) = 1.9639 \ \Omega$$

The location of the ground is found as

$$L = \frac{1.9639 \ \Omega}{0.259 \ \Omega/\text{mi}} = 7.582 \text{ mi from station } A$$

If the line with the fault and the spare line are the same size, then the following relationship exists:

$$x = \frac{R_1}{R_1 + R_2} L$$

where L is the total length of the joined pair and x is the distance to the ground point.

example 15–2 A ground occurs between power stations A and B. A line of the same size is connected to the grounded line, at station B. The total length $L = 16.253$ mi. Measurements at station A determine that $R_1 = 27.82$ Ω and $R_2 = 36.77$ Ω. Determine the fault location.

solution:

$$x = \frac{R_1}{R_1 + R_2} L = \frac{27.82}{27.82 + 36.77}(16.253)$$

$$= 7.000 \text{ mi}$$

A combination type of meter, called a *multimeter* or *V-O-M*, is a popular, commercially available meter which is used widely. This type of instrument provides a variety of ac–dc ranges for the measurement of voltage and current. A number of ranges for the measurement of resistance are available also. A typical instrument of this type is shown in Figure 15–7.

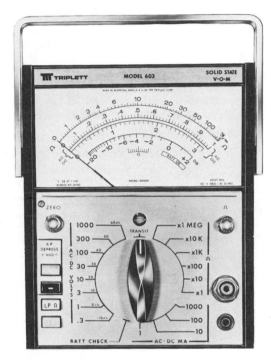

FIGURE 15–7
Typical Commercial Multimeter (V-O-M)
(Courtesy of Triplett Corporation)

V-O-Ms are versatile, rugged, and relatively inexpensive. They provide a means for measuring a wide range of values of resistance, current, and voltage, as shown in Figure 15–7, with a reasonable degree of accuracy.

EXERCISE 15–1

1. Using the Wheatstone bridge of Figure 15–3, what is the value of R_x if $R_1 = 30 \ \Omega$, $R_2 = 40 \ \Omega$, and $R_3 = 21.52 \ \Omega$?

2. What is the actual galvanometer reading in problem 1 if $V_{R_1} = V_{R_x}$ and $V_{R_2} = V_{R_3}$?

3. Using the Wheatsone bridge of Figure 15–4, if $R_1 = 67.1\ \Omega$ and $R_2 = 36.2\ \Omega$ and the potentiometer of R_{3_B} reads 16, what is the value of R_x?

4. The slide wire of the bridge in Figure 15–5 has a total resistance of 152 Ω and is 100 units long. On balance, R_1 is 16.5 units from the 0 point. If $R_3 = 61.3\ \Omega$, what is the resistance of R_x?

5. If the wire used in problem 4 had a total resistance of 1,675 Ω and balance occurred when the R_2 point was at 76.2 units and $R_3 = 1,211\ \Omega$, what would be the value of R_x?

6. Using a Murray loop, determine the ground-fault distance from point A if a spare line of the same size is connected to line 1 at point B. The spare line has a resistance of 3.625 Ω/1,000 ft. Point B is located 5,000 ft from A. Balance occurs when $R_1 = 8.62\ \Omega$ and $R_2 = 5.37\ \Omega$.

7. Using the Wheatstone bridge of Figure 15–3, the scale of the dial of R_3 was damaged so that the value of R_3 could not be read. However, balance was obtained when $R_1 = 26.52\ \Omega$, $R_2 = 37.57\ \Omega$, and R_x was known to be 53.65 Ω. What should the dial of R_3 have read?

8. If the wire in problem 4 had twice the total resistance and the balance occurred at the same point, what would be the value of R_x?

16

BATTERIES

In previous chapters, we have used the battery as a source of electrical potential. In this chapter, the battery as a source of electromotive force (emf) will be examined more closely.

The battery is a device made up of individual identical chemical cells. A battery produces an emf as a result of the chemical action of its cells. The purpose of this chapter is to examine the structure of a battery and investigate its operation as a source of electrical potential.

16–1 CHEMICAL CELLS

The *chemical cell* is a device in which chemical energy is converted into electrical energy. As a result of the chemical action an emf, E, is developed. If the cell supplies no current, the chemically generated emf, E, will equal the terminal voltage, V_t, of the cell. However, if the cell is supplying current, it will be found that the terminal voltage is less than the emf generated by the cell. This is the result of a voltage drop that occurs because of the internal resistance, r, of the cell. This is shown schematically in Figure 16–1.

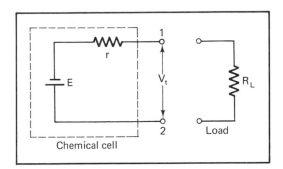

FIGURE   16–1
Schematic Representation of Chemical Cell

If no load were connected to the cell, no current would flow. Hence no voltage drop would occur across r, and the voltage between the cell terminals 1 and 2, V_t, would equal the chemically generated emf, E. This voltage, E, could be measured using a voltmeter of high sensitivity. The internal resistance of a cell is quite small, often below 1 Ω. Measurement of E with a voltmeter with a sensitivity of 20,000 Ω/V would cause an extremely small current flow. As a result, V_t would be approximately equal to E.

If the load R_L, shown in Figure 16–1, were now connected to the cell terminals 1 and 2, current would be drawn from the cell. The voltage across the cell terminals, V_t, would no longer be equal to the cell emf, E. The voltage relationship that would now exist could be expressed as

$$V_t = E - Ir$$

This indicates, of course, that the terminal voltage of the cell decreases with increasing current drawn from the cell and the resultant voltage drop that occurs across the internal resistance of the cell.

16–2 STRUCTURE OF A BATTERY

A *battery* is a device that consists of one or more cells. A cell that cannot be recharged when chemically depleted is called a *primary cell*. Cells that are capable of being recharged are called *secondary cells*. The carbon–zinc cell, the alkaline–manganese cell, and the mercury cell are examples of primary cells. The lead–acid storage cell and the nickel–cadmium storage cell are examples of secondary cells.

A battery, when composed of two or more cells, may have the identical individual cells arranged either in series or in parallel. This permits a battery to be structured to meet the desired voltage and current requirements of the particular application involved.

Figure 16–2 shows a schematic arrangement of a battery formed by placing three cells in series. When cells are connected in series,

FIGURE 16–2
Battery Composed of Three Cells in Series

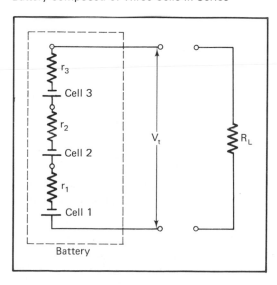

the battery formed has an emf developed which is the sum of the emfs of the individual cells:

$$E = E_1 + E_2 + E_3 + \cdots \quad \text{or} \quad E = aE_{\text{ind}}$$

where a is the number of identical cells in series. The internal resistances are seen to be in series. So the total internal resistance of the battery is

$$r = r_1 + r_2 + r_3 + \cdots \quad \text{or} \quad r = ar_{\text{ind}}$$

example 16–1   A battery is to be formed of three identical cells. Each cell has an emf of 1.21 V and an internal resistance of 0.82 Ω. Find the total voltage and internal resistance of the battery.

solution: The voltage is found as follows:

$$E = E_1 + E_2 + E_3 = 1.21 + 1.21 + 1.21 = 3.63 \text{ V}$$

or

$$E = aE_{\text{ind}} = 3 \times 1.21 = 3.63 \text{ V}$$

The internal resistance is

$$r = r_1 + r_2 + r_3 = 0.82 + 0.82 + 0.82 = 2.46 \text{ Ω}$$

or

$$r = 3r_{\text{ind}} = 3 \times 0.82 = 2.46 \text{ Ω}$$

The battery thus formed is shown schematically in Figure 16–3.

A battery formed by placing three cells in parallel is shown in Figure 16–4. The voltages of individual cells are all in parallel; hence

$$E = E_1 = E_2 = E_3$$

The internal resistances of each cell are also in parallel. These are handled as resistance in parallel and

$$\frac{1}{r} = \frac{1}{r_1} + \frac{1}{r_2} + \frac{1}{r_3} + \cdots \quad \text{or} \quad r = \frac{r_{\text{ind}}}{a}$$

where r_{ind} is the internal resistance of individual identical cells and a represents the number of cells in parallel.

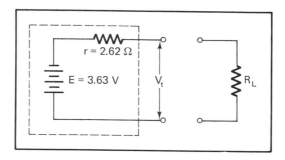

FIGURE 16–3
Schematic Representation of Battery
of Example 16–1

example 16–2 A battery is to be formed by placing four identical cells in parallel. Each cell has $E_{ind} = 1.48$ V and $r_{ind} = 0.96\ \Omega$. Determine the total voltage and internal resistance of the battery.

solution: The voltage of the battery is

$$E = E_1 = E_2 + E_3 = E_4 = E_{ind}$$
$$= 1.48 \text{ V}$$

FIGURE 16–4
Battery Formed of Three Cells in Parallel

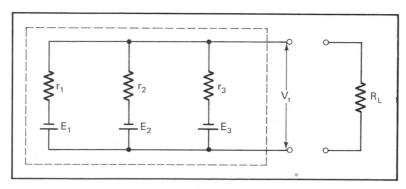

The internal resistance is found as

$$\frac{1}{r} = \frac{1}{r_1} + \frac{1}{r_2} + \frac{1}{r_3} + \frac{1}{r_4} = \frac{1}{0.96} + \frac{1}{0.96} + \frac{1}{0.96} + \frac{1}{0.96}$$

$$= 1.042 + 1.042 + 1.042 + 1.042 = 4.167$$

$$r = 0.24 \ \Omega$$

or

$$r = \frac{r_{\text{ind}}}{a}, \quad \text{where } a = 4$$

$$= \frac{0.96}{4} = 0.24 \ \Omega$$

The schematic representation of the battery thus formed is shown in Figure 16–5.

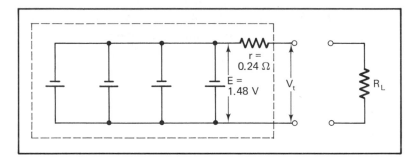

FIGURE 16–5
Schematic Representation of Battery
of Example 16–2

EXERCISE 16–1

1. A battery is to be formed of 15 identical cells in series. Each cell has an emf of 1.41 V and an internal resistance of 0.31 Ω. Determine the voltage and internal resistance of this battery.

2. A battery is formed of 6 identical cells in series. The battery has voltage measured with a high-sensitivity voltmeter of 9.56 V. The internal resistance of the battery is 1.56 Ω. What is the internal resistance and emf of each cell?

3. What is the voltage and internal resistance of a battery formed of 10 parallel, identical cells of 1.34 V and $r = 1.58 \ \Omega$ each?

4. A battery has a terminal voltage of 1.17 V under no-load conditions and an $r = 0.86 \ \Omega$. If the battery is composed of 8 cells

in parallel, what is the voltage and internal resistance of each cell?

The formation of a battery from individual identical cells was shown in the previous section. An examination of how a battery functions under load conditions will now be discussed. This is best seen with individual examples.

example 16–3   Determine the terminal voltage of the battery of Example 16–1 if the load current is 36 mA.

solution: Using the schematic shown in Figure 16–3, it is seen that

$$V_t = E - Ir$$

$$= 3.63 - 0.036 \times 2.62 = 3.63 - 0.094 = 3.54 \text{ V}$$

example 16–4   The battery shown in Figure 16–6 has an $E = 12.6$ V and $r = 0.68 \ \Omega$. It is connected to a load of $R_L = 1.85 \ \Omega$. What current flows in the circuit?

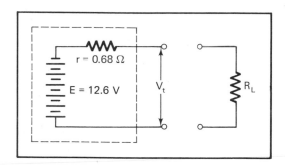

FIGURE 16–6
Schematic Representation of Battery
of Example 16–4

solution: The equation $V_t = E - Ir$ may be rearranged as

$$E = V_t + Ir$$

in which case the voltage across the load, R_L, is seen to be equal to V_t, or

$$V_t = IR_L$$

which, if substituted in the above equation, results in

$$E = IR_L + Ir$$

Factoring produces

$$E = I(R_L + r)$$

Solving for I,

$$I = \frac{E}{R_L + r}$$

$$= \frac{12.6}{1.85 + 0.68} = \frac{12.6}{2.53} = 4.98 \text{ A}$$

example 16–5   Calculate the internal resistance of a battery of $E = 24$ V which supplies 6.2 A to a load of $R_L = 3.16$ Ω.

solution: Solving the relationship

$$I = \frac{E}{R_L + r}$$

for r produces

$$R_L + r = \frac{E}{I}$$

$$r = \frac{E}{I} - R_L$$

$$= \frac{24}{6.2} - 3.16 = 0.711 \text{ Ω}$$

EXERCISE 16–2

1.   Calculate the terminal voltage of a battery whose emf, $E = 15.3$ V, and internal resistance, $r = 0.67$ Ω, when connected to a load that draws 375 mA from the battery.

2.   What is the internal resistance of a battery with $E = 64.2$ V that is connected to a load of $R_L = 3.82$ Ω? The current supplied by the battery is 1.73 A.

3.   Determine the terminal voltage of a 36.42-V battery with an internal resistance of 1.07 Ω and a voltage across the load of 35.12 V.

4.   In problem 3, what current flows through the load?

5. Calculate the current drain from a battery whose $E = 12.6$ V and $r = 0.167$ Ω when connected to a load of 3.17 Ω.

6. What is the load resistance that is connected to a battery whose $E = 6.3$ V and $r = 0.718$ Ω if the current supplied by the battery is $I = 1.2$ A?

7. The battery voltage measured with a voltmeter with high sensitivity is 16.17 V. The current delivered by the battery when connected to a load of $R_L = 27.05$ Ω is 560 mA. Determine r.

8. What is the terminal voltage, V_t, of a battery with an $E = 45.3$ V and $r = 0.396$ Ω that delivers 5.6 A to an unknown load?

17

FUNCTIONS
AND GRAPHS

In previous chapters, we have worked with various formulas and equations. It was seen in these relationships that one or more of the terms or elements were dependent upon others. This chapter will examine these interrelationships and develop various methods for their graphical presentation and analysis.

17-1 FUNCTIONS

In our work with Ohm's law, it was found that the current that flowed in a circuit was dependent upon the voltage and the resistance. Expressed in another way, the current was found to be a function of the voltage and resistance.

A function, then, may be described as the relationship that exists between elements of equations or formulas. It is a relationship that permits evaluation of one element by assigning values to the other. For example, using Ohm's law, for a fixed value of circuit voltage, the current may be determined for various values of resistance. The variation of current is developed as a function of the individual values of resistance selected and the constant circuit voltage chosen.

17-2 INDEPENDENT AND DEPENDENT VARIABLES

A key concept in the definition of a function was that of the dependence of one element of an equation or formula on another. In the Ohm's law example, for a constant value of E, the current, I, was seen to be dependent upon the values selected for R. The current, I, is referred to as the *dependent variable*. The resistance, R, is called the *independent variable*, in that the values assigned were arbitrary or independent.

Examples of the independent and dependent variables are shown in the following equations:

1. $C = \pi D$
2. $\omega = 2\pi f$
3. $E = 3V - 2$

In example 1, π is a constant and C is the dependent variable, with D the independent variable. Example 2 has 2π as constant, with f the independent variable and ω the dependent variable. In example 3, the values 3 and 2 are constants, with V as the independent variable and E as the dependent variable.

A method of notation that is often called *functional notation* is in common use to designate the relationship between the elements of an expression or an equation. In this notation, the letter f is generally used to replace the phrase "a function of." For example, in the equation

$$C = \pi D$$

the element C is said to be "a function of " D. This may be expressed as

$$C = f(D), \quad \text{where } f(D) = \pi D$$

In the equation $E = 5e + 2$,

$$E = f(e), \quad \text{where } f(e) = 5e + 2$$

This may be written

$$E = f(e) = 5e + 2$$

When expressed in this manner, e is designated as the independent variable. This also establishes that E is the dependent variable.

Functional notation also provides a means of designating the specific value to be assigned to the independent variable. For example, using the equation

$$X = 3y + 5$$

we may be asked to determine X if $y = 2$. In functional notation this would be expressed as

$$x = f(y) = 3y + 5 \quad \text{find } f(2)$$

This would mean that the numerical quantity 2 is to be substituted for the independent variable, y, and the dependent variable, x, determined. This would be found as

$$x = f(y) = 3y + 5 \quad \text{find } f(2)$$
$$x = 3(2) + 5 = 6 + 5 = 11$$

In many instances it would not be possible to obtain the dependent variable in this absolute numerical form. For example,

$$E = f(I) = IR \quad \text{evaluate } f(15)$$

Substitution of the value 15 for the independent variable, I, produces the value of the dependent variable, E, as

$$E = IR = (15)R = 15R$$

It would be necessary for this to remain in this form unless the value of R were known.

Often more than one element of an equation could be considered as the independent variable. The following procedure shows how one is indicated as the independent variable. If R were to be considered, as the independent variable in Ohm's law in the form $E = IR$, it would be designated as

$$E = f(R) = IR$$

The element I could be designated as the independent variable in a similar manner:

$$E = f(I) = IR$$

The independent variable of an equation may be considered the dependent variable by rearranging the equation. For example,

$$a = f(c) = 5c + 1$$

where a is the dependent variable and c is the independent variable. Rearranging the equation as

$$c = \frac{a}{5} - \frac{1}{5}$$

c will now be considered the dependent variable and a the independent variable. Expressed in functional notation this becomes

$$c = g(a) = \frac{a}{5} - \frac{1}{5}$$

Note that the letter f is used to designate operations on the independent variable, c, above. The letter g is used to designate operations when a is considered the independent variable, as shown.

EXERCISE 17–1 In problems 1–12, determine the value of the dependent variable.

1. $a = f(b) = 2b + 3;\ f(4)$

2. $c = f(d) = d^2 - 3;\ f(-6)$

3. $e = f(g) = \dfrac{g}{2} - \dfrac{5}{2}; f(2)$

4. $h = f(j) = j^3 + 2j^2 + 3; f(0)$

5. $k = f(m) = m^2 + m + 3; f(-1)$

6. $n = f(p) = p^3 + 2p; f(6)$

7. $g = f(r) = r + 2r + 16; f(13)$

8. $s = f(t) = t^3 - 2t^2 - 12; f(4)$

9. $V = f(w) = \dfrac{1}{w^2} + \dfrac{2}{w} - 6; f(2)$

10. $x = f(y) = y^3 - 2y^2 + y - 2; f(0)$

11. $a = f(b) = 3b^2 + b; f(-3)$

12. $d = f(e) = e^2 + e + 2; f(6)$

17-4 GRAPHS

A graph is a device that depicts pictorially relationships that exist between quantities. The graph provides a means of visually presenting data in a manner that permits the interrelationship between the quantities involved to be understood more readily.

Graphs take various forms and shapes. Common types are the bar graph, the circle graph, the broken-line graph, and the smooth-curve graph. Examples of these as shown in Figures 17–1, 17–2,

FIGURE 17-1
Types of Graphs (a) Circle (b) Bar

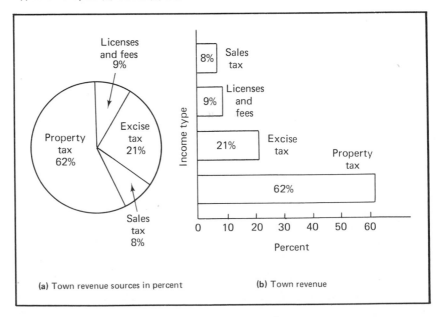

(a) Town revenue sources in percent   (b) Town revenue

and 17–3. Most of the graphs used in electronics are of the smooth-curve type. These are often plotted from measured data. Note in Figure 17–3 that a "smooth" curve has been drawn, "averaging" the individual data points.

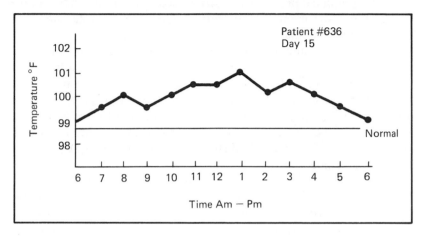

FIGURE 17–2
Broken-Line Graph

FIGURE 17–3
Smooth-Curve Graph

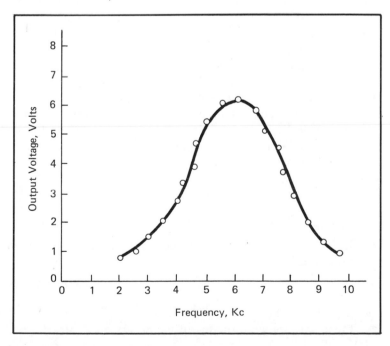

In order to locate points accurately on a graph, a system of coordinate notation was developed. This is generally referred to as the *Cartesian coordinate system*.

The graphical procedures used in Chapter 3 with signed numbers involved measurements to the left or right from a reference point. This procedure is inadequate for our present needs. In giving directions to a lost motorist, you would give him information that would take him from his present position to the desired location. These directions must provide him with accurate information as to the direction and distance that he must travel on each leg toward his destination. Giving the motorist only the distance but not the direction to the next point, or vice versa, would be of no help. In a similar manner, the location of points on a graph must be accurate, in that both "direction" and the "distance" must be provided.

Algebra, as we have seen, involves negative as well as positive quantities. The location of a point on a graph, then, could involve various combinations of positive and negative directions and distances from the origin. The coordinate notation system provides for this requirement. This coordinate system involves the construction of two perpendicular axes, one horizontal and one vertical, on graph paper. The point of intersection is called the *origin* or *reference point*. The horizontal axis is called the *x axis* and the vertical axis is called the *y axis*. These axes result in a division of the plane into four sections, called *quadrants*. *X* axis measurements to the right of the origin are considered positive; those to the left, negative. *Y* axis measurements above the origin are considered positive; those below, negative. These are shown in Figure 17-4.

The location of individual points is made using a system of *xy*, or rectangular, coordinates. The point location is provided by means of the intersection of perpendicular lines erected from the *x* and *y* axis. The *x*-axis location of a point is given first and is called the *abscissa*. The *y*-axis point is then given and is called the *ordinate*. The location of four points, one in each quadrant, is shown in Figure 17-5. Each point is located by specifying its (x, y) location, in that order.

EXERCISE 17-2

1. In which quadrant are the points given by the following coordinates?

a: $-3, 5$ $\quad$ b: $5, -1$ $\quad$ c: $-6, -2$

d: $5, 6$ $\quad$ e: $-4, 7$ $\quad$ f: $-a, -c$

2. Designate the coordinates of the points on Figure 17-6.

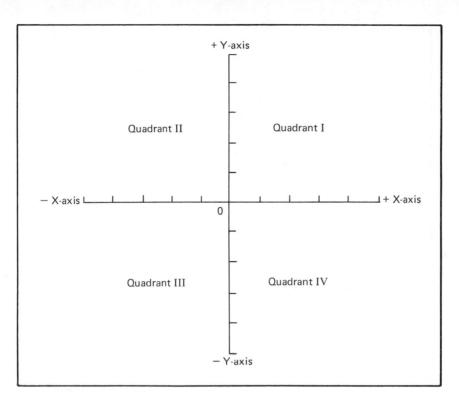

FIGURE 17-4
Coordinate Notation System

17-6 GRAPH OF A FUNCTION

Using the coordinate system developed in Section 17-5, we may now obtain a graph of a function. In the equation

$$y = x - 4$$

y is seen to be a function of x, or

$$y = f(x) = x - 4$$

Using arbitrary values of the independent variable x, the value of the dependent variable may be obtained. The independent variable is customarily plotted along the x axis, while the dependent variable is plotted along the y axis:

POINT	a	b	c	d	e	f	g
x	−4	−2	0	2	4	6	8
y	−8	−6	−4	−2	0	2	4

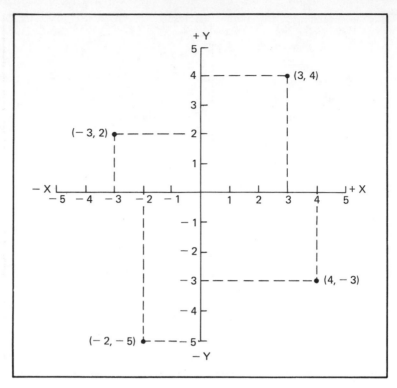

FIGURE 17–5
Location of Rectangular Coordinate (x, y) Points

The plotting of these points results in the graph or the curve of this function, shown in Figure 17–7. This is seen to be a straight-line "curve" when plotted.

Every plotted point on the curve satisfies the equation, in that the coordinates of each point were found using the equation. Let us now check another point on the curve. For example, choosing point z, y is found to equal 8 and x is seen to equal 12. Substituting in the equation we have

$$y = x - 4$$

At point z,

$$y = 8, \qquad x = 12$$
$$8 = 12 - 4$$
$$= 8$$

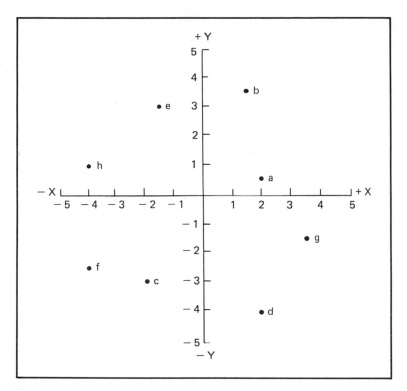

FIGURE 17–6
Figure for Problem 2, Exercise 17–2

The equation is seen to be satisfied.

Let us now examine what the result would be of selecting a point not on the curve. Point W, shown in Figure 17–7, is chosen for this purpose. Point W has coordinates of $y = 8$ and $x = 4$. Substituting, we have

$$y = x - 4$$
$$8 = 4 - 4$$

$\neq 0$ which does not satisfy the equation

The conclusion may be made that any point on the curve satisfies the equation, whereas any point not on the curve will not satisfy the equation.

The graph for any function may be plotted in a similar manner. As noted previously, it is standard practice to use the x axis for the independent variable and the y axis for the dependent variable, as in Figure 17–7.

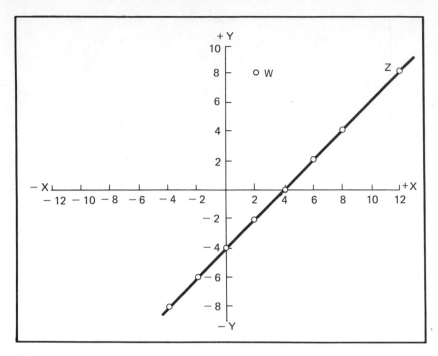

FIGURE 17–7
Graph of the Function $x + y$

example 17–1 Graph the power equation, $P = I^2R$ when $R = 5$.

solution: Here we would plot $P = f(I) = 5I^2$:

Point	a	b	c	d	e
I	0	1	2	3	4
P	0	5	20	45	90

All the coordinate points are positive and fall in quadrant I. This graph is shown in Figure 17–8.

example 17–2 Graph the equation $m = n^2 - 2$.

solution: In this example we would plot $m = f(n) = n^2 - 2$:

Point	a	b	c	d	e	f	g	h	i	j	k
n	−5	−4	−3	−2	−1	0	1	2	3	4	5
m	23	14	7	2	−1	−2	−1	2	17	14	23

At this point it would be well to point out the differences between linear and nonlinear equations and their differences when graphically

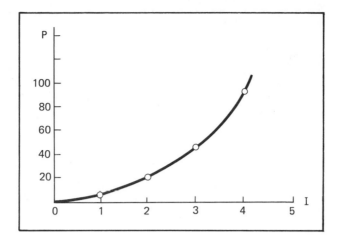

FIGURE 17–8
Graph of the Function $5I^2$

plotted. A *linear equation* is one in which each term contains either no unknown or a single unknown to the first power. An equation is also considered linear if each of its terms contains either no unknowns, or the single unknown to the first power occurs only in the numerator of fractional terms. The equation $y = x - 4$ is linear. The equations $P = 5I^2$ and $m = n^2 - 2$ are not linear. Linear equations result in a straight line when plotted, as shown in Figure 17–7. Equations that are not linear do not result in a straight line when plotted, as shown in Figures 17–8 and 17–9.

17–7 GRAPH FROM MEASURED DATA

In Section 17–6, the method of plotting the graph of a function was demonstrated. In practical applications, such an equation may not be known or may not, in fact, exist. Often only experimentally obtained measured data on a particular device are all that is available.

A single measurement made on a device will often tell very little. A number of measurements made under different conditions of operation, when plotted on a graph, provide a visual picture of the characteristics of the device. The graph often permits the nature and behavior of the device to be predicted. Often an equation that mathematically describes the operation of the device may be developed from the graph.

Prior to analyzing graphs obtained from measured data, a few general rules relative to plotting these data will be provided:

1. Choose appropriate x and y axis scales so that the graph may be easily plotted with the measured values.
2. Always use the intersection of the axes as the zero point of the scales.

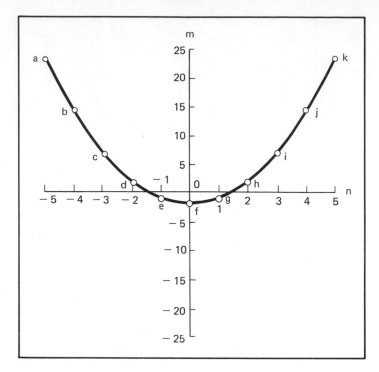

FIGURE   17–9
Graph of the Function $n^2 - 2$

3. Choose scales so that the plotted data are displayed over a reasonable portion of the graph area. Inappropriate scale selection results in distorted or "squeezed" graphs, which are difficult to use and interpret.

4. Label x and y axes clearly and indicate scale units.

5. Indicate accurately the location of each point. This is often best done by enclosing a small dot in a circle, triangle, or square.

6. Draw a straight line, or a smooth curve, that averages the points. Some curves will pass through each point; others will average the variations among points to produce a smooth curve.

7. Error curves and instrument calibration curves are normally the only types of broken-line curves used in electronics. All others are of the smooth-curve type.

17–8   GRAPHICAL ANALYSIS

The correct interpretation of graphically presented data is extremely important. In many electronic applications the slope of a curve or line is of particular significance.

The voltage–current characteristic of a 5-Ω resistor is shown in Figure 17–10. The slope of a curve is the ratio of the vertical rise that occurs for an arbitrarily selected horizontal run. In carpentry the slope of a roof is the rise in inches that occurs in a horizontal run of 1 ft.

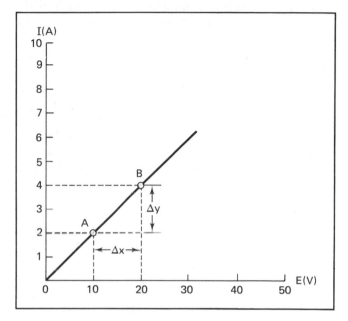

FIGURE   17–10
Voltage-Current Characteristic of 5-Ω Resistor

In electronics, we are only concerned with the ratio of the rise to the selected run. In Figure 17–10, it is desired to obtain the slope of the curve. Points A and B are chosen for this purpose. The rise that occurs between A and B is seen to be from

$I = 2A$ to $I = 4A$ or   2 units

The horizontal run between these points is from

$E = 10V$ to $E = 20V$ or   10 units

The slope is found to be:

$$\text{slope} = m = \frac{\text{rise}}{\text{run}} = \frac{IB - IA}{EB - EA} = \frac{4 - 2}{20 - 10} = \frac{2}{10} = \frac{1}{5}$$

Often the slope will be indicated as

$$\text{slope} = m = \frac{\text{rise}}{\text{run}} = \frac{\Delta y}{\Delta x}$$

where Δ is the Greek capital letter delta and is used to indicate the "change of." The Δy and Δx quantities are shown in Figure 17–10.

17–9 GRAPH OF A LINEAR EQUATION

In Figure 17–7, the graph of the equation $y = x - 4$ is plotted and is seen to be a straight line. In Figure 17–10, the equation of $I = \dfrac{E}{R}$, where $R = 5$, is plotted. This is also seen to be a straight line. Each of these equations contain two unknowns of the first power. Such equations are linear equations and always result in a straight line when plotted.

A general form of a linear equation, the equation of a straight line, may be written

$$y = mx + b$$

where

y = dependent variable, plotted vertically

x = independent variable, plotted horizontally

m = slope of the curve, $\Delta y/\Delta x$

b = value of y when $x = 0$, the y intercept

example 17–3 Draw the graph of $5y = 20 + 10x$.

solution: Factoring and rearranging to the general form as above we have

$$5y = 20 + 10x$$
$$y = 4 + 2x$$
$$= 2x + 4$$

Only two points are required to draw the graph of the linear equation, a straight line. By definition, the y intercept, b, is equal to 4 when $x = 0$. This establishes one point. Any other value of x may be used to obtain the second point needed. Let us arbitrarily select $x = 2$. Substituting and solving for y produces

$y = 2x + 4$

$\quad = (2)(2) + 4 = 8$

The resulting curve is shown in Figure 17–11.

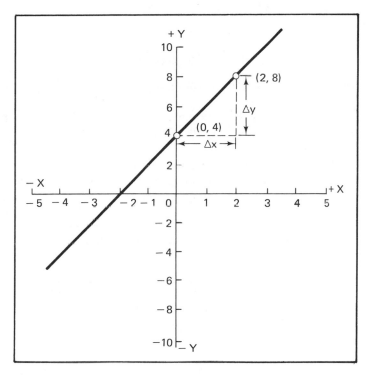

FIGURE 17–11
Graph of $y = 2x + 4$

Checking the slope of the curve between these points,

$$m = \frac{\Delta y}{\Delta x} = \frac{8 - 4}{2 - 0} = \frac{4}{2} = 2$$

This corresponds, of course, to the equation written in the general form:

$y = mx + b$

$\quad = 2x + 4$

Let us return to the Ohm's law relationship which we previously plotted in Figure 17–10, $I = \dfrac{E}{R}$, where $R = 5$. Written in the general form this would appear as

$$y = mx + b$$

$$I = \frac{1}{5}E + 0$$

This would tell us that the slope is $\dfrac{1}{5}$ and b, the y intercept when $x = 0$, would be zero. Again examine Figure 17–10 to prove the validity of these statements.

Several interesting comments regarding the V–I graph shown in Figure 17–10 will be helpful in the future:

1. The slope may be found by dividing the y value (I) at any point by the x value (v) at any point. This is *only* true when a straight-line curve passes through the zero point.
2. The slope of the curve is the reciprocal of the resistance. That is, $m = \dfrac{1}{R} = \dfrac{1}{5}$, where $R = 5\ \Omega$.

---

example 17–4　Draw the graph of $3x = -y - 1$.

---

solution:　Rearranging the equation in the general form of a linear equation, we have

$$y = -3x - 1$$

The y intercept when $x = 0$ is -1. To obtain one other graph point, let $x = 2$. Then

$$y = -3x - 1$$
$$= -3(2) - 1 = -6 = -7$$

Plotting and drawing the curve produces the graph of Figure 17–12. Selecting values for Δy and Δx shows that the Δx segment represents a movement to the right (positive), while the Δy segment represents a downward movement (negative). Using this relationship we have

$$m = \frac{\Delta y}{\Delta x} = \frac{5 - 2}{2 - 1} = \frac{-3}{+1} = -3$$

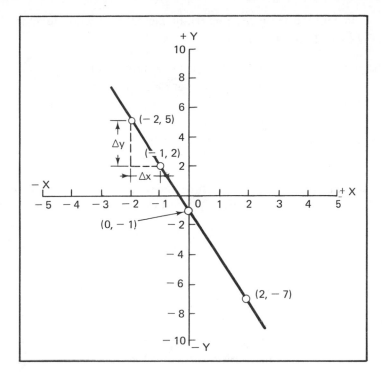

FIGURE 17–12
Graph of $y = -3x - 1$

This corresponds with the slope indicated in the equation $y = -3x - 1$.

Examples 17–2 and 17–3 were purposely chosen to show the differences between a $+m$ slope and a $-m$ slope. Note that the $+m$ slope of Example 17–2 results in a curve upward to the right. The $-m$ slope of Example 17–3 results in a curve upward to the left.

17-10 EQUATIONS FROM THE GRAPH OF A STRAIGHT LINE

If a straight line results when measured data are plotted, the graphical relationship may be expressed in equation form. This will, of course, involve the equation of the straight line that we have examined in previous sections. It would be well to review this equation and the significance of its elements. Stated again, the equation of the straight line is

$$y = mx + b$$

Summarizing the important factors that were developed relative to this equation:

1. y: the dependent variable, plotted on the vertical axis.
2. x: the independent variable, plotted on the horizontal axis.
3. m: the slope; positive slope upward to right, negative slope upward to left.
4. b: y intercept when $x = 0$; if the curve passes through the origin, the equation has the form $y = mx$.

example 17–5 Plot the graph of the measured data and express in the form of the equation of a straight line.

x	-4	0	4	8
y	-1	0	1	2

Plotting these data produces the following curve shown in Figure 17–13.

solution: As curve passes through origin, $b = 0$ and the equation reduces to the form $y = mx$. The slope is found using the construction shown in Figure 17–13.

FIGURE 17–13
Graph for Example 17–4

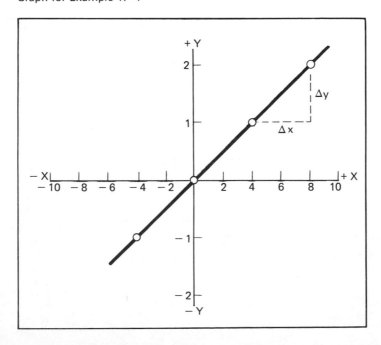

$$m = \frac{\Delta y}{\Delta x} = \frac{2 - 1}{8 - 4} = \frac{1}{4}$$

The slope is upward to the right, so we have a positive slope of $m = +\frac{1}{4}$. The equation of this graph may be written

$$y = +mx = \frac{1}{4}x$$

example 17–6 Plot the graph for the measured data and express in the form of the equation of a straight line.

x	4	2	0	−2	−4	−6
y	−30	−20	−10	0	10	20

solution: Plotting the graph produces Figure 17–14. The y intercept is at $y = -10$; therefore, $b = -10$. The slope is found from the construction shown in Figure 17–14:

$$m = \frac{\Delta y}{\Delta x} = \frac{30 - 10}{8 - 4} = \frac{20}{4} = 5$$

FIGURE 17–14
Graph for Example 17–5

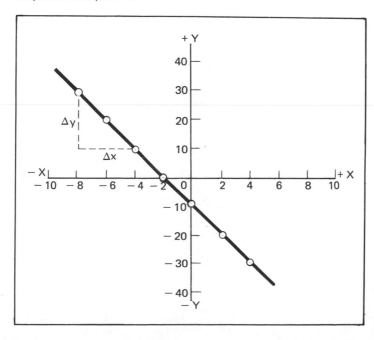

As the slope is upward to the left, we have a negative
slope of $m = -5$. The equation then takes the form

$$y = -mx - b = -5x - 10$$

EXERCISE 17-3

1. In the following equations, determine the y intercept:

   (a) $3x + y = 4$ (b) $2x - 1 = y$ (c) $4y - 2x = 0$

   (d) $5x = 2y + 10$ (e) $6y = -5x - 10$ (f) $7x = 6y - 5$

2. What is the slope of the curve in each equation of problem 1?
   Is the slope positive or negative?

3. Plot the graphs of the equations

   $$y = 4x + 10$$
   $$8x = -2y - 40$$

   What is the x and y intercept of each equation? Are the curves
   parallel? Why?

4. Plot the graphs of the equations

   $$3y = \frac{x}{5} + 5$$

   $$\frac{6}{10}x = -6y - 30$$

   Determine the x and y intercepts of each. Are the curves parallel?
   Would it have been possible, without plotting the curves, to
   determine if the curves were parallel?

5. Plot the graph from the following data and write the equation
   of the graph:

x	−3	0	3	6	9
y	−1	0	1	2	3

6. Plot the graph from the following data and write the equation of
   the graph.

A	0	1	2	3	4
B	0	50	100	150	200

7. Would the equation of problem 6 represent Ohm's law if $A = I$ and $B = E$? What would be the resistance of the circuit? How is this related to the slope?

8. Plot the graph from the following data and write the equation of the graph.

m	6	2	-2	-6	-10
n	13	0	3	6	9

18

SIMULTANEOUS EQUATIONS

In electronics circuits we often have situations that result in equations with two unknowns. Under such circumstances, without additional information, such an equation cannot be solved for the unknown quantities.

In Chapter 17, we were involved with linear equations in the form

$$y = mx + b$$

It was seen that an infinite number of values of x and y will satisfy the equation. Frequently, another equation, involving the same unknown quantities, may be written. In electronics these two such equations represent circuit conditions that exist *simultaneously*. These two equations, each involving the same two unknowns, must be solved *simultaneously* and the values of the unknowns must satisfy each equation *simultaneously*. For obvious reasons, then, these equations are called *simultaneous linear equations*.

In this chapter, graphical and algebraic methods of solving these linear equations of two or more unknowns will be presented. At this point it would be well to emphasize that as many equations are required as there are unknowns. However, most of our work here will involve two equations with two unknowns.

18-1 SOLUTION BY GRAPHICAL METHODS

Linear equations when plotted on a graph result in a straight line. If the lines of two simultaneous equations cross when graphically plotted, the coordinates of this intersection, and no other, would satisfy each equation.

example 18-1 Solve the following simultaneous equations graphically:

$$y = x + 4, \qquad y = -x + 10$$

solution: Plot each equation graphically, using only intercepts obtained when $x = 0$ and $y = 0$ in each equation (Figure 18-1). The coordinates of the point of intersection are (3, 7) or $x = 3$, $y = 7$. Substituting these values in each of the equations we have

$$y = x + 4 \qquad y = -x + 10$$
$$7 = 3 + 4 \qquad 7 = -3 + 10$$
$$= 7 \qquad \qquad = 7$$

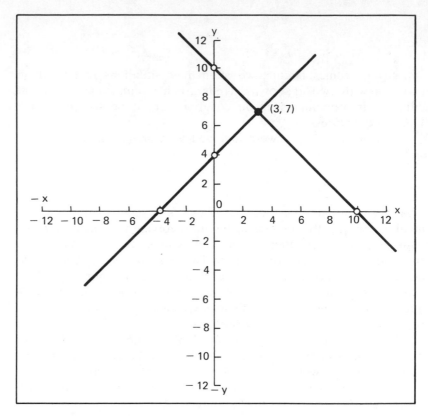

FIGURE 18–1
Graph for Example 18–1

We see that the equations are simultaneously satisfied by the x and y coordinates of the point of intersection.

example 18–2 Solve the following simultaneous equations graphically:

$$y = -x + 4, \qquad y = -x + 2$$

solution: Plotting the graphs of each equation produces Figure 18–2. When these two equations are plotted, the curves are found to be parallel. There is no intersection of the lines and therefore no simultaneous solution for the equations. Such equations are called *inconsistent equations*.

example 18–3 Solve graphically the following simultaneous equations:

$$3y = -2x - 6, \qquad y = 3x - 6$$

solution: Plotting the graphs produces Figure 18–3. Substituting these coordinate values of $x = 1.09$ and $y = -2.72$ in

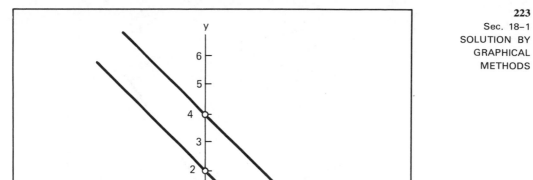

FIGURE 18–2
Graph for Example 18–2

each equation shows that the equations are satisfied and the solution is correct.

The purpose of the previous example was to show the care required in plotting and reading the graph coordinates. The graphical method of solution leaves a great deal to be desired from a point of view of accuracy. In addition, it is an inconvenient and time-consuming procedure. The graphical method of solution has, therefore, been replaced by algebraic methods.

EXERCISE 18–1 Solve the following simultaneous linear equations graphically.

1. $a = 3b - 3$
   $2a = 3b + 12$

2. $2m + n = 6$
   $3m = 2n + 2$

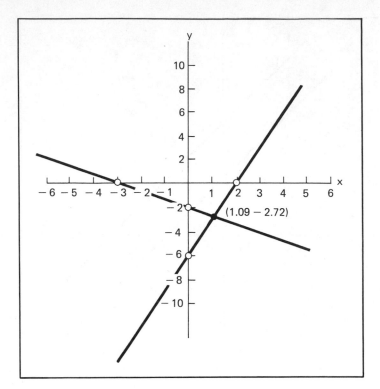

FIGURE 18-3
Graph for Example 18-3

3. $2y + x = 4$
$y = 2x - 3$

4. $5w - 3z = -6$
$z - 2w = 1$

5. $3s - t - 6 = 0$
$s - t - 4 = 0$

6. $2c - 3d = 15$
$c - 2d = 12$

7. $5e - f = 10$
$6f - 6e = 12$

8. $4g - 2h = -4$
$-2g - 3h = 10$

18-2 SOLUTION BY ADDITION AND SUBTRACTION

This algebraic method of solution involves the elimination by addition or subtraction of equal terms in each equation, combining, and then solving for the remaining unknown. This value is then substituted back in one of the original equations to obtain the remaining unknown.

example 18-4 Solve the following equations by addition and subtraction:

$$y - x = -1 \tag{1}$$

$$-y - 2x = -8 \tag{2}$$

solution: Adding the two equations results in

$$y - x = -1$$
$$\underline{-y - 2x = -8}$$
$$-3x = -9$$
$$x = 3$$

Substituting $x = 3$ in Equation (1), we have

$$y - 3 = -1$$
$$y = 2$$

To check, substitute values of $x = 3$ and $y = 2$ into Equations (1) and (2):

(1) $\qquad 2 - 3 = -1, \qquad -1 = -1$

and

(2) $\quad -2 - 2(3) = -8, \qquad -8 = -8$

The solution is correct.

example 18–5 Solve the following equations by addition and subtraction:

$$3y + 2b = 16 \qquad\qquad\qquad\qquad\qquad \textbf{(1)}$$
$$6y - 3b = 18 \qquad\qquad\qquad\qquad\qquad \textbf{(2)}$$

solution: Multiply Equation (1) by 2, which produces

$$6y + 4b = 32 \qquad\qquad\qquad\qquad\qquad \textbf{(3)}$$
$$6y - 3b = 18 \qquad\qquad\qquad\qquad\qquad \textbf{(2)}$$

Subtracting Equation (2) from (3) results in

$$7b = 14$$
$$b = 2$$

Substituting the value $b = 2$ in Equation (1) and solving for y,

$$3y + 2(2) = 16$$
$$3y + 4 = 16$$

$$3y = 12$$

$$y = 4$$

To check: Substitute values of $b = 2$ and $y = 4$ in Equations (1) and (2):

(1) $3(4) + 2(2) = 16$ (2) $6(4) - 3(2) = 18$

$12 + 4 = 16$ $24 - 6 = 18$

$16 = 16$ $18 = 18$

The solution is correct.

EXERCISE   18–2   Solve the following equations by addition and subtraction.

1. $x + y = 2$
$-x + y = 4$

2. $3c + 4d = -15$
$c - d = 2$

3. $2e - 4f = 0$
$4e - 4f = -12$

4. $3a + 4b = -4$
$-2a + 2b = 12$

5. $3x + 2y = 21$
$-4x - 3y = -29$

6. $4f + 3g = 1$
$2f + g = -1$

7. $2b - 5c = 6$
$3b - 6c = 12$

8. $5y + z = 2$
$3y + 2z = -3$

18–3 SOLUTION BY COMPARISON

This method involves solving each equation for the same variable. As both equations are then equal to the same quantity, they are equal to each other.

example 18–6 Solve the following equations by comparison:

$$2a + b = 8 \tag{1}$$

$$a - b = 1 \tag{2}$$

solution: Solving (1) for b, we have

$$b = -2a + 8 \tag{3}$$

Solving (2) for b, we have

$$-b = -a + 1$$

Multiplying both sides by -1,

$$b = a - 1 \qquad (4)$$

Equating (3) and (4),

$$-2a + 8 = a - 1$$

Solving for a,

$$-3a = -9$$
$$a = 3$$

Substituting in (1) and solving for b,

$$2(3) + b = 8$$
$$b = 2$$

example 18–7 Solve the following equations by comparison:

$$x - 1 = 2y \qquad (1)$$
$$-3x + 5y = -6 \qquad (2)$$

solution: Solving (1) for x,

$$x = 2y + 1 \qquad (3)$$

Solving (2) for x,

$$-3x = -5y - 6$$
$$-x = \frac{-5y - 6}{3}$$

Multiplying both sides by -1,

$$x = \frac{5y + 6}{3} \qquad (4)$$

Equating (3) and (4),

$$2y + 1 = \frac{5y + 6}{3}$$

Multiplying both sides by 3,

$$6y + 3 = 5y + 6$$

$$y = 3$$

Substituting in (1) and solving for x,

$$x - 1 = 2(3)$$

$$x = 7$$

EXERCISE 18–3 Solve the following equations by comparison.

1. $2a + 2b = 4$
   $-2a + 2b = 8$

2. $12c + 9d = 3$
   $6c + 3d = -3$

3. $e + 5f - 2 = 0$
   $2e + 3f + 3 = 0$

4. $2g - 2h = -6$
   $2g - 4h = 0$

5. $-5m + 2n = 6$
   $-6m + 3n = 12$

6. $p + q = 1$
   $2p - 12 = 8q$

18–4 SOLUTION BY SUBSTITUTION

In this method of solution, one of the unknowns of one equation is expressed in terms of the other member of that equation. This value is then substituted for the same unknown in the remaining equation. The second equation, now with only one unknown, may then be solved. This value is then substituted back in the first equation to obtain the remaining unknown.

example 18–8 Solve the following equations by substitution:

$$2a + b = -3 \tag{1}$$

$$3a + 3b = 3 \tag{2}$$

solution: Solving Equation (1) for b,

$$b = -2a - 3$$

which is substituted for b in (2) as

$$3a + 3(-2a - 3) = 3$$

which is solved for a:

$$3a - 6a - 9 = 3, \qquad -3a = 12$$

$$a = -4$$

This is substituted back in Equation (1),

229
Sec. 18–5
SIMULTANEOUS
EQUATIONS
INVOLVING
FRACTIONS

$$2(-4) + b = -3, \qquad -8 + b = -3$$

$$b = 5$$

example 18–9 Solve the following equations by substitution:

$$c - 2d = 0 \tag{1}$$

$$2c - 3d - 1 = 0 \tag{2}$$

solution: Solving Equation (1) for c,

$$c = 2d$$

Substituting in (2) results in

$$2(2d) - 3d = 1$$

$$4d - 3d = 1$$

$$d = 1$$

Substituting the value of d in (1),

$$c - 2(1) = 0$$

$$c = 2$$

EXERCISE 18–4 Solve the following equations by substitution.

1. $w - 3z = -3$
    $2w + 3z = 12$

2. $a - 2b = -3$
    $2a = -b + 4$

3. $c = 2d + 1$
    $5d = 3c - 6$

4. $-n = -6m + 10$
    $2n - m = 13$

5. $u - v + 3 = 0$
    $2u + 4v = 0$

6. $2s + 3t = 16$
    $-s = -2t + 6$

18–5 SIMULTANEOUS EQUATIONS INVOLVING FRACTIONS

Simultaneous equations involving fractions may be solved using any of the previous methods. Some equations with fractions may be solved more readily by clearing the fractions. Other equations may be solved more conveniently in the fractional form.

example 18–10   Solve the following equations:

$$c - 3d = -3 \tag{1}$$

$$\frac{c}{3} + \frac{d}{2} = 2 \tag{2}$$

solution: First, clear the fractions of Equation (2). Multiplying by the LCD, 6, produces

$$2c + 3d = 12 \tag{3}$$

The equations, in conventional form, are

$$c - 3d = -3 \tag{1}$$

$$2c + 3d = 12 \tag{3}$$

Solving (1) for c,

$$c = 3d - 3$$

Substituting in (3),

$$2(3d - 3) + 3d = 12$$

$$6d - 6 + 3d = 12$$

$$9d = 18$$

$$d = 2$$

Substituting in (1) and solving for c,

$$c - 3(2) = -3$$

$$c = 3$$

example 18–11   Solve the following equations:

$$\frac{1}{x} - \frac{1}{y} = 2 \tag{1}$$

$$-\frac{2}{x} - \frac{3}{y} = 1 \tag{2}$$

solution: Multiplying (1) by 2 produces

$$\frac{2}{x} - \frac{2}{y} = 4 \tag{3}$$

231

Sec. 18–6
SIMULTANEOUS
EQUATIONS
INVOLVING
LITERAL
QUANTITIES

$$-\frac{2}{x} - \frac{3}{y} = 1 \tag{2}$$

By addition of (2) and (3),

$$-\frac{5}{y} = 5$$

$$y = -1$$

Substituting in (1),

$$\frac{1}{x} - \frac{1}{-1} = 2$$

$$\frac{1}{x} + 1 = 2$$

$$x = 1$$

EXERCISE 18–5 Solve the following simultaneous equations involving fractions.

1. $p - q = 4$

   $p - \dfrac{q}{3} = 2$

2. $2w = -x - 1$

   $2w = -\dfrac{3x}{2} + \dfrac{1}{2}$

3. $\dfrac{c}{2} - \dfrac{d}{4} = 1$

   $2c + \dfrac{2d}{3} = \dfrac{22}{3}$

4. $\dfrac{2}{a} + \dfrac{6}{b} = 3$

   $\dfrac{15}{b} - \dfrac{6}{a} = 2$

18–6 SIMULTANEOUS EQUATIONS INVOLVING LITERAL QUANTITIES

A simultaneous equation may have literal coefficients in place of the more conventional numerical coefficients. In either instance the solution is similar to those developed in previous sections.

example 18–12 Solve the following simultaneous equations, where x and y are the unknowns:

$$ax - cy = d \tag{1}$$

$$bx + ey = f \tag{2}$$

solution: The first step will be to eliminate x. Multiply (1) by b:

$$abx - bcy = bd \qquad\qquad (3)$$

Multiply (2) by a:

$$abx + aey = af \qquad\qquad (4)$$

Subtract (4) from (3):

$$-bcy - aey = bd - af \qquad\qquad (5)$$

Factor y from (5):

$$y(-bc - ae) = bd - af$$

Solve for y:

$$y = \frac{bd - af}{-bc - ae} \qquad\qquad (6)$$

The substitution of this value of y in (1) and solving for x would become rather involved. A simpler procedure would be to use (1) and (2) and eliminate y, thus solving for x, as follows. Multiply (1) by e:

$$aex - cey = de \qquad\qquad (7)$$

Multiply (2) by c:

$$bcx + cey = cf \qquad\qquad (8)$$

Add (7) and (8):

$$aex + bcx = de + cf \qquad\qquad (9)$$

Factor x from (9):

$$x(ae + bc) = de + cf$$

Solve for x:

$$x = \frac{de + cf}{ae + bc}$$

Solve the following equations, where x and y are the unknown quantities.

1. $ex - fy = 2$
   $-ex + gy = 3$

2. $-mx - ny = p$
   $-rx + sy = 5$

18–7 SIMULTANEOUS EQUATIONS
WITH MORE THAN TWO UNKNOWNS

Simultaneous equations with two unknowns, second order, require two equations for their solution. Equations with more than two unknowns require as many equations as there are unknowns. The following examples will show the solution procedures for equations involving three unknowns, third order. Equations with more than three unknowns would be handled in a similar manner.

The solutions of such equations involves the elimination of a common unknown from a different pair of the three equations. This results in two equations and two unknowns. These are then solved in the conventional manner.

example 18–13 Solve the following simultaneous equations:

$$a + 2b - c = 2 \tag{1}$$

$$a + b - 2c = 3 \tag{2}$$

$$2a + b + c = 1 \tag{3}$$

solution: The unknown, a, will be eliminated from (1) and (2) and then from (2) and (3). Subtracting (2) from (1) results in

$$b + c = -1 \tag{4}$$

Multiplying (2) by 2,

$$2a + 2b - 4c = 6 \tag{5}$$

Subtracting (3) from (5),

$$2a + b + c = 1 \tag{3}$$

resulting in

$$b - 5c = 5 \tag{6}$$

Eliminating b from (4) and (6),

$$b + c = -1 \tag{4}$$

$$\underline{b - 5c = 5} \tag{6}$$

Subtracting (6) from (4),

$$6c = -6$$

$$c = -1 \tag{7}$$

Substituting in (4),

$$b - 1 = -1$$

$$b = 0 \tag{8}$$

Substituting (7) and (8) into (1),

$$a + 2(0) - (-1) = 2$$

$$a = 1 \tag{9}$$

To check, the values of a, b, and c in (9), (8), and (7) are substituted back in (1), (2), and (3), and the solution is found to be correct.

example 18-14 An Ayrton shunt-meter circuit is shown in Figure 18–4. Determine R_1, R_2, and R_3.

solution: The reader should review Section 13–5. Ayrton shunts were discussed at that point but this type of problem was not solved as simultaneous equations had not yet been discussed. Solutions require writing three equations, as there are three unknowns. With the switch in the A position, 0–10 mA, the shunt will consist of $R_1 +$ $+ R_2 + R_3$, with value equal to a ratio of $\frac{1}{9}$, as 1 mA is required for full-scale meter deflection, leaving 9 mA to flow through the shunt. As $R_m = 90 \ \Omega$, we may write

$$R_1 + R_2 + R_3 = \frac{1}{9}(90) \tag{1}$$

In the B position, 0–100 mA, the shunt consists of $R_1 + R_2$, with R_3 in series with R_m. The shunt must pass

235
Sec. 18–7
SIMULTANEOUS
EQUATIONS WITH
MORE THAN TWO
UNKNOWNS

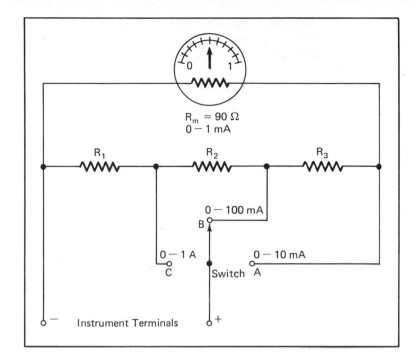

FIGURE 18–4
Ayrton Shunt Circuit for Example 18–14

99 mA while 1 mA flows through the meter, resulting in a $\frac{1}{99}$ ratio.

$$R_1 + R_2 = \frac{1}{99}(R_3 + 90) \qquad (2)$$

Similarly, in the C position, 0–1 A, we may write

$$R_1 = \frac{1}{999}(R_2 + R_3 + 90) \qquad (3)$$

We may now proceed to solve the three simultaneous equations.

Multiply (1) by 99: $\qquad 99R_1 + 99R_2 + 99R_3 = 990$

Rearrange and multiply (2) by 99: $\qquad 99R_1 + 99R_2 - R_3 = 90$

Subtracting, $\qquad\qquad\qquad\qquad\qquad 100R_3 = 900$

$$R_3 = 9\ \Omega$$

Multiply (1) by 999: $\quad 999R_1 + 999R_2 + 999R_3 = 9{,}990$

Rearrange and multiply (3) by 999: $\quad 999R_1 - \quad R_2 - \quad R_3 = 90$

Subtracting, $\qquad\qquad 1{,}000R_2 + 1{,}000R_3 = 9{,}900$

Substituting the value of R_3, we have

$$1{,}000R_2 + 1{,}000(9) = 9{,}900$$

$$R_2 = 0.90 \ \Omega$$

Substituting values of R_3 and R_2 in (1):

$$R_1 + 0.90 + 9 = 10$$

$$R_1 = 0.10 \ \Omega$$

To check the solution, substitute the values of R_1, R_2, and R_3 in (1), (2), and (3).

EXERCISE 18–7

1. $x + 2y - z = 8$
   $2x + y + z = 7$
   $4x + 2y - z = 11$

2. $2e_1 + e_2 + 4e_3 = 5$
   $3e_1 - e_2 + 5e_3 = -9$
   $-2e_1 - 2e_2 + e_3 = -17$

3. $R_1 + R_2 + R_3 = 65$
   $2R_1 + 3R_2 - R_3 = 75$
   $-R_1 - R_2 + 2R_3 = 10$

4. $L_1 + \dfrac{L_2}{2} + \dfrac{L_3}{3} = 6$
   $2L_1 + 3L_2 - L_3 = -3$
   $-L_1 - 2L_2 + L_3 = -2$

18–8 SIMULTANEOUS-EQUATION PROBLEMS

In the previous sections simultaneous equations were provided in examples and exercises. Often problems will occur in which the necessary equations must be formulated. Under such conditions it will be necessary to designate the unknowns and write equations involving the interrelation between the quantities involved. Once the equations have been written, the solution may be carried out by the most convenient method.

example 18–15 The sum of two currents is 100 mA. Twice the larger current is equal to 8 times the smaller. What are the two currents?

solution: We have two currents involved, one smaller than the other. If we let

I_1 = smaller current

I_2 = larger current

we may write the equations involved. The problem states that the sum of the two is 100 mA. We may write as the first equation

$$I_1 + I_2 = 100 \tag{1}$$

The problem also states that twice the larger, or $2I_2$, is equal to 8 times the smaller, or $8I_1$. We may write the second equation as

$$2I_2 = 8I_1 \tag{2}$$

These form the two simultaneous equations, with two unknowns. The solution follows:

$$I_1 + I_2 = 100 \tag{1}$$
$$2I_2 = 8I_1 \tag{2}$$

Rearranging,

$$I_1 + I_2 = 100 \tag{1}$$
$$-8I_1 + 2I_2 = 0 \tag{3}$$

Multiplying (1) by 8,

$$8I_1 + 8I_2 = 800 \tag{4}$$
$$-8I_1 + 2I_2 = 0 \tag{3}$$

Adding (3) and (4),

$$10I_2 = 800$$
$$I_2 = 80$$

Substituting I_2 in (1),

$$I_1 + 80 = 100$$
$$I_1 = 20$$

The answers are $I_1 = 20$ mA and $I_2 = 80$ mA.

example 18-16 A voltage divider results in two voltages whose difference is 50 V. One half of the smaller voltage plus one third of the larger is equal to twice the larger divided by 3. What are the two voltages?

solution: Let E_1 = smaller voltage and E_2 = larger voltage. Then

$$E_2 - E_1 = 50 \tag{1}$$

$$\frac{E_1}{2} + \frac{E_2}{3} = \frac{2E_2}{3} \tag{2}$$

Clearing the fractions in (2) results in

$$3E_1 + 2E_2 = 4E_2 \quad \text{or}$$
$$3E_1 - 2E_2 = 0 \tag{3}$$

The two equations for solution, after rearranging (3), are

$$E_2 - E_1 = 50 \tag{1}$$
$$-2E_2 + 3E_1 = 0 \tag{3}$$

Multiplying (1) by (2) gives

$$2E_2 - 2E_1 = 100 \tag{4}$$
$$-2E_2 + 3E_1 = 0 \tag{3}$$

Adding (4) and (3),

$$E_1 = 100 \text{ V}$$

And substituting in (1),

$$E_2 - 100 = 50 \quad \text{or}$$
$$E_2 = 150 \text{ V}$$

EXERCISE 18-8

1. The sum of two capacitors is 22 microfarads (μF). The larger is equal to one more than twice the smaller. What is the size of each capacitor?

2. The difference between two resistors is 52 Ω. The larger resistor is equal to one half of fifty-four times the smaller. What are the two resistors?

3. The sum of two inductors is 7 millihenrys (mH). The larger inductor is two and one-half times the smaller. What is the size of each inductor?

4. A voltage divider is composed of two resistors in series. This total resistance is 52 Ω. The larger resistor is two less than twenty-six time the smaller. What are the two resistors?

5. The total voltage drop across two resistors in series is 67 V. The voltage drop across the smaller resistor is 7 V more than one half the larger. What are the voltages?

6. The difference between two voltages is 152 V. The larger voltage is 48 V less than twice the smaller voltage. What are the voltages?

7. The sum of two inductors is 15 H, while the difference between them is 3 H. What is the size of each inductor?

8. The sum of three resistors, R_1, R_2, and R_3, in series is 500 Ω. The sum of R_1 and R_2 is 450 Ω, while R_2 is seven times R_3. What are the resistors?

19

DETERMINANTS

In Chapter 18, simultaneous equations of the second order—two equations—and of the third order—three equations—were solved. The solution process often involved many operations. In this chapter we shall examine a method of solution involving the arrangement of equation quantities in a particular configuration and using "mechanical" procedures to solve the equations. This method is referred to as *solution by determinants.*

To solve simultaneous equations by determinants, it is necessary to establish a general form in which to arrange the equations. The usual form, using literal numbers, is

$$a_1x + b_1y = c_1 \tag{1}$$

$$a_2x + b_2y = c_2 \tag{2}$$

If Equations (1) and (2) were solved for x and y, respectively, using the method shown in Example 18–12, the result would be

$$x = \frac{c_1b_2 - c_2b_1}{a_1b_2 - a_2b_1} \tag{3}$$

$$y = \frac{a_1c_2 - a_2c_1}{a_1b_2 - a_2b_1} \tag{4}$$

Examination of Equations (3) and (4) shows the following:

1. The denominators of both are identical.
2. The denominators contain only the coefficients of x and y.
3. The x equation numerator contains no x coefficients, whereas the y equation numerator contains no y coefficients.

The significance of these characteristics will become apparent as our work progresses.

At this time it would be well to introduce the determinant. A determinant is merely a manner of data arrangement. For example, the common denominators in Equations (3) and (4) may be expressed as

$$a_1 b_2 - a_2 b_1 = \begin{vmatrix} a_1 & b_1 \\ a_2 & b_2 \end{vmatrix}$$

This new form of arrangement is called a *determinant*.

The designation of the parts and functions of the determinant are as follows:

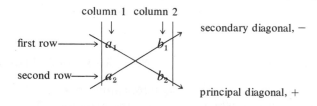

determinant elements: a_1, a_2, b_1, b_2

The evaluation of the determinant is obtained by first determining the product of the elements along the principal diagonal, multiplication in this direction, downward to the right, is designated as *positive, +, multiplication*. This is shown as

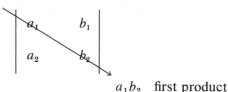

$$a_1 b_2 \quad \text{first product}$$

The second product is found by multiplying elements along the secondary diagonal. Multiplication in this direction, upward to the right, is designated as *negative, —, multiplication*. This is shown as

$$-a_2 b_1 \quad \text{second product}$$

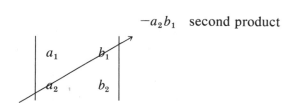

Addition of the two products thus obtained results in the evaluation of the determinant as

$$a_1 b_2 - a_2 b_1$$

The evaluation of any determinant is made in a similar manner.

243
Sec. 19–3
SIMULTANEOUS
EQUATIONS IN
DETERMINANT
FORM

example 19–1   Evaluate the determinant

solution: The individual products are obtained by diagonal multiplication and added as

$$+S_1t_2 - S_2t_1$$

example 19–2   Evaluate the determinant

$$\begin{vmatrix} 5 & 3 \\ 6 & -2 \end{vmatrix}$$

solution: Diagonal multiplication produces

$$+(5)(-2) - (6)(3) = -10 - 18 = -28$$

EXERCISE 19–1   Evaluate the following determinants.

1. $\begin{vmatrix} -M_1 & N_1 \\ M_2 & N_2 \end{vmatrix}$ 2. $\begin{vmatrix} r_a & S_a \\ r_b & S_b \end{vmatrix}$

3. $\begin{vmatrix} 4 & -6 \\ 5 & 7 \end{vmatrix}$ 4. $\begin{vmatrix} -3 & 5 \\ -2 & -4 \end{vmatrix}$

5. $\begin{vmatrix} 6 & -2 \\ -4 & 7 \end{vmatrix}$ 6. $\begin{vmatrix} 17 & -17 \\ 15 & 12 \end{vmatrix}$

7. $\begin{vmatrix} X_6 & -Y_5 \\ X_7 & -Y_6 \end{vmatrix}$ 8. $\begin{vmatrix} a & d \\ b & -e \end{vmatrix}$

19–3 SIMULTANEOUS EQUATIONS IN DETERMINANT FORM

In Section 19–1, the general form for writing simultaneous equations was seen to be

$$a_1x + b_1y = c_1 \tag{1}$$

$$a_2x + b_2y = c_2 \tag{2}$$

These equations were solved for x and y and the common denominator was expressed in determinant form in Section 19–2, which is shown again:

$$\begin{vmatrix} a_1 & b_1 \\ a_2 & b_2 \end{vmatrix} \tag{5}$$

To express Equations (1) and (2) in determinant form, it is now only necessary to write the numerators of x and y using Equations (3) and (4) of Section 19–1.

The x numerator is formed from the common denominator of (5). The x coefficients of column 1 are replaced with the constants c_1 and c_2. The x numerator then becomes

$$\begin{vmatrix} c_1 & b_1 \\ c_2 & b_2 \end{vmatrix}$$

The x equation in determinant form, using the common denominator and x numerator, is written

$$x = \frac{\begin{vmatrix} c_1 & b_1 \\ c_2 & b_2 \end{vmatrix}}{\begin{vmatrix} a_1 & b_1 \\ a_2 & b_2 \end{vmatrix}}$$

The y numerator is formed in a similar manner, again using the common denominator. Here, however, it is the y coefficients of column 2 that are replaced by the constants c_1 and c_2. The y numerator is written as

$$\begin{vmatrix} a_1 & c_1 \\ a_2 & c_2 \end{vmatrix}$$

The y equation may now be written

$$y = \frac{\begin{vmatrix} a_1 & c_1 \\ a_2 & c_2 \end{vmatrix}}{\begin{vmatrix} a_1 & b_1 \\ a_2 & b_2 \end{vmatrix}}$$

The evaluation of the numerators is made in exactly the same manner as the denominator. Division of the value of the numerator by the value of the denominator results in the evaluation of the equation.

In summary the procedure for writing and evaluating simultaneous equations in determinant form is as follows:

1. Express each equation in the form

245
Sec. 19–3
SIMULTANEOUS
EQUATIONS IN
DETERMINANT
FORM

$$a_1x + b_1y = c_1 \qquad \textbf{(1)}$$

$$a_2x + b_2y = c_2 \qquad \textbf{(2)}$$

2. Write the common denominator in determinant form using the x and y coefficients. These are placed in the same vertical arrangement as in Equations (1) and (2).
3. Write the x numerator, replacing the x coefficients with the constants, using the same vertical arrangement as in Equations (1) and (2).
4. The y numerator is similarly formed, replacing the y coefficients with the constants.
5. Write the x and y equations.
6. Evaluate the x and y equations.

example 19–3 Solve the following simultaneous equations using determinants:

$$3x + 4y = -6$$

$$4x - 2y - 14$$

solution: The common denominator is formed,

$$\begin{vmatrix} 3 & 4 \\ 4 & -2 \end{vmatrix}$$

The x numerator is formed replacing the x coefficients with the constants:

$$x \text{ numerator} = \begin{vmatrix} -6 & 4 \\ 14 & -2 \end{vmatrix}$$

The y numerator is similarly formed as

$$y \text{ numerator} = \begin{vmatrix} 3 & -6 \\ 4 & 14 \end{vmatrix}$$

The individual equations are then written and evaluated:

$$x = \frac{\begin{vmatrix} -6 & 4 \\ 14 & -2 \end{vmatrix}}{\begin{vmatrix} 3 & 4 \\ 4 & -2 \end{vmatrix}}$$

$$= \frac{+(-6)(-2) - (14)(4)}{+(3)(-2) - (4)(4)} = \frac{12 - 56}{-6 - 16} = \frac{-44}{-22} = 2$$

$$y = \frac{\begin{vmatrix} 3 & -6 \\ 4 & 14 \end{vmatrix}}{\begin{vmatrix} 3 & 4 \\ 4 & -2 \end{vmatrix}}$$

$$= \frac{+(3)(14) - (4)(-6)}{+(3)(-2) - (4)(4)} = \frac{42 + 24}{-6 - 16} = \frac{66}{-22} = -3$$

The solution of the simultaneous equations is $x = 2$, $y = -3$. Check by substituting these values in the original equations as before.

example 19-4 Solve using determinants:

$$5a - 41 = 6b$$

$$95 + 10b = 3a$$

solution: Rewriting the equations in the standard form,

$$5a - 6b = 41$$

$$-3a + 10b = -95$$

Forming the common denominator,

$$\begin{vmatrix} 5 & -6 \\ -3 & 10 \end{vmatrix}$$

The x numerator is written

$$\begin{vmatrix} 41 & -6 \\ -95 & 10 \end{vmatrix}$$

The y numerator is written

$$\begin{vmatrix} 5 & 41 \\ -3 & -95 \end{vmatrix}$$

Forming the a and b equations using the common denominator and the x and y numerators,

$$a = \frac{\begin{vmatrix} 41 & -6 \\ -95 & 10 \end{vmatrix}}{\begin{vmatrix} 5 & -6 \\ -3 & 10 \end{vmatrix}}$$

247
Sec. 19–4
DETERMINANTS
WITH THREE
SIMULTANEOUS
EQUATIONS

$$= \frac{+(41)(10) - (-95)(-6)}{+(5)(10) - (-3)(-6)} = \frac{410 - 570}{50 - 18} = \frac{-160}{32} = -5$$

$$b = \frac{\begin{vmatrix} 5 & 41 \\ -3 & -95 \end{vmatrix}}{\begin{vmatrix} 5 & -6 \\ -3 & 10 \end{vmatrix}}$$

$$= \frac{+(5)(-95) - (-3)(41)}{+(5)(10) - (-3)(-6)} = \frac{-475 + 123}{50 - 18} = \frac{-352}{32} = 11$$

EXERCISE 19–2 Solve, using determinants.

1. $3c - 4d = -11$
   $5c + 7d = 50$

2. $-5e + 4f = -55$
   $6e - 3f = 57$

3. $g + h = 32$
   $2g - h = 13$

4. $-13j - 13k = 26$
   $11j + 11k = -22$

5. $-7m - 6n = -126$
   $6m + 7n = 121$

6. $-13p + 7q = 18$
   $16p - 8q = -24$

7. $-r - s = 25$
   $2r - 6s = 54$

8. $121t + 152u = 273$
   $56t - 76u = 20$

19–4 DETERMINANTS WITH THREE SIMULTANEOUS EQUATIONS

In previous sections, determinants were used to solve second-order, or two simultaneous, equations. In this section determinants will be used to solve third-order, or three simultaneous, equations.

The three simultaneous equations would first be written in the general form,

$$a_1 x + b_1 y + c_1 z = d_1$$

$$a_2 x + b_2 y + c_2 z = d_2$$

$$a_3 x + b_3 y + c_3 z = d_3$$

The determinants are written in a similar manner as with two equations, except that there would now be three columns and three rows. These are shown as

$$\begin{vmatrix} a_1 & b_1 & c_1 \\ a_2 & b_2 & c_2 \\ a_3 & b_3 & c_3 \end{vmatrix}$$

In this form the diagonal multiplication of elements often creates some difficulties because of the necessity of "folding" or "twisting" the diagonals. To avoid this and permit the use of diagonals as developed previously, a modification is made. This consists of repeating columns 1 and 2, outside and to the right of the determinant. This is shown as

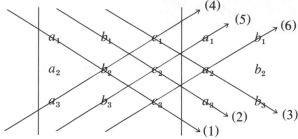

As before, the principal diagonal is positive multiplication. These diagonals are downward to the right. The secondary diagonal is negative multiplication and is upward to the right. Multiplication would be performed using diagonals (1), (2), and (3), which would be followed by diagonals (4), (5), and (6). Evaluation of this determinant would produce

$$a_1b_2c_3 + b_1c_2a_3 + c_1a_2b_3 - a_3b_2c_1 - b_3c_2a_1 - c_3a_2b_1$$

Normally the factors of each product are arranged in alphabetical sequence. This is done while forming the product in the multiplication process. This would produce, on rearranging,

$$a_1b_2c_3 + a_3b_1c_2 + a_2b_3c_1 - a_3b_2c_1 - a_1b_3c_2 - a_2b_1c_3$$

Arranged either way the evaluation of the determinant will be the same.

In solving three simultaneous equations, procedures similar to those used for solving two equations are used. These consist of forming the common-denominator determinant and then the x, y, and z numerators. Evaluation of each and the determination of each unknown then follows. The formation of each determinant is shown:

$$\text{denominator} = \begin{vmatrix} a_1 & b_1 & c_1 \\ a_2 & b_2 & c_2 \\ a_3 & b_3 & c_3 \end{vmatrix} \begin{matrix} a_1 & b_1 \\ a_2 & b_2 \\ a_3 & b_3 \end{matrix}$$

$$x \text{ numerator} = \begin{vmatrix} d_1 & b_1 & c_1 \\ d_2 & b_2 & c_2 \\ d_3 & b_3 & c_3 \end{vmatrix} \begin{matrix} d_1 & b_1 \\ d_2 & b_2 \\ d_3 & b_3 \end{matrix}$$

$$y \text{ numerator} = \begin{vmatrix} a_1 & d_1 & c_1 \\ a_2 & d_2 & c_2 \\ a_3 & d_3 & c_3 \end{vmatrix} \begin{matrix} a_1 & d_1 \\ a_2 & d_2 \\ a_3 & d_3 \end{matrix}$$

$$z \text{ numerator} = \begin{vmatrix} a_1 & b_1 & d_1 \\ a_2 & b_2 & d_2 \\ a_3 & b_3 & d_3 \end{vmatrix} \begin{matrix} a_1 & b_1 \\ a_2 & b_2 \\ a_3 & b_3 \end{matrix}$$

249
Sec. 19–4
DETERMINANTS
WITH THREE
SIMULTANEOUS
EQUATIONS

Evaluation would then follow as

$$x = \frac{x \text{ numerator}}{\text{denominator}}$$

$$y = \frac{y \text{ numerator}}{\text{denominator}}$$

$$z = \frac{z \text{ numerator}}{\text{denominator}}$$

example 19–5 Solve the simultaneous equations

$$x + y + z = 6$$

$$-x + 2y + 3z = 12$$

$$3x - 2y - 4z = -13$$

solution: Forming the common-denominator determinant and repeating columns 1 and 2,

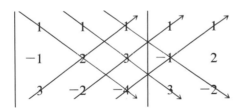

Multiplication produces the value of the common denominator:

$$+(1)(2)(-4) + (1)(3)(3) + (1)(-1)(-2) - (3)(2)(1) -$$
$$(-2)(3)(1) - (-4)(-1)(1)$$
$$= -8 + 9 + 2 - 6 + 6 - 4 = -1$$

Forming the *x*-numerator determinant:

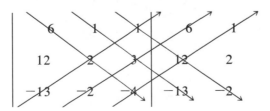

Evaluating,

$$(6)(2)(-4) + (1)(3)(-13) + (1)(12)(-2) - (-13)(2)(1) -$$
$$(-2)(3)(6) - (-4)(12)(1)$$
$$= -48 - 39 - 24 + 26 + 36 + 48 = -1$$

Using the value of the common-denominator and the value of the x-numerator, the value of x may be determined as:

$$x = \frac{-1}{-1} = 1$$

Forming the y-numerator determinant:

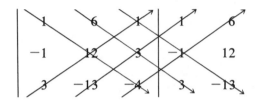

Evaluating,

$$(1)(12)(-4) + (6)(3)(3) + (1)(-1)(-13) - (3)(12)(1) -$$
$$(-13)(3)(1) - (-4)(-1)(6)$$
$$= -48 + 54 + 13 - 36 + 39 - 24 = -2$$

$$y = \frac{-2}{-1} = 2$$

Forming the z-numerator determinant:

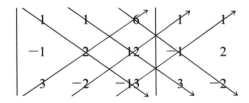

Evaluating,

251
Sec. 19–4
DETERMINANTS
WITH THREE
SIMULTANEOUS
EQUATIONS

$$(1)(2)(-13) + (1)(12)(3) + (6)(-1)(-2) - (3)(2)(6) -$$
$$(-2)(12)(1) - (-13)(-1)(1)$$
$$= -26 + 36 + 12 - 36 + 24 - 13 = -3$$
$$z = \frac{-3}{-1} = 3$$

EXERCISE 19–3 Using determinants, solve the simultaneous equations of Exercise 18–7.

20
EXPONENTS AND RADICALS

$\blacksquare$n previous chapters, we have developed some basic mathematical concepts involving both exponents and radicals. In this chapter a much more comprehensive study of these important topics will be presented. There will, of necessity, be some repetition of previously presented material. However, this will serve as a review and will also bring together in one chapter the laws of exponents and radicals and their use in mathematical operations.

20-1 LAWS OF EXPONENTS—MULTIPLICATION

An exponent indicates how many times a number is to be multiplied by itself. Expressed another way, the exponent indicates how many times the base is to be used as a factor.

Expressed mathematically,

$$3^3 = 3 \cdot 3 \cdot 3$$

$$a^5 = a \cdot a \cdot a \cdot a \cdot a$$

$$b^3 \cdot b^2 = b \cdot b \cdot b \cdot b \cdot b = b^{3+2} = b^5$$

$$c^2 \cdot c^3 \cdot c = c \cdot c \cdot c \cdot c \cdot c \cdot c = c^{2+3+1} = c^6$$

These relationships show that the product of two or more powers with the same base is obtained by adding the exponents. This law is conventionally expressed in this form:

$$a^m \cdot a^n = a^{m+n}, \quad \text{where } a \neq 0$$

20-2 LAWS OF EXPONENTS—DIVISION

Division involving exponents with the same base may be shown as

$$\frac{s^5}{s^3} = \frac{\not s \cdot \not s \cdot \not s \cdot s \cdot s}{\not s \cdot \not s \cdot \not s} = s^2,$$

or

$$\frac{s^5}{s^3} = s^{5-3} = s^2,$$

$$\frac{t^7}{t^2} = t^{7-2} = t^5$$

$$\frac{v^9}{v^6} = v^{9-6} = v^3$$

These examples show that the quotient of the division of powers with the same base is obtained by subtracting the exponents. The law of the division of exponents is expressed as

$$\frac{a^m}{a^n} = a^{m-n}, \quad \text{where } a \neq 0$$

20-3 NEGATIVE EXPONENTS

The question might be asked: If an exponent is negative, such as C^{-5}, how is it possible to multiply a number by itself a minus-five times? This may be shown using the law of exponents in division, where

$$\frac{a^m}{a^n} = a^{m-n}, \quad \text{where } n > m$$

$$\frac{c^3}{c^5} = \frac{\not{c} \cdot \not{c} \cdot \not{c}}{\not{c} \cdot \not{c} \cdot \not{c} \cdot c \cdot c} = \frac{1}{c^2}$$

Therefore,

$$\frac{c^3}{c^5} = c^{3-5} = c^{-2} \quad \text{or} \quad \frac{1}{c^2}$$

The law involving negative exponents is stated as:

$$a^{-n} = \frac{1}{a^n}, \quad \text{where } a \neq 0$$

20-4 ZERO EXPONENTS

In our discussion of multiplication and division involving exponents, a question might be asked regarding the significance of a number with a zero exponent. The answer may be shown in the following examples of multiplication and division involving zero exponents:

$$e^5 \cdot e^0 = e^{5+0} = e^5$$

$$\frac{e^5}{e^0} = e^{5-0} = e^5$$

Expressed in general form,

$$a^m \cdot a^0 = a^m, \quad \text{where } a \neq 0 \tag{1}$$

$$\frac{a^m}{a^0} = a^m, \quad \text{where } a \neq 0 \tag{2}$$

It should be noted that $a^0 = 1$ (see Section 6–1). This is shown using Equations (1) and (2), where

$$a^m \cdot a^0 = a^m \cdot 1 = a^m, \quad \text{where } a \neq 0$$

$$\frac{a^m}{a^0} = \frac{a^m}{1} = a^m, \qquad \text{where } a \neq 0$$

20–5 POWER OF A POWER

Often a mathematical expression contains a power of a power as

$$(3^5)^2$$

This means that the base is raised to a power equal to the product of the exponents. That is,

$$(3^5)^2 = 3^{5 \cdot 2} = 3^{10}$$

In general form,

$$(a^m)^n = a^{mn}, \quad \text{where } a \neq 0$$

20–6 POWER OF A PRODUCT

A power of a product may be shown as

$$(xy)^2$$

This means that

$$(xy)^2 = x^2 y^2 \quad \text{or} \quad (cde)^2 = c^2 d^2 e^2$$

In general form this is written

$$(ab)^m = a^m b^m, \quad \text{where } a \neq 0, \ b \neq 0$$

20–7 FRACTIONAL EXPONENTS

Using the law of multiplication of exponents

$$a^m \cdot a^n = a^{m+n}$$

It follows that

$$s^{\frac{1}{2}} \cdot s^{\frac{1}{2}} = s^{\frac{1}{2} + \frac{1}{2}} = s^1 = s$$

From our basic mathematics we learned that the square root of a number is a process of obtaining a number that when multiplied by itself would result in the given number. Therefore,

$$\sqrt{s} = s^{\frac{1}{2}}$$

Similarly,

$$t^{\frac{1}{4}} \cdot t^{\frac{1}{4}} \cdot t^{\frac{1}{4}} \cdot t^{\frac{1}{4}} = t^{\frac{1}{4}+\frac{1}{4}+\frac{1}{4}+\frac{1}{4}} = t^1 = t$$

Or, expressed differently,

$$(t^{\frac{1}{4}})^4 = t$$

Or, in general form,

$$(a^{\frac{1}{n}})^n = a$$

Then

$$v^{\frac{3}{4}} \cdot v^{\frac{3}{4}} \cdot v^{\frac{3}{4}} \cdot v^{\frac{3}{4}} = v^{\frac{3}{4}+\frac{3}{4}+\frac{3}{4}+\frac{3}{4}} = v^{\frac{12}{4}} = v^3$$

or

$$(v^{\frac{3}{4}})^4 = v^3$$

Then

$$v^{\frac{3}{4}} = \sqrt[4]{v^3}$$

The above examples indicate that the denominator of a fractional exponent indicates the root of the base, while the numerator indicates the power of the base. Expressed in mathematical form,

$$a^{\frac{m}{n}} = \sqrt[n]{a^m}, \quad \text{where } a \neq 0$$

It should be obvious that the root of a power may be extracted by reversing this procedure. That is,

$$\sqrt[n]{a^m} = a^{\frac{m}{n}}, \quad \text{where } a \neq 0$$

20–8 POWER OF A FRACTION

A fraction raised to a power is equal to the numerator of the fraction raised to that power divided by the denominator raised to that power.

Shown mathematically,

$$\left(\frac{2}{5}\right)^2 = \frac{2^2}{5^2} = \frac{4}{25}$$

This relationship may often be used to simplify operations using scientific notation. For example,

$$\left(\frac{10^6}{10^2}\right)^3 = \frac{10^{6\cdot3}}{10^{2\cdot3}} = \frac{10^{18}}{10^6} = 10^{18-6} = 10^{12}$$

We may also perform the indicated division within the parentheses and then raise the quotient to the indicated power. Using the example above, we have

$$\left(\frac{10^6}{10^2}\right)^3 = (10^{6-2})^3 = (10^4)^3 = 10^{12}$$

The answer is, of course, the same.

Expressed mathematically, this rule is

$$\left(\frac{a}{b}\right)^m = \frac{a^m}{b^m}, \quad \text{where } a \neq 0, \text{ and } b \neq 0$$

20–9 LAWS OF EXPONENTS—SUMMARY

The laws of exponents are shown in summary form in Table 20–1. The reference section and the limitations, if any, are listed in this table. It should be noted that the general limitation of $a \neq 0$ (and $b \neq 0$, where used), applies to all operations and so is not listed.

TABLE 20–1 Laws of Exponents Summarized

OPERATION	LAW	LIMITATION	REFERENCE SECTION
Multiplication	$a^m \cdot a^n = a^{m+n}$		20–1
Division	$a^m \div a^n = a^{m-n}$	$m > n$	20–2
	$= \dfrac{1}{a^{n-m}}$	$n > m$	20–2
Negative exponent	$a^{-n} = \dfrac{1}{a^n}$		20–3
Zero exponent	$a^m \cdot a^0 = a^m$		20–4
	$\dfrac{a^m}{a^0} = a^m$		20–4

TABLE 20-1 Laws of Exponents Summarized (*cont.*)

OPERATION	LAW	LIMITATION	REFERENCE SECTION
Power of a power	$(a^m)^n = a^{mn}$		20–5
Power of a product	$(ab)^m = a^m b^n$		20–6
Fractional exponent	$a^{\frac{m}{n}} = \sqrt[n]{a^m}$		20–7
	$(a^{\frac{1}{n}})^n = a$		20–7
Root of a power	$\sqrt[n]{a^m} = a^{\frac{m}{n}}$		20–7
Power of a fraction	$\left(\dfrac{a}{b}\right)^m = \dfrac{a^m}{b^m}$		20–8

20-10 RADICALS

In arithmetic we learned that the radical sign is $\sqrt{}$. In previous sections we saw that the vinculum or bar, $\overline{}$, is a sign of grouping. Normally, the radical sign and vinculum are used thus $\sqrt{}$, and called the *radical*.

If we have $\sqrt[n]{a}$, the n is the *index* of the root and the a is called the *radicand*.

20-11 OPERATIONS WITH RADICALS

In Section 20–7 it was shown how a fractional exponent could be expressed in radical form. Similarly, it was seen that a radical could be expressed as a fractional exponent. This procedure could be considered as a simplification of the radical. We shall now examine a number of other operations with radicals, which in combination with the laws of exponents will permit their simplification and increase the ease with which they may be worked.

20-12 LAWS OF RADICALS

There are three basic laws of radicals. Note that they are related to the laws of exponents. These laws are shown in Table 20–2. The limitations which apply are that a, $b \neq 0$, and m and n are positive integers.

TABLE 20–2 Laws of Radicals

259

Sec. 20–13
SIMPLIFICATION OF
RADICALS

1. $a^{\frac{m}{n}} = \sqrt[n]{a^m} = \left(\sqrt[n]{a}\right)^m$

2. $\sqrt[n]{ab} = \sqrt[n]{a} \cdot \sqrt[n]{b}$

3. $\sqrt[n]{\dfrac{a}{b}} = \dfrac{\sqrt[n]{a}}{\sqrt[n]{b}}$

20–13 SIMPLIFICATION OF RADICALS

The application of the laws of radicals will be shown in the following examples.

example 20–1 Simplify: $\sqrt{16x^4y^6}$.

solution: $\sqrt{16x^4y^6} = (4^2x^4y^6)^{\frac{1}{2}} = 4^{\frac{2}{2}}x^{\frac{4}{2}}y^{\frac{6}{2}} = 4x^2y^3$

In Example 20–1, the radicand was a perfect square and was easily solved in the manner indicated. If the radicand were not a perfect square, it might be rearranged into two factors, one a perfect square. This perfect square might then be extracted from the radicand, resulting in a simplification of the radical.

example 20–2 Simplify: $\sqrt{72x^5y^7z^3}$.

solution: $\sqrt{72x^5y^7z^3} = \sqrt{36x^4y^6z^2} \cdot \sqrt{2xyz}$

$\qquad\qquad = \pm 6x^2y^3z\sqrt{2xyz}$

E X E R C I S E 20–1 Simplify by factoring.

1. $\sqrt{162}$ 2. $\sqrt{128}$ 3. $\sqrt{36y^2}$

4. $\sqrt{98a^3b^5}$ 5. $\sqrt{121c^3}$ 6. $\sqrt{288d^5e^7}$

7. $5a\sqrt{25b^2c^4}$ 8. $6n\sqrt{50m^3p^5q^{11}}$

The simplification of radicals containing fractions is handled somewhat differently. Those with perfect squares in both the numerator and denominator are handled in the following manner. As

$\sqrt{16} = 4$

$\sqrt{81} = 9$

$\dfrac{\sqrt{16}}{\sqrt{81}} = \pm\dfrac{4}{9}$

it follows that

$$\sqrt{\frac{16}{81}} = \pm\frac{4}{9}$$

example 20-3 Simplify: $\sqrt{\dfrac{36x^2}{64y^4}}$.

solution:

$$\sqrt{\frac{36x^2}{64y^4}} = \frac{\sqrt{36x^2}}{\sqrt{64y^4}} = \frac{6x}{8y^2}$$

However, if the denominator is not a perfect square, the simplification is performed in a different manner. In this case both the numerator and denominator are multiplied by a number that will make the denominator a perfect square. This procedure is called *rationalizing the denominator*. The resulting perfect square may then be extracted from the denominator, simplifying the radical.

example 20-4 Simplify: $\sqrt{\dfrac{5}{12}}$.

solution: Multiplication of both the numerator and denominator by 3 will make the denominator a perfect square.

$$\sqrt{\frac{5}{12}} = \sqrt{\frac{5 \cdot 3}{12 \cdot 3}} = \sqrt{\frac{15}{36}} = \frac{\sqrt{15}}{\sqrt{36}} = \pm\frac{1}{6}\sqrt{15} = \pm\frac{\sqrt{15}}{6}$$

example 20-5 Simplify: $\sqrt{\dfrac{3a^3}{7b^4}}$.

solution: Multiplying both the numerator and denominator by 7 produces a perfect square. This is shown as

$$\sqrt{\frac{3a^3}{7b^4}} = \sqrt{\frac{3a^3 \cdot 7}{7b^4 \cdot 7}} = \sqrt{\frac{21a^3}{49b^4}} = \frac{\sqrt{21a^3}}{\sqrt{49b^4}} = \pm\frac{1}{7b^2}\sqrt{21a^3}$$

EXERCISE 20-2 Simplify.

1. $\dfrac{\sqrt{4}}{\sqrt{49}}$ 2. $\dfrac{\sqrt{4a^2}}{\sqrt{16b^4}}$ 3. $\sqrt{\dfrac{49b^4c^6}{81d^8}}$

4. $\dfrac{\sqrt{5e}}{\sqrt{3f^2}}$ 5. $\sqrt{\dfrac{6g^3}{9h^2}}$ 6. $\sqrt{\dfrac{5m^3n^5}{6p^2q^4}}$

7. $\sqrt{\dfrac{3stv}{5w^2x^4y^6}}$ **8.** $\sqrt{\dfrac{13}{7a}}$

Radicals that are the same may be added or subtracted in a similar manner as adding or subtracting similar terms. Similar radicals would be those with the same index and the same radicand.

example 20-6 Simplify: $3\sqrt{x} + 2\sqrt{x} - 5\sqrt{x} + 6\sqrt{x}$.

solution: As the index and the radicands are the same, the radicals may be combined. Adding terms,

$$11\sqrt{x} - 5\sqrt{x} = 6\sqrt{x}$$

example 20-7 Simplify: $\sqrt{8} + 3\sqrt{2} - \sqrt{2}$.

solution: The $\sqrt{8}$ term may be simplified by

$$\sqrt{8} = \sqrt{4 \cdot 2} = 2\sqrt{2}$$

We then have

$$2\sqrt{2} + 3\sqrt{2} - 2\sqrt{2}$$

Combining produces $3\sqrt{2}$.

example 20-8 Simplify:

$$\sqrt{\dfrac{2a}{9}} + \sqrt{\dfrac{a}{8}}$$

solution: Rationalizing the denominator of the second term, we have

$$\sqrt{\dfrac{2a}{9}} + \sqrt{\dfrac{a}{8} \cdot \dfrac{2}{2}} = \dfrac{\sqrt{2a}}{\sqrt{9}} + \dfrac{\sqrt{2a}}{\sqrt{16}} = \dfrac{1}{3}\sqrt{2a} + \dfrac{1}{4}\sqrt{2a}$$

$$= \dfrac{4}{12}\sqrt{2a} + \dfrac{3}{12}\sqrt{2a} = \dfrac{7}{12}\sqrt{2a}$$

EXERCISE 20–3 Simplify.

1. $\sqrt{2} - 3\sqrt{2} + 5\sqrt{2}$ **2.** $\sqrt[3]{a} - 3\sqrt[3]{a}$

3. $\dfrac{\sqrt{a^3}}{3} - \dfrac{2\sqrt{a^3}}{5}$

4. $\sqrt{8} + 3\sqrt{2}$

5. $3\sqrt{72} - \sqrt{8}$

6. $\sqrt{36a^5} + 3\sqrt{a^5} - 2\sqrt{a^5}$

7. $\sqrt{\dfrac{m^2}{8}} + \dfrac{3\sqrt{8m^2}}{\sqrt{16}}$

8. $-2x\sqrt{y} + 3x\sqrt{16y}$

20-15 MULTIPLICATION AND DIVISION OF RADICALS

Laws 2 and 3 in the laws of radicals, Section 10–12, indicate the procedures involved in the multiplication and division of radicals. These are repeated here.

$$\sqrt[n]{ab} = \sqrt[n]{a} \cdot \sqrt[n]{b}$$

$$\sqrt[n]{\frac{a}{b}} = \frac{\sqrt[n]{a}}{\sqrt[n]{b}}$$

Using the above laws, radicals with the *same index* may be multiplied and divided in the same manner as in other algebraic expressions. In other words, we may consider the radical as a sign of grouping, which of course the vinculum establishes, and perform the indicated operation accordingly.

example 20-9 Perform the indicated operation and simplify:

$$3\sqrt{ab^3} \cdot 4\sqrt{a^3b^2}$$

solution: Multiplication of the coefficients and the terms within the radicals is followed by the simplification of the product.

$$3\sqrt{ab^3} \cdot 4\sqrt{a^3b^2} = 3 \cdot 4\sqrt{(ab^3) \cdot (a^3b^2)} = 12\sqrt{a^4b^5}$$

$$= 12\sqrt{a^4b^4b} = 12a^2b^2\sqrt{b}$$

example 20-10 Perform the indicated operation and simplify: Multiply $\sqrt{5} + 2\sqrt{3}$ by $3\sqrt{3}$.

solution: This involves the multiplication of a binomial by a monomial. This differs from our previous algebraic multiplication in that only radicals are involved.

$$\begin{array}{r} \sqrt{5} \quad + 2\sqrt{3} \\ 3\sqrt{3} \\ \hline 3\sqrt{5 \cdot 3} + 6\sqrt{3} \cdot \sqrt{3} \end{array}$$

As $\sqrt{3} \cdot \sqrt{3} = 3$, we have

$$3\sqrt{15} + 6 \cdot 3 = 3\sqrt{15} + 18$$

example 20–11 Perform the indicated operation and simplify:

$$\frac{3\sqrt{a^5}}{\sqrt{4a}}$$

solution:

$$\frac{3\sqrt{a^5}}{\sqrt{4a}} = 3\sqrt{\frac{a^5}{4a}}$$

Dividing both numerator and denominator by a produces

$$3\sqrt{\frac{a^4}{4}} = \frac{3\sqrt{a^4}}{\sqrt{4}} = \frac{3a^2}{2}$$

An expression often found in electronics is in the form $\sqrt{3} + 5$ or $3 - \sqrt{2}$. This is called an *irrational binomial*. When this occurs in fractional form, that is, when division is indicated, rationalization of the denominator is necessary. This will require the multiplication of both the numerator and denominator by the *conjugate* of the denominator. The conjugate is the same as the denominator except that the sign of the second term is changed. For example,

$3 + \sqrt{5}$ is the conjugate of $3 - \sqrt{5}$

$\sqrt{2} - 5$ is the conjugate of $\sqrt{2} + 5$

example 20–12 Perform the indicated operation and simplify:

$$\frac{1}{\sqrt{5} + 1}$$

solution: Multiplying both the numerator and the denominator by the conjugate of the denominator, we have

$$\frac{\sqrt{5} - 1}{(\sqrt{5} + 1)(\sqrt{5} - 1)}$$

For purposes of understanding, the multiplication of the denominator is shown as

$$\begin{array}{r} \sqrt{5} + 1 \\ \sqrt{5} - 1 \\ \hline -\sqrt{5} - 1 \\ 5 + \sqrt{5} \\ \hline 5 \qquad -1 = 4 \end{array}$$

The similarity between the use of conjugates and the
difference of binomial squares in the form $(x + y)(x - y)$
should be observed. Remember that in this form the
$+xy$ and $-xy$ terms cancel, as do the $+\sqrt{5}$ and the
$-\sqrt{5}$ terms in this example. Combining with the
numerator, we have

$$\frac{\sqrt{5} - 1}{4}$$

example 20–13 Perform the indicated operation and simplify:

$$\frac{\sqrt{2} + 5}{\sqrt{2} - 1}$$

solution: Multiplying both the numerator and the denominator by
the conjugate of the denominator and simplifying,

$$\frac{\sqrt{2} + 5}{\sqrt{2} - 1} = \frac{(\sqrt{2} + 5)(\sqrt{2} + 1)}{(\sqrt{2} - 1)(\sqrt{2} + 1)} = \frac{6\sqrt{2} + 7}{1} = 6\sqrt{2} + 7$$

EXERCISE 20–4   Perform the indicated operation and simplify.

1. $\sqrt{10} \cdot \sqrt{12}$ 2. $\sqrt{2} \cdot 3\sqrt{10}$

3. $5\sqrt{8} \cdot 7\sqrt{12}$ 4. $\sqrt[3]{6} \cdot \sqrt[3]{12}$

5. $(\sqrt{5} + 2) \cdot \sqrt{5}$ 6. $(3\sqrt{8} + 5) \cdot 2\sqrt{6}$

7. $\dfrac{4\sqrt{x^3}}{\sqrt{16x}}$ 8. $\dfrac{1}{\sqrt{3} + 2}$

20–16   THE *j* OPERATOR

In this section, an extremely important concept in electronics will be
introduced. This is the *j* operator. In much the same manner as the
signs of operation with which we are so familiar, $+, -, \times, \div, \sqrt{\ }$, the
j operator indicates an operation.

In our previous work it was developed that multiplication of a
graphical quantity by -1 was the same as rotating it through $180°$.
The use of the *j* operator indicates counterclockwise (CCW) rotation
through $90°$. This is shown in Figure 20–1. A quantity, *m*, is placed
on the *x* axis, as shown. When "operated on" by the *j* operator, it is
designated as *jm*. This quantity is now shown on the *y* axis. It has,
then, through the use of the *j* operator, been rotated through $90°$ in
a CCW direction. In Figure 20–1 the quantity *jm* now lies along the
y axis.

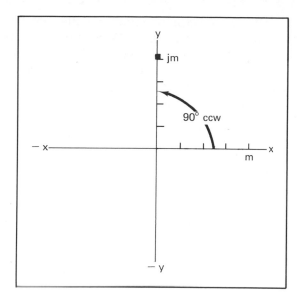

FIGURE 20–1
Effect of the *j* Operator on a Quantity

What would be the effect of again using the *j* operator to rotate it CCW through another 90°? We would now be operating on the quantity represented by *jm* with the *j* operator. In effect, then, we have $j \cdot jm$, or j^2m. This result of this operation is shown in Figure 20–2.

FIGURE 20–2
Effect of the *j* Operator on Quantity *jm*

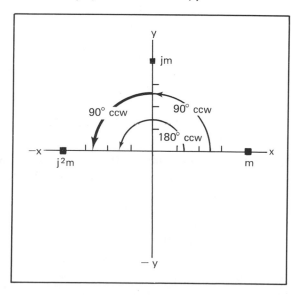

We have seen that the operation on the quantity m by the j operator results in a 90° CCW rotation. Operating on the quantity jm results in another CCW rotation of 90°. In effect, then, two operations on the quantity m by the j operator, or j^2m, results in a 180° CCW rotation. As noted above, our previous graphical work established that the multiplication of a quantity by -1 was the same as rotation through 180°. If this is so, we may now equate

$$j^2 = -1$$

as both represent rotation through 180°. Therefore, if

$$j^2 = -1 \quad \text{then} \quad j = \sqrt{-1}$$

Carrying this analysis still further we see that as

$$j = \sqrt{-1} = 90° \text{ CCW rotation}$$
$$j^2 = -1 = 180° \text{ CCW rotation}$$

use of the j operator on the quantity represented by j^2m will rotate it another 90° in a CCW direction. In other words, as

$$j^2 = -1 = 180° \text{ CCW rotation}$$
$$j \cdot j^2 = j \cdot -1 = -j = 180° + 90° = 270° \text{ CCW rotation}$$
$$-j = 270° \text{ CCW rotation}$$

This is shown graphically in Figure 20–3, which shows that $-jm$ represents CCW rotation of 270°. This may also be represented as

$$-jm = 270° \text{ CCW}$$

or

$$-\sqrt{-1} \cdot m = 270° \text{ CCW}$$

or

$$-jm = 360° - 270° = 90° \text{ CW}$$

In effect, then, operation by the $-j$ operator on quantity m represents a 270° CCW rotation or a $-90°$ rotation. We may then say that

$$j = 90° \text{ rotation CCW}$$

and

$$-j = 90° \text{ rotation CW}$$

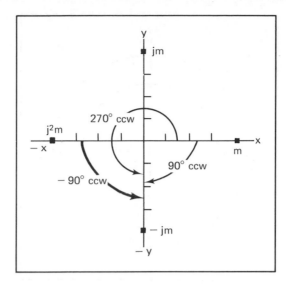

FIGURE 20–3
Effect of *j* Operator on Quantity *j²m*

Then, through this means, rotation in a CCW or CW direction will result from our choice of operators; this is,

$$j = \sqrt{-1} \quad \text{or} \quad -j = -\sqrt{-1}$$

For example,

$$-jm = 90° \text{ CW}$$
$$-j \cdot -jm = j^2m = -\sqrt{-1} \cdot -\sqrt{-1} \cdot m = -1m = -m = 180° \text{ CW}$$

This is, of course, the same point as shown in Figure 20–2. Rotation through another 90° CW is represented by

$$-j \cdot -j \cdot -j \cdot m = -\sqrt{-1} \cdot -\sqrt{-1} \cdot -\sqrt{-1} \cdot m$$
$$= -1 \cdot -\sqrt{-1} \cdot m = -1 \cdot -j \cdot m = jm$$

A summary of the CCW and CW rotations with the *j* and −*j* operators is best shown graphically. Figure 20–4 shows CCW rotations using the *j* operator and Figure 20–5 shows CW rotations using the −*j* operator. Notice carefully the similarities in each of the figures. The results obtained through rotation are the same. The only difference that exists is in the direction of rotation. Each of these procedures will be very useful in our later work with electronic circuits.

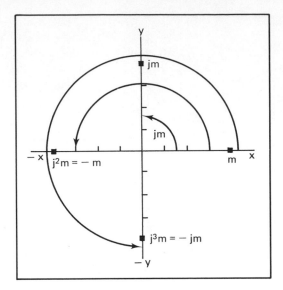

FIGURE 20–4
CCW Rotation of Quantity *m* Using *j* Operator

20–17 SIMPLIFICATION OF RADICALS WITH NEGATIVE NUMBERS

Our work with radicals has always involved positive numbers. In Section 20–16, we used as an operator a radical with a negative number. We know, however, that no "real" number, when multiplied by itself, will result in a −1. The indicated square root of a negative number is referred to as an *imaginary number*. The use of the *j* operator permits us to simplify the indicated square root of a negative or imaginary number. For example, the indicated square root of $\sqrt{-16}$ could be represented as

$$\sqrt{(-1)(16)} \quad \text{or} \quad \sqrt{-1} \cdot \sqrt{16} \quad \text{or} \quad \sqrt{-1} \cdot 4$$

and as $\sqrt{-1} = j$, we may write

$$\sqrt{-1} \cdot 4 = j4$$

Similarly, $\sqrt{-9a^2}$ may be simplified as

$$\sqrt{(-1)(9a^2)} = \sqrt{-1} \cdot \sqrt{9a^2} = j3a$$

In these examples we have been able to represent an imaginary quantity using the *j* operator.

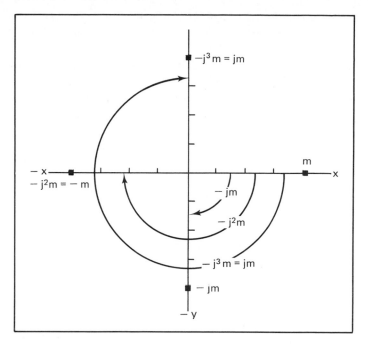

FIGURE 20–5
CW Rotation of Quantity *m* Using the −*j*
Operator

20-18 COMPLEX NUMBERS

Combining a real number with an imaginary number results in a *complex number*. The following are examples of complex numbers:

$$3 + j4 \qquad 2 - j5 \qquad -3 + j6 \qquad -7 - j3 \qquad m - jn \qquad 3x - j^2y$$

Note in the above examples that

1. The real number may be positive or negative.
2. The imaginary number may be positive or negative.
3. The complex number may be composed of numerical quantities, literal quantities, or combinations.

In later chapters, the use of complex numbers will be applied to vectors. In this chapter, we shall deal only with basic algebraic operations involving complex numbers.

At this point, questions arise: What is the significance of a complex number? What does it mean to have a real and an imaginary number combined? How is it possible to depict such a number? Figure 20–6 will perhaps answer all these questions. Figure 20–6a shows the complex numbers $3 + j4$ and $-3 - j4$, and Figure 20–6b shows $-3 + j4$ and $3 - j4$. The figures should be helpful in understanding the representation of complex numbers. Note that in each case the real number is laid off in the appropriate direction. The imaginary part is then laid off and rotated through 90° to form the point that the particular complex number represents. In later sections our understanding of complex numbers will be more thoroughly developed. Questions that may arise as a result of the method of the representation of complex numbers shown in Figure 20–6 will be answered as our knowledge of this subject is expanded.

20–19 COMPLEX NUMBERS—ADDITION AND SUBTRACTION

As shown in Figure 20–6, complex numbers are represented with the real number measured along the x axis, whereas the imaginary number is rotated 90° parallel to the y axis after being measured on the x axis. The 90° angle between the two parts of the complex number does not, at this point, allow us to combine the two parts. The complex number may be treated as a binomial and addition or subtraction performed in this manner.

example 20–14   Add the following complex numbers:

$$3 - j4 \text{ and } 5 + j6 \qquad 6 + j5 \text{ and } -4 - j2$$

solution:

$$
\begin{array}{cc}
3 - j4 & 6 + j5 \\
5 + j6 & -4 - j2 \\
\hline
8 + j2 & 2 + j3
\end{array}
$$

example 20–15   Perform the indicated operation: Subtract $-3 + j5$ from $6 - j8$ and subtract $2 - j3$ from $6 + j9$.

solution:

$$
\begin{array}{cc}
6 - \ j8 & 6 + \ j9 \\
-3 + \ j5 & 2 - \ j3 \\
\hline
9 - j13 & 4 + j12
\end{array}
$$

20–20 COMPLEX NUMBERS—MULTIPLICATION AND DIVISION

In multiplication and division, the complex number is handled as in addition and subtraction, as a binomial. The process of division is performed in a manner similar to the division of radicals. That is, both the numerator and the denominator are multiplied by the conjugate of the denominator. These processes are shown in the following examples.

271
Sec. 20–20
COMPLEX
NUMBERS—
MULTIPLICATION
AND DIVISION

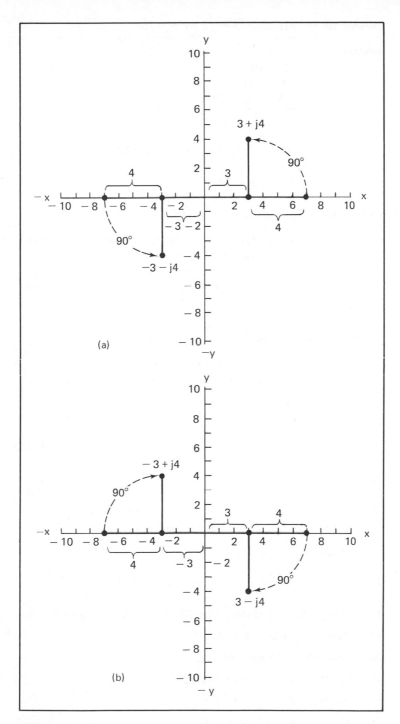

FIGURE 20–6
(a) Representation of $3 + j4$ and $-3 - j4$ (b) Representation of $-3 + j4$ and $3 - j4$

example 20-16 Multiply $3 - j4$ by $5 + j6$.

solution:

$$
\begin{array}{r}
3 - j4 \\
5 + j6 \\
\hline
15 - j20 \\
j18 - j^2 24 \\
\hline
15 - j2 \;\; - j^2 24
\end{array}
$$

As $j^2 = -1$, the $-j^2 24$ term becomes $+24$. Then

$$15 - j2 + 24 = 39 - j2$$

example 20-17 Divide 1 by $3 + j4$.

solution: Multiplying both the numerator and denominator by the conjugate of $3 + j4$, we have

$$\frac{1}{3 + j4} = \frac{1(3 - j4)}{(3 + j4)(3 - j4)} = \frac{3 - j4}{9 - j^2 16} = \frac{3 - j4}{25}$$

example 20-18 Divide $2 + j3$ by $1 - j4$.

solution: $\dfrac{2 + j3}{1 - j4} = \dfrac{(2 + j3)(1 + j4)}{(1 - j4)(1 + j4)} = \dfrac{-10 + j11}{17}$

E X E R C I S E   20-5   Simplify.

1. $\sqrt{20}$ 2. $\sqrt{48}$ 3. $\sqrt{128}$

4. $\sqrt{\dfrac{3}{7}}$ 5. $\sqrt{\dfrac{7}{12}}$ 6. $\sqrt{\dfrac{3}{5}}$

7. $4\sqrt{5} + 6\sqrt{5}$ 8. $3\sqrt[3]{4} - 2\sqrt[3]{4}$

9. $\sqrt{32} + 3\sqrt{2}$ 10. $2\sqrt{48} + 3\sqrt{27}$

11. Multiply: $2\sqrt{8} \cdot 3\sqrt{6}$.

12. Divide: $\dfrac{10}{4 - \sqrt{3}}$.   13. Divide: $\dfrac{3 + \sqrt{3}}{4 + \sqrt{3}}$.

14. Using the j operator, simplify $\sqrt{-9}$, $\sqrt{-81}$, and $\sqrt{-36}$.

15. Add $6 - j5$ and $8 + j6$.

16. Add $16 - j12$ and $30 + j5$.

17. Subtract $4 - j5$ from $3 + j2$.

18. Subtract $2 - j2$ from $3 + j3$.

19. Multiply $6 + j3$ by $2 - j2$.

20. Multiply $3 - j6$ by $2 + j12$.

21. Multiply $12 + j11$ by $3 - j4$.

22. Divide 1 by $6 - j4$.

23. Divide 10 by $3 + j2$.

24. Divide $2 + j2$ by $3 - j2$.

273

Sec. 20–20
COMPLEX
NUMBERS—
MULTIPLICATION
AND DIVISION

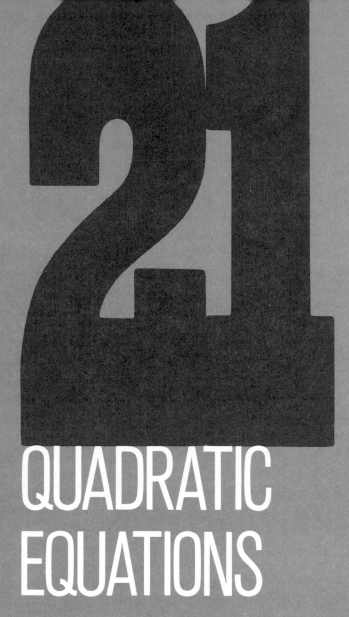

21

QUADRATIC EQUATIONS

In our previous work, we have been primarily concerned with equations of the first degree, that is, equations in which the highest degree of any term was 1. Such equations, called *linear equations*, when plotted on a graph resulted in a straight line. The equation

$$5x + 4 = 0$$

is an example of an equation of the first degree.

In this chapter we shall work with equations of the second degree. The highest degree of any term of an equation of the second degree is 2. Such equations are not linear and when plotted on a graph will not result in a straight line. The equation

$$3x^2 + 2x + 3 = 0$$

is an example of an equation of the second degree. An equation of this type is called a *quadratic equation*.

21–1 QUADRATIC EQUATIONS

The quadratic equation is seen to be an equation of the second degree. The quadratic equation may take two general forms: the first is called the *pure quadratic*, the second is called the *complete quadratic*.

The pure quadratic is also called the *incomplete* or *simple quadratic*. There are no first-degree terms present in this form of the quadratic equation. The equation

$$x^2 + 3 = 0$$

is an example of the pure quadratic equation.

A quadratic equation that has both second- and first-degree terms is a complete quadratic equation. The equations

$$5x^2 - 3x + 2 = 0$$
$$a^2 - 2a = 0$$

are examples of this type.

The complete form of the quadratic equation is often written in general terms as

$$ax^2 + bx + c = 0$$

In this form, a, b, and c are constants. Note that if the first term is missing, that is, if $a = 0$, then $ax^2 = 0$, the equation would be $bx + c = 0$, which is no longer a quadratic but an equation of the first degree.

If, $b = 0$, then $bx = 0$, and the equation would be $ax^2 + c = 0$, a quadratic of the pure or incomplete form.

21–2 SOLUTION OF A PURE QUADRATIC EQUATION

As seen above, the pure quadratic equation is written in the general form as

$$ax^2 + c = 0$$

The solution of an equation of this type is shown in the following example.

example 21–1 Solve $2x^2 - 72 = 0$.

solution: Adding 72 to each side, we have

$$2x^2 = 72$$
$$x^2 = 36$$
$$x = \sqrt{36} = \pm 6$$

Note that the $\sqrt{36}$ produces two solutions. The multiplication of $(+6)(+6) = 36$ and the multiplication of $(-6)(-6) = 36$. To check the correctness of the answer, substitute back in the original equation.

$$2x^2 - 72 = 0$$
$$2(6)(6) - 72 = 0, \qquad 72 - 72 = 0$$
$$2(-6)(-6) - 72 = 0, \qquad 72 - 72 = 0$$

example 21–2 Solve $a^2 - 52 = -36$.

solution: Adding 52 to both sides, we have

$$a^2 = 16$$
$$a = \pm 4$$

To check: $(\pm 4)^2 - 52 = -36$. The answer is correct.

EXERCISE 21–1 Solve the following equations.

1. $a^2 - 64 = 0$ 2. $b^2 = 144$

3. $c^2 - 100 = 69$ 4. $3d^2 = 243$

5. $2e^2 - 392 = 0$ 6. $5f^2 - 70 = 250$

7. $17g^2 + 306 = 578$ 8. $13g^2 + 39 = 507$

21–3 COMPLETE QUADRATICS—SOLUTION BY FACTORING

It was noted previously that if $b = 0$ or $x = 0$, then the product, bx, must be equal to zero. That is, if $b = 0$, then $(0)(x) = 0$, or if $x = 0$, then $(b)(0) = 0$. This principle is used to solve quadratic equations by factoring.

example 21–3   Solve by factoring the complete quadratic equation $2a^2 - 4a = 0$.

solution: It is seen that the equation may be factored as

$2a(a - 2) = 0$

We now have two quantities, $2a$ and $a - 2$. If their product is equal to zero, then either

$2a = 0$ or $a - 2 = 0$

Solving the first equation, $2a = 0$, for a, we have

$a = 0$

Solving the second equation, $a - 2 = 0$, for a, we have

$a = 2$

We now have the two solutions that must satisfy the original equation.

to check: Substituting $a = 2$ into $2a^2 - 4a = 0$,

$2(2)^2 - 4(2) = 0$

$8 - 8 = 0$

Substituting $a = 0$, we have

$2(0)^2 - 4(0) = 0$ or $0 = 0$

The solution is therefore correct.

example 21-4 Solve the equation $(b + 2)(b - 3) = 0$.

solution: Equating each factor to zero and solving for b, we have

$$b + 2 = 0 \qquad b - 3 = 0$$
$$b = -2 \qquad b = 3$$

to check: Substituting $b = -2$ into the original equation, we have

$$(b + 2)(b - 3) = 0$$
$$(-2 + 2)(-2 - 3)$$
$$(0)(-5) = 0 \quad \text{or} \quad 0 = 0$$

Now substituting $b = 3$ into the original equation, we have

$$(3 + 2)(3 - 3) = 0$$
$$(5)(0) = 0 \quad \text{or} \quad 0 = 0$$

The solution is therefore correct.

example 21-5 Solve $c^2 + 6c + 8 = 0$.

solution: When factored,

$$(c + 4)(c + 2) = 0$$

Equating both factors to zero and solving, we have

$$c + 4 = 0 \qquad c + 2 = 0$$
$$c = -4 \qquad c = -2$$

to check: Substituting each value in the original equation,

$$c^2 + 6c + 8 = 0$$

we have, for $c = -4$,

$$(-4)^2 + 6(-4) + 8 = 0 \qquad 16 - 24 + 8 = 0 \qquad 0 = 0$$

For $c = -2$.

$$(-2)^2 + 6(-2) + 8 = 0 \qquad 4 - 12 + 8 = 0 \qquad 0 = 0$$

The solution is correct.

EXERCISE 21-2   Solve the following equations by factoring.

279

Sec. 21–4
SOLUTION BY
COMPLETING THE
SQUARE

1. $a^2 + a = 0$

2. $2b^2 + 2b = 0$

3. $4c^2 + 8c + 12c = 0$

4. $\dfrac{x^2}{2} = -3x$

5. $-3d = -d^2 + 18$

6. $16S^2 - 4S = -20$

7. $(m + 2)(m - 2) = 0$

8. $\dfrac{a^2}{3} = \dfrac{a}{6}$

21–4 SOLUTION BY COMPLETING THE SQUARE

Often the solution of a complete quadratic by factoring is not easily obtained. In such cases, a method called *completing the square* may be used. Although not often used in practice as a method of solving quadratic equations, it is of interest.

In previous chapters we became familiar with perfect trinomial squares. It was seen that the middle term of a perfect trinomial square was equal to twice the product of the square roots of the first and third terms:

$$4a^2 + 16a + 16$$

That is, the middle term is equal to $(2)(\sqrt{4a})(\sqrt{16}) = 16a$. In a similar manner, we may complete the square of the following trinomial by supplying the missing term in

$$b^2 + \underline{\quad\quad} + 4$$

This is found by

$$2(\sqrt{b^2})(\sqrt{4}) = 4b$$

Substituting,

$$b^2 + 4b + 4$$

which is now a perfect trinomial square and factors as $(b + 2)^2$. Similarly, a perfect trinomial square may be formed from a complete quadratic equation that is not readily factored.

example 21-6 Solve the equation $a^2 + 8a - 11 = 0$.

solution: It is seen that this equation is not readily factored. Rewriting the equation, we have

$$a^2 + 8a = 11$$

Using the method above, a perfect trinomial square would exist if the third term were equal to one half the coefficient of the second term, squared, $(\frac{1}{2} \times 8)^2 = 16$. The trinomial square would be written

$$a^2 + 8a + 16$$

This could be obtained in the example by adding 16 to each side of the equation:

$$a^2 + 8a + 16 = 11 + 16 \quad \text{or}$$

$$a^2 + 8a + 16 = 27$$

Factoring, we have

$$(a + 4)^2 = 27$$

Taking the square root of each side produces

$$a + 4 = \pm\sqrt{27}$$

This may be further simplified by factoring the radicand as

$$a + 4 = \pm\sqrt{9 \cdot 3} = \pm 3\sqrt{3} \quad \text{or}$$

$$a = -4 \pm 3\sqrt{3}$$

The value of a may be obtained by solving this equation. The accuracy, however, is dependent upon the value used for $\sqrt{3}$. Normally, the solution is left in the radical form as above.

example 21-7   Solve the equation $4b^2 + 16b - 20 = 0$.

solution: Rearranging, we have

$$4b^2 + 16b = 20$$

Dividing both sides of the equation by 4 produces

$$b^2 + 4b = 5$$

A perfect trinomial square would exist if

$$b^2 + 4b + 4$$

Adding 4 to each side of the equation,

$$b^2 + 4b + 4 = 5 + 4$$

Factoring:

$$(b + 2)^2 = 9 \quad \text{or} \quad b + 2 = \pm\sqrt{9} \quad \text{or} \quad b = -2 \pm 3$$

Then

$$b = 1 \quad \text{or} \quad -5$$

EXERCISE 21–3   Solve by completing the square.

1. $a^2 + 4a = 15$ 2. $b^2 + 8a - 14 = 0$
3. $c^2 + 18c + 52 = 0$ 4. $16d^2 + 24d = 31$

21–5 SOLUTION BY THE QUADRATIC FORMULA

As noted, the general form of the quadratic equation is written

$$ax^2 + bx + c = 0$$

If we solve this equation for x, a formula will result that can be used in the solution of quadratic equations.

The solution of this general form equation involves the method of completing the square. The procedure is as follows:

1. Remove the constant, c, to the right side:

$$ax^2 + bx = -c$$

2. Remove the x^2 coefficient, a, by dividing both sides by a, resulting in

$$x^2 + \frac{b}{a} x = -\frac{c}{a}$$

3. To make the left member a perfect square, the third term is found by dividing the coefficient of the x term by 2, as in $\frac{b}{2a}$, and squaring the result. This produces

$$\left(\frac{b}{2a}\right)^2 = \frac{b^2}{4a^2}$$

This is added to both sides, resulting in

$$x^2 + \frac{b}{a}x + \frac{b^2}{4a^2} = \frac{b^2}{4a^2} - \frac{c}{a}$$

The left member may now be factored as

$$\left(x + \frac{b}{2a}\right)^2 = \frac{b^2}{4a^2} - \frac{c}{a}$$

Adding the terms in the right member produces

$$\left(x + \frac{b}{2a}\right)^2 = \frac{b^2 - 4ac}{4a^2}$$

Taking the square root of both sides,

$$x + \frac{b}{2a} = \pm\frac{\sqrt{b^2 - 4ac}}{2a}$$

Subtracting the term $\frac{b}{2a}$ from both sides produces

$$x = -\frac{b}{2a} \pm \frac{\sqrt{b^2 - 4ac}}{2a}$$

Combining the terms in the right member,

$$x = \frac{-b \pm \sqrt{b^2 - 4ac}}{2a}$$

The result is known as the *quadratic formula*. Its use in solving quadratic equations is shown in the following examples.

---

example 21–8   Using the quadratic formula, solve $x^2 = x + 6$.

---

solution: Arranging the equation in the general form,

$$x^2 - x - 6 = 0$$

where $a = 1$, $b = -1$, and $c = -6$. Substituting in the quadratic formula,

$$x = \frac{-b \pm \sqrt{b^2 - 4ac}}{2a}$$

$$= \frac{-(-1) \pm \sqrt{(-1)^2 - 4 \cdot 1 \cdot (-6)}}{2 \cdot 1}$$

$$= \frac{1 \pm \sqrt{1 + 24}}{2}$$

$$= \frac{1 \pm \sqrt{25}}{2}$$

$$= \frac{1 + 5}{2} = 3 \quad \text{or} \quad x = \frac{1 - 5}{2} = -2$$

to check: Substituting in the original equation, we have

$x = 3$: $x^2 = x + 6,$ $(3)^2 = 3 + 6,$ $9 = 9$

$x = -2$: $x^2 = x + 6,$ $(-2)^2 = -2 + 6,$ $4 = 4$

The solution is therefore correct.

example 21–9   Solve $x^2 + 2x - 8 = 0$, using the quadratic formula.

solution: In this equation, $a = 1$, $b = 2$, and $c = -8$. Substituting,

$$x = \frac{-2 \pm \sqrt{(2)^2 - 4(1)(-8)}}{2(1)}$$

$$= \frac{-2 \pm \sqrt{4 + 32}}{2} = \frac{-2 \pm \sqrt{36}}{2}$$

$$= \frac{-2 \pm 6}{2}$$

$$= \frac{-2 + 6}{2} = \frac{4}{2} = 2 \quad \text{or}$$

$$= \frac{-2 - 6}{2} = \frac{-8}{2} = -4$$

Check using the regular method.

EXERCISE   21–4   Solve, using the quadratic formula.

1. $x^2 + 4x - 12 = 0$ 2. $x^2 - 2x - 3 = 0$

3. $6x^2 = -9x - 3$ 4. $x^2 + x + 1 = 0$

5. $6x^2 + 36x + 48 = 0$ 6. $\dfrac{x^2}{2} = -x - 4$

7. $\dfrac{3x^2}{2} + 4x + 1 = 0$ 8. $\dfrac{x^2}{4} + \dfrac{3x}{2} - \dfrac{16}{8} = 0$

In Chapter 17, linear equations in the form $y = mx + b$ were plotted. The determination of the x and y intercepts and the slope of the curve were demonstrated. For example, in Figure 17–11 the graph of the equation $y = 2x + 4$ was plotted. The point where the curve crossed the x axis was obtained when $y = 0$. The point where the curve crossed the y axis was obtained when $x = 0$.

In a similar manner, the graph of the quadratic equation may be plotted. In the algebraic solution, the quadratic equation was equated to zero. In other words, we solved the equation of the quadratic written in the standard form of

$$y = ax^2 + bx + c$$

for only one condition, that is, for $y = 0$.

If we were to assign arbitrary values to x, the independent variable, we would be able to obtain values for y, the dependent variable. These points when plotted result in the graph of the quadratic equation. This is shown in the following example.

example 21-10 Plot the graph of the quadratic equation, $y = x^2 + 6x + 8$

solution: For arbitrarily selected values of x, the values of y are calculated as follows:

x	−8	−7	−6	−5	−4	−3	−2	−1	0	1	2
y	24	15	8	3	0	−1	0	3	8	15	24

Plotting these values and drawing the curve, we have Figure 21–1. This is the characteristic curve of the quadratic equation. It is called a *parabola*. Several features of this curve should be noted.

1. This quadratic equation was solved algebraically in Example 21–7. The roots of the equation were found to be −2 and −4. Note that these are the two points where the curve crosses the x axis, that is, when $y = 0$.

2. The curve has a minimum value. This point is called the *turning point*. This curve is seen to be symmetrical about the turning point. The line shown in Figure 21–2, which divides the curve into two mirror-image sections, is called the *axis of symmetry*. The quadratic equation in the standard form has values

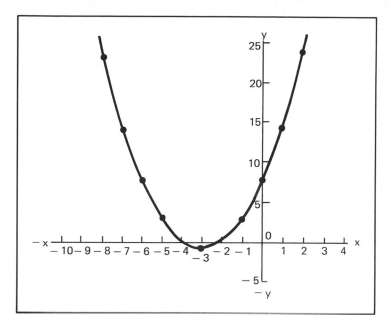

FIGURE 21–1
Graph of $y = x^2 + 6x + 8$

of $a = 1$, $b = 6$, and $c = 8$. The value of x, where the minimum or turning point occurs, is found to be at a value of

$$x = -\frac{b}{2a}$$

For this equation this is found as

$$x = -\frac{6}{2 \cdot 1} = \frac{-6}{2} = -3$$

The axis of symmetry then occurs at a value of $x = -3$. This corresponds to the graph. If this value of x were substituted into the original equation, the y value of the minimum or turning point could be determined. This is found as

$$y = x^2 + 6x + 8$$
$$= (-3)^2 + (6)(-3) + 8$$
$$= 9 - 18 + 8$$
$$= -1$$

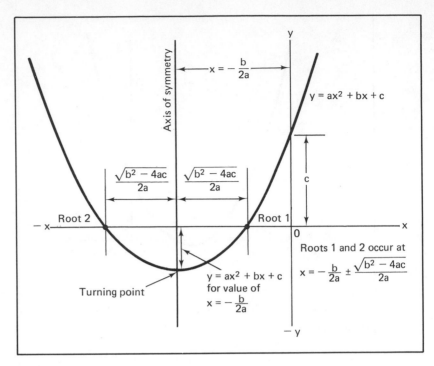

FIGURE 21–2
Characteristics of Graph of Quadratic Equation

Observe that this corresponds to the y value of the turning point on the graph.

3. The quadratic formula as developed in Section 21–5 may be written

$$x = \frac{-b}{2a} \pm \frac{\sqrt{b^2 - 4ac}}{2a}$$

It was seen that the x value of the turning point was $\frac{-b}{2a}$. The roots of the equation, where the curve crosses the x axis, are seen to be displaced from the turning point by the amount represented by

$$\pm \frac{\sqrt{b^2 - 4ac}}{2a}$$

If we calculate this value, it is found to be

$$\pm \frac{\sqrt{(6)^2 - (4)(1)(8)}}{(2)(1)}$$

$$\pm \frac{\sqrt{36 - 32}}{2}$$

$$\pm \frac{\sqrt{4}}{2}$$

$$\pm 1$$

287
Sec. 21-7
CURVES OF
QUADRATIC
EQUATIONS IN
THE FORM
$y = ax^2$

Examination of the curve shows that the curve crosses the x axis at -4 and -2. This is a displacement of ± 1 from the x value of the turning point, or the axis of symmetry, which is -3.

4. Another interesting point to observe is that the y-axis intercept occurs at the value of $c = 8$. It is seen that this occurs at $x = 0$. If this value of $x = 0$ were substituted in the original equation, the y intercept would be found as

$$y = x^2 + 6x + 8$$

$$= (0)^2 + (6)(0) + 8$$

$$= 8$$

These points are shown in Figure 21-2.

In the following sections, a variety of curves of the quadratic equation will be plotted. The effect of the values of the constants, a, b, and c, on the shape of the curves will be examined.

21-7 CURVES OF QUADRATIC EQUATIONS IN THE FORM $y = ax^2$

A number of curves of the quadratic equation in the form $y = ax^2$ are plotted in Figure 21-3 for various values of a. As before, values of y are obtained for arbitrarily assumed values of x.

There are a number of interesting observations that may be made examining these curves.

1. The curve for $a = 1$, often called the *standard parabola,* is rather shallow compared to the curves for the larger values of a, which are narrower curves with steeper sides.

2. The curves with positive values of a have their openings upward. The curves with negative values of a have their openings downward.

3. All curves are symmetrical about the y axis and intercept the a axis at only one point, where $y = 0$, $x = 0$.

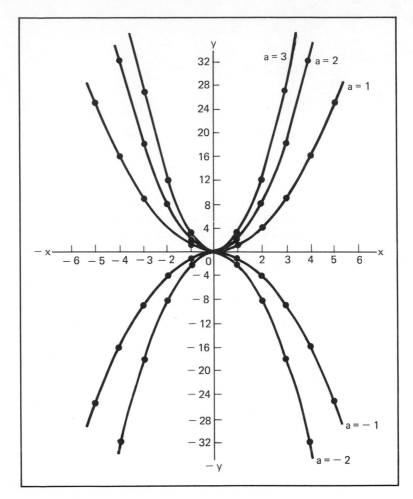

FIGURE 21–3
Graph of Quadratic Equation in the Form $y = ax^2$

21–8 CURVES OF QUADRATIC EQUATIONS
IN THE FORM $y = x^2 + bx$

In this section, we shall examine the effect of the coefficient, b, on the shape of the curves of the quadratic equation in the form $y = x^2 + bx$. As before, values of y are obtained for arbitrarily assumed values of x. The resultant curves are shown in Figure 21–4.

Examination of the curves of Figure 21–4 shows the following regarding the effect of the coefficient, b:

1. When $b = 0$, the term $bx = 0$, and the equation takes the form $y = x^2$, resulting in a standard parabola.

289
Sec. 21–8
CURVES OF
QUADRATIC
EQUATIONS IN
THE FORM
$y = x^2 + bx$

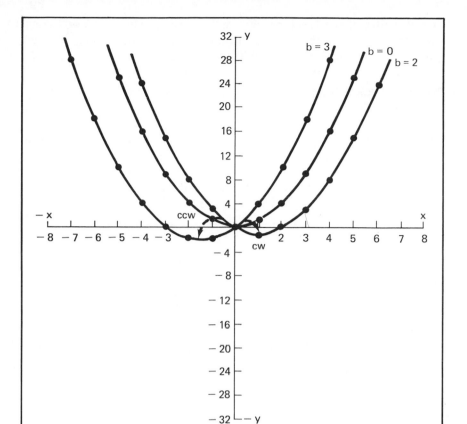

FIGURE 21–4
Graph of Quadratic Equation in the Form $y = x^2 + bx$

2. A positive value of b results in a counterclockwise (CCW) shift of the minimum or turning point of the curve.

3. A negative value of b results in a clockwise (CW) shift of the minimum or turning point of the curve.

4. The shifts that occur in the turning point result in curves that are symmetrical about a line parallel to the y axis.

5. The absolute value of b determines the amount of the CW or CCW shift that occurs.

These curves are plotted for a value of $a = 1$ for the equation in the form $y = ax^2 + bx$ or $y = x^2 + bx$. If negative values of a were used, the resultant parabolas would have their openings downward, as shown in Figure 21–3. For such curves, positive values of b will result in

CCW shifts of the turning point, and negative values of b will result in CW shifts. As before, the absolute value of the value of b will determine the amount of the shift that occurs.

21–9 CURVES OF QUADRATIC EQUATIONS
IN THE FORM $y = x^2 + c$

This section will examine the effect of the value of c on the shape of curves of the quadratic equation in the form $y = x^2 + c$. Such curves are shown in Figure 21–5. Note that when $c = 0$, we have $y = x^2$, which results in the curve for the standard parabola.

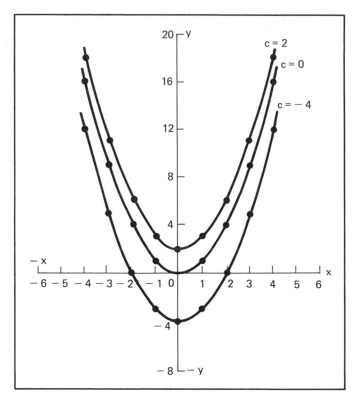

FIGURE 21–5
Graph of Quadratic Equation in the Form $y = x^2 + c$

Examination of the curves of Figure 21–5 shows the following regarding the effect of the constant, c.

1. A positive value of c results in an upward shift of the curve.
2. A negative value of c results in a downward shift of the curve.

3. The absolute value of c determines the amount of the shift that occurs. This, in effect, determines where the y intercept occurs.

The curves plotted in previous sections were observed to have maximum and minimum values. In Figure 21-2, the minimum value was seen to occur at the axis of symmetry whose position was $x - \dfrac{-b}{2a}$ from the y axis. Substitution of this value of x into a quadratic equation in the general form yielded the y value of the minimum point. In a similar manner, the determination of the maximum point for a downward-opening curve could be determined.

A practical application of these principles involves the determination of the maximum power transfer in electronics circuits. This is demonstrated in the following example.

example 21-11 Determine the value of load resistor R in Figure 21-6 that will result in a maximum transfer of power to the load.

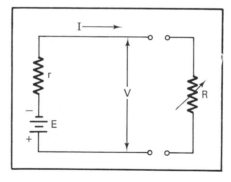

FIGURE   21-6
Circuit for Example 21-11

solution: The voltage source V is obtained from a battery whose voltage is E and whose internal resistance is r. When the load is connected to the source, the circuit current is

$$I = \frac{E}{r + R} \tag{1}$$

The voltage delivered to the load is

$$V = E - Ir \tag{2}$$

The power delivered to the load is

$$P = VI \tag{3}$$

As the load resistance R is changed, the current will also change, which results in a change in the voltage, V. This is because of the change in the voltage drop that occurs in the internal resistance of the source. The power delivered to the load is thus seen to be a function of both the voltage V and the current I. We may substitute Equation (2) into (3), which produces

$$P = (E - Ir)I \quad \text{or}$$
$$= EI - I^2 r$$

This may be rearranged in the general form of the quadratic equation as

$$P = -rI^2 + EI \tag{4}$$

where the value of $a = -r$ and $b = E$. The maximum power delivered would occur when

$$I = \frac{-b}{2a}$$

Substituting the values for a and b, we have

$$I = \frac{-E}{2(-r)} \quad \text{or}$$
$$= \frac{E}{2r}$$

This value may be substituted into (1), which produces

$$\frac{E}{2r} = \frac{E}{r + R}$$

which if solved for R gives

$$\frac{r + R}{2r} = \frac{E}{E}$$
$$\frac{R}{r} = 1$$
$$R = r$$

This means that the maximum transfer of power occurs when the load resistance, R, is equal to the internal resistance of the source. This is a procedure that is extremely important in electronics. In many instances, a circuit designer will use great care in matching the load to the source in order to obtain this maximum power transfer.

21-11   DISCRIMINANTS

Examination of the curves plotted in Figures 21-4 and 21-5 shows that the curves of the quadratic equations may

1. Not touch the x axis.
2. Touch the x axis at one point.
3. Intercept the x axis at two points.

The quadratic formula provides a means of quickly establishing which of these three conditions exist for a particular equation. The quadratic formula shows the roots of the equation as

$$x_1 = \frac{-b}{2a} + \frac{\sqrt{b^2 - 4ac}}{2a}$$

$$x_2 = \frac{-b}{2a} - \frac{\sqrt{b^2 - 4ac}}{2a}$$

The quantity $b^2 - 4ac$ under the radical is referred to as the *discriminant*. The significance of the quantity $\frac{\sqrt{b^2 - 4ac}}{2a}$ is seen when Figure 21-2 is examined. In this figure this quantity respresents the displacement of the equation roots from the axis of symmetry. For this to occur, the value of $b^2 - 4ac$ must be positive and greater than zero; $b^2 - 4ac > 0$.

If the discriminant is equal to zero, that is, $b^2 - 4ac = 0$, then the equation reduces to

$$x_1 = x_2 = \frac{-b}{2a}$$

The quadratic equation under such conditions is a perfect square. We have no distance between the axis of symmetry and the roots in Figure 21-2, that is, $\frac{\sqrt{b^2 - 4ac}}{2a} = 0$. This means that the curve does not cross the x axis but touches it at only one point.

If the discriminant is negative, that is, $b^2 - 4ac < 0$, we are faced with taking the square root of a negative number. On this basis, we know that there is *no real solution*, and our answers are *imaginary*. Graphically, this is represented by a curve that does not touch the x axis, such as the surve for $c = 2$ in Figure 21-5. In our original algebraic solutions of quadratic equations, we let $y = 0$. In this curve, y never reaches zero. The discriminant indicates that this is a curve that does not touch the x axis and the equation is one whose roots are imaginary.

There is one other condition that should be examined: the case where $b^2 - 4ac > 0$ but is not a perfect square. Under such circumstances, while a solution to the equation is obtained, the answer is *irrational*. The curve could not be depicted graphically because of the irrational nature of the quantities involved. So what we are saying is that while the equation yields a solution, the answer is an irrational one that is physically meaningless or impractical.

EXERCISE 21-5

Determine the discriminant in the following equations. What information does the discriminant provide?

1. $x^2 - 4x + 16 = 0$
2. $4x^2 - 20x + 35 = 0$
3. $x^2 - 6x + 8 = 0$
4. $16x^2 - 40x + 35 = 0$

22
NETWORK
ANALYSIS

Until now we have dealt with relatively simple electrical circuits. With more complex circuits, their analysis and solution become more difficult. There are, however, several circuit theorems and procedures that simplify our work with these more difficult circuits. This chapter will develop these theorems and their application in the simplification of complex circuits.

22-1 KIRCHHOFF'S FIRST LAW

In our work with electrical circuits, it was found that most circuits could be simplified and evaluation performed with relative ease. For example, a series–parallel circuit combination of resistors, consisting of one resistor in series with two resistors in parallel, could be easily simplified. This process consisted of obtaining the equivalent resistance of the parallel branch, which is then added to the series resistor. The result is a single resistance and an equivalent circuit that is easily analyzed.

As circuits become more complex, the processes of circuit simplification becomes more difficult and more time consuming. In certain instances a circuit cannot be simplified using usual methods. As noted, several laws and theorems have been developed in order that these more complex circuits may be simplified and as a result be more easily evaluated. The first of these laws we shall examine is Kirchhoff's first law.

Laboratory experimentation of circuit voltages and currents by a German physicist, Gustav R. Kirchhoff, led to the development of these laws in 1847. Kirchhoff's first law, often called *Kirchhoff's current law*, is stated as:

> THE ALGEBRAIC SUM OF CURRENTS ENTERING AND LEAVING ANY POINT IN A CIRCUIT IS ZERO.

This means that the sum of the currents entering a point in a circuit is equal to the sum of the currents leaving that point. This is really the same principle that we used in our solution of parallel circuits. For example, in the following circuit, we show the current division as in Figure 22–1. The current entering ① is 7 A, while the current leaving 1 is 5 A and 2 A. The current entering ② is 2 A and 5 A, while the current leaving ② is 7 A. In terms of Kirchhoff's law, at ①,

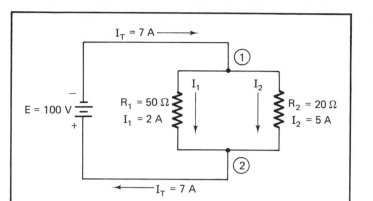

FIGURE 22–1
Current Division in a Parallel Circuit

$$I_T - I_1 - I_2 = 0 \qquad \text{or} \qquad I_T = I_1 + I_2$$
$$7\text{ A} = 2\text{ A} - 5\text{ A} = 0, \qquad 7\text{ A} = 2\text{A} + 5\text{ A}$$
$$7\text{ A} - 7\text{ A} = 0, \qquad 7\text{ A} = 7\text{ A}$$

22–2 KIRCHHOFF'S SECOND LAW

Kirchhoff's second law is often called Kirchhoff's voltage law:

> THE ALGEBRAIC SUM OF THE EMFS AND THE VOLTAGE DROPS IN A CIRCUIT IS ZERO.

Stated differently, this means that the algebraic sum of the emfs and the voltage drops in a circuit are equal.

This is the same principle that we used earlier in our solution of series circuits. For example, in the following circuit we show the voltage distribution as in Figure 22–2. The voltage drops are seen to be $V_1 = 20$ V, $V_2 = 40$ V, and $V_3 = 60$ V, while the single emf source is 120 V. Written in terms of Kirchhoff's law,

$$E - IR_1 - IR_2 - IR_3 = 0 \qquad \text{or} \qquad E = IR_1 + IR_2 + IR_3$$
$$E - V_1 - V_2 - V_3 = 0, \qquad E = V_1 + V_2 + V_3$$
$$120\text{ V} - 20\text{ V} - 40\text{ V} - 60\text{ V} = 0, \qquad 120\text{ V} = 20\text{ V} + 40\text{ V} + 60\text{ V}$$
$$120\text{ V} - 120\text{ V} = 0, \qquad 120\text{ V} = 120\text{ V}$$

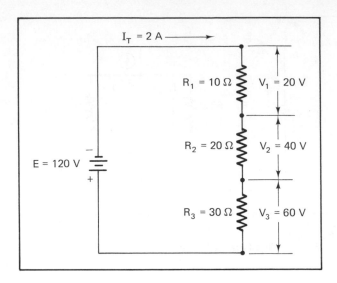

FIGURE 22–2
Voltage Distribution in a Series Circuit

Both of these laws are seen to be nothing more than a statement of the procedures and principles developed in our earlier circuit work. When appropriately applied, however, these laws will permit complex circuits to be handled with relative ease.

22–3 CONVENTIONS AND METHODS

Through the use of Kirchhoff's laws it is possible to write circuit equations that will permit us to evaluate complex circuits. In order to develop a systematic procedure for writing these equations, a number of conventions and methods have been developed.

In our previous discussions we have established that in this text, unless otherwise indicated, we shall consider electron flow and current flow to be synonomous. That is, current will flow from a negative to a positive potential.

Current flow through any passive device such as a resistor will be considered to move in a negative to a positive direction. As we know, this current causes a voltage *drop* across the resistor. In writing Kirchhoff's law relationships, such voltage drops will be written as a negative voltage.

A circuit current is supplied by an emf source. Current flow is considered to leave from the negative terminal of the source and return to the positive terminal. Such a source of emf is written as a positive voltage.

A series circuit containing an emf source and two resistors is used to demonstrate the application of Kirchhoff's laws. This circuit is shown in Figure 22–3. If we start at point ①, the first step is to draw

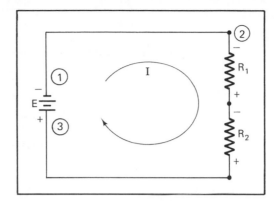

FIGURE 22–3
Circuit Showing Polarities and Current Loop

the current loop indicating the direction of current flow. The next step is to write the voltages around the current loop designating the proper emf polarities. This is done in the following manner:

1. At point ② resistor R_1 is encountered. Current flow through R_1 causes a voltage drop which is considered negative. This is written $-V_{R_1}$.
2. The current entering R_2 flows from a point of negative polarity to one of positive polarity. As such, the voltage drop through R_2 is also considered negative and written $-V_{R_2}$.
3. At point ③, the battery is encountered. Here the current flow is from a positive to a negative polarity, which is considered a voltage rise and is designated as positive. It is written as $+E$.
4. Then writing the voltages around the current loop from ① to ①, we have

$$-V_{R_1} - V_{R_2} + E = 0$$

22–4 APPLICATIONS USING KIRCHHOFF'S LAW

One application of Kirchhoff's laws is shown in Example 22–1. In this example two voltage sources with internal resistances are used.

example 22–1 Determine the current flow in the circuit shown in Figure 22–4.

solution: Starting at point ①, the current loop is first drawn. In some circuits the direction of current would have to be assumed. In such a case, if the answer is preceded by a negative sign, the incorrect direction was assumed. The

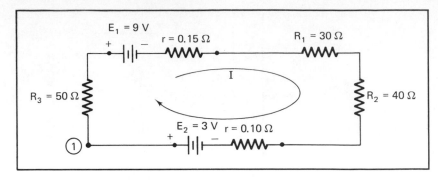

FIGURE 22-4
Circuit for Example 22-1

absolute value obtained is the correct answer, with the negative sign indicating only a direction of current flow opposite to that chosen.

Starting at point ① and writing the voltages around the current loop, we have

$$-V_{R_3} + E_1 - V_{r_1} - V_{R_1} - V_{R_2} - V_{r_2} - E_2 = 0$$

$$-50I + 9 - 0.15I - 30I - 40I - 0.10I - 3 = 0$$

Note that the polarity of E_2 is such as to oppose the direction of current flow. This voltage is designated as negative and is considered a voltage drop.

Combining, we have

$$-120.25I + 6 = 0$$

Then

$$I = 49.9 \text{ mA}$$

If we had assumed the opposite current direction, starting at point ①, we would write

$$3 - 0.10I - 40I - 30I - 0.15I - 9 - 50I = 0$$

$$-120.25I - 6 = 0$$

$$I = -49.9 \text{ mA}$$

The negative sign, as noted, indicates that this assumed current direction was incorrect.

The preceding example involved only Kirchhoff's voltage law. The following examples will require a combination of Kirchhoff's voltage and current laws.

example 22-2 Determine the source voltage in the circuit of Figure 22–5.

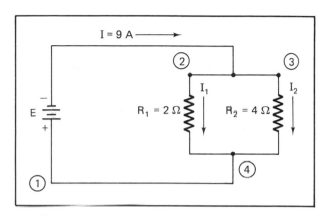

FIGURE 22–5
Circuit for Example 22–2

solution: Writing Kirchhoff's voltage equations, we have

loop ①, ②, ④, ①: $E - I_1 R_1 = 0$ and as $R_1 = 2\,\Omega$

$$E - 2I_1 = 0$$

$$I_1 = \frac{E}{2} \tag{1}$$

loop ①, ③, ④, ①: $E - I_2 R_2 = 0$ and as $R_2 = 4\,\Omega$

$$E - 4I_2 = 0$$

$$I_2 = \frac{E}{4} \tag{2}$$

Writing Kirchhoff's current equation we have

$$I - I_1 - I_2 = 0 \tag{3}$$

Equations (1) and (2) may be substituted in (3) and, knowing I, we may write

$$9 - \frac{E}{2} - \frac{E}{4} = 0 \quad \text{or}$$

$$-\frac{E}{2} - \frac{E}{4} = -9 \quad \text{and}$$

$$-\frac{2E}{4} - \frac{E}{4} = -9$$

$$-\frac{3E}{4} = -9$$

$$-3E = -36$$

$$E = 12 \text{ V}$$

Then, substituting in (1) and (2) we have

$$I_1 = \frac{E}{2} = \frac{12}{2} = 6 \text{ A}$$

$$I_2 = \frac{E}{4} = \frac{12}{4} = 3 \text{ A}$$

example 22–3 Determine the current flow through R_1, R_2, and R_3 in Figure 22–6.

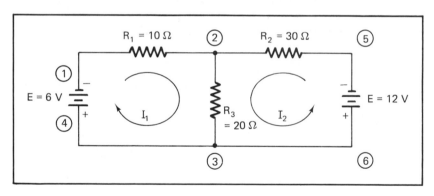

FIGURE 22–6
Circuit for Example 22–3

solution:

The current loops are drawn first. These are shown in Figure 22–6. Note that I_1 and I_2 both flow through R_3. Writing the voltage loop equations, we have:

loop ①, ②, ③, ④, ①:

$$-10I_1 - 20I_1 - 20I_2 + 6 = 0 \tag{1}$$

loop ⑤, ②, ③, ⑥, ⑤:

$$-30I_2 - 20I_2 - 20I_1 + 12 = 0 \qquad (2)$$

Combining terms and rearranging

$$-30I_1 - 20I_2 = -6 \qquad (3)$$

$$-20I_1 - 50I_2 = -12 \qquad (4)$$

Solving (3) and (4) simultaneously produces

$$I_1 = 0.054 \text{ A} = 54 \text{ mA}$$

$$I_2 = 0.219 \text{ A} = 219 \text{ mA}$$

and the current flow through R_3 is

$$I_{R_3} = I_1 + I_2 = 54 + 219 = 273 \text{ mA}$$

example 22-4 Determine the circuit currents in the circuit of Example 22–3 if the 12-V battery were replaced with a 24-V battery with the same polarity.

solution: Writing the loop equations for

loop ①, ②, ③, ④, ①:

$$-10I_1 - 20I_1 - 20I_2 + 6 = 0 \qquad (1)$$

loop ⑤, ②, ③, ⑥, ⑤:

$$-30I_2 - 20I_2 - 20I_1 + 24 = 0 \qquad (2)$$

Combining terms and rearranging,

$$-30I_1 - 20I_2 = -6 \qquad (3)$$

$$-20I_1 - 50I_2 = -24 \qquad (4)$$

Solving (3) and (4) simultaneously,

$$I_2 = 0.545 \text{ A}$$

$$I_1 = -0.163 \text{ A}$$

$$I_{R_3} = I_1 + I_2 = (-0.163) + (0.545) = 0.382 \text{ A}$$

Check answers by substitution in original equations.

The negative value of I_1, as noted previously, indicates that the direction chosen for the current in the I_1 loop was incorrect. The magnitude of I_1 calculated is correct, the sign indicates only that we assumed an incorrect direction of the current flow. This example was chosen to point out that arbitrary selection of the direction of the current loops may be made. The answer obtained will be correct regardless of the current direction chosen. A negative answer only establishes that the current direction is opposite to that chosen.

example 22–5 Determine the current flow through the 20-Ω resistor in Figure 22–7. The batteries have the internal resistance shown.

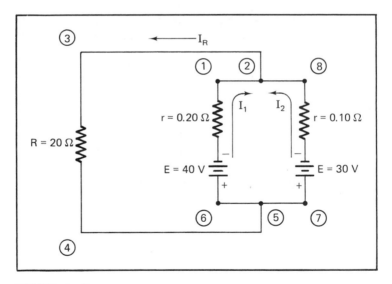

FIGURE 22–7
Circuit for Example 22–5

solution: The direction of current flow is first assumed and labeled as shown. The loop equations are then written. Note that the current flow through R is $I_R = I_1 + I_2$:

loop ①, ②, ③, ④, ⑤, ⑥, ①:

$$-20(I_1 + I_2) + 40 - 0.20I_1 = 0 \quad \text{or} \qquad (1)$$

$$-20.20I_1 - 20I_2 = -40 \qquad (2)$$

loop ⑧, ②, ③, ④, ⑤, ⑦, ⑧:

$$-20(I_1 + I_2) + 30 - 0.10I_2 = 0 \quad \text{or} \qquad (3)$$

$$-20I_1 - 20.10I_2 = -30 \qquad (4)$$

Solving (2) and (4) simultaneously produces

$$I_1 = 34 \text{ A}, \qquad I_2 = -32.34 \text{ A}$$

$$I_R = I_1 + I_2$$

$$= 1.66 \text{ A}$$

Note that the arbitrary assumed direction of the current flow in the I_2 loop was incorrect, as indicated by the negative sign. Check answers by substituting answers in original equations.

EXERCISE 22-1 Using Kirchhoff's laws, solve the following:

1. Three resistors of 5 Ω, 6 Ω, and 10 Ω are connected in series across a power supply of 9 V with negligible internal resistance. Determine the current flow.

2. In the circuit shown in Figure 22-8, determine the current flow.

FIGURE 22-8
Circuit for Problem 2

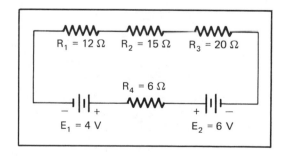

3. In the circuit shown in Figure 22–9, determine the value of I.

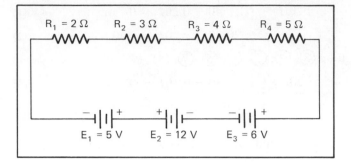

FIGURE 22–9
Circuit for Problem 3

4. In Figure 22–10, determine the current flow.

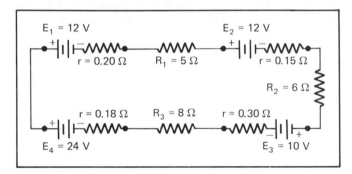

FIGURE 22–10
Circuit for Problem 4

5. Determine the current flow through the 30 Ω resistor in the circuit shown in Figure 22–11.

FIGURE 22–11
Circuit for Problem 5

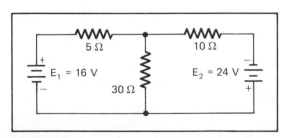

6. Determine the current flow through resistor R in the circuit shown in Figure 22–12.

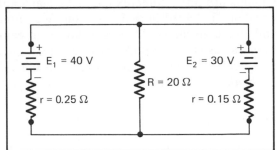

FIGURE 22–12
Circuit for Problem 6

7. Determine the current flow through resistor R_1, R_2 shown in Figure 22–13.

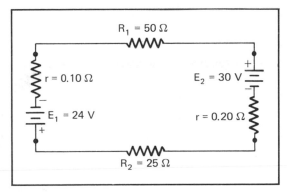

FIGURE 22–13
Circuit for Problem 7

8. Determine the current flow through resistor R shown in Figure 22–14.

FIGURE 22–14
Circuit for Problem 8

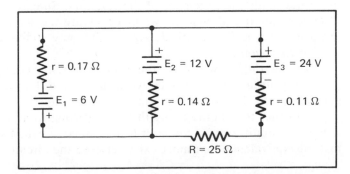

Circuits are often complex and have many unknowns, requiring many equations involved in their solution. Such procedures become tedious and time consuming. There are, however, equivalent circuits that may often be used to simplify these complex circuits and permit a much easier solution. One such equivalent is the *delta* (Δ) or π and the Y or T *circuits*. These circuit arrangements are shown in Figure 22–15.

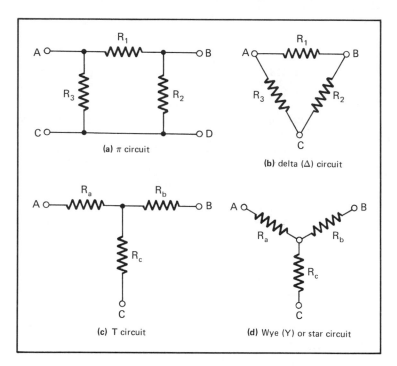

FIGURE   22–15
Common Transformation Circuits

Examination of circuits (a) and (b) of Figure 22–15 shows that these are the same circuit. They are electrically identical. The only difference is the arrangement of the resistors. Similarly, examination of circuits (c) and (d) also shows that they are the same circuit. They are also electrically identical. Again, the only difference is in the resistor arrangement.

In electrical power work the Δ and Y resistor configurations are commonly used. In electronics work, the π and T arrangements are generally used. In either case, the electrical analysis is the same.

In order to simplify a circuit by converting from a π to a T or a Δ to a Y circuit, or vice versa, it is necessary to establish the mathematical equivalence that must exist between the circuits. We must be able to replace a π circuit with a T circuit, or vice versa, without altering the electrical effect on the circuit. In other words, the resistance between any two terminals in the π circuit must be identical with the same two terminals in the T circuit.

Examination of Figure 22–15a shows that the resistance between terminals A and B is made up of R_1 in parallel with $R_2 + R_3$ or

$$R_{AB} = \frac{R_1(R_2 + R_3)}{R_1 + R_2 + R_3}$$

Examination of Figure 22–15c shows that the resistance between terminals A and B is made up of R_a and R_b in series, or

$$R_{AB} = R_a + R_b$$

Inasmuch as the resistance between these two points must be equivalent, we may write

$$R_a + R_b = \frac{R_1(R_2 + R_3)}{R_1 + R_2 + R_3} = \frac{R_1 R_2 + R_1 R_3}{R_1 + R_2 + R_3}$$

In the same manner the relationships between the other two pairs of terminals may be developed. As the configurations are similar to that between terminals A and B, we find that

$$R_b + R_c = \frac{R_1 R_2 + R_2 R_3}{R_1 + R_2 + R_3}$$

$$R_a + R_c = \frac{R_1 R_3 + R_2 R_3}{R_1 + R_2 + R_3}$$

We now have three equations, which may be solved simultaneously for R_a, R_b, and R_c. This produces

$$R_a = \frac{R_1 R_3}{R_1 + R_2 + R_3}$$

$$R_b = \frac{R_1 R_2}{R_1 + R_2 + R_3}$$

$$R_c = \frac{R_2 R_3}{R_1 + R_2 + R_3}$$

In a similar manner, the relationship between T and π circuits may be developed. This will permit us to simplify a circuit by converting a T configuration to its equivalent π circuit. The mathematical relations that exist for this conversion are found to be

$$R_1 = \frac{R_a R_b + R_b R_c + R_a R_c}{R_c}$$

$$R_2 = \frac{R_a R_b + R_b R_c + R_a R_c}{R_a}$$

$$R_3 = \frac{R_a R_b + R_b R_c + R_a R_c}{R_b}$$

The use of these equivalents to simplify a circuit is shown in the following examples.

example 22–6 Convert the π circuit of Figure 22–16a to its equivalent T circuit and convert the T circuit of Figure 22–16b to its equivalent π circuit.

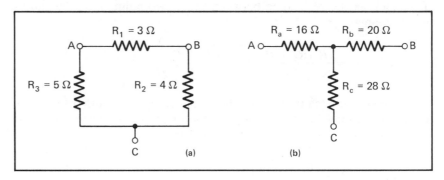

FIGURE 22–16
Circuits for Example 22–6

solution: Converting the π circuit of (a) to its T-circuit equivalent, we calculate

$$R_a = \frac{R_1 R_3}{R_1 + R_2 + R_3} = \frac{(3)(5)}{3 + 4 + 5} = \frac{15}{12} = 1.25 \ \Omega$$

$$R_b = \frac{R_1 R_2}{R_1 + R_2 + R_3} = \frac{(3)(4)}{3 + 4 + 5} = \frac{12}{12} = 1.0 \ \Omega$$

$$R_c = \frac{R_2 R_3}{R_1 + R_2 + R_3} = \frac{(4)(5)}{3 + 4 + 5} = \frac{20}{12} = 1.66 \ \Omega$$

Converting the T circuit of (b) to its π-circuit equivalent, we calculate

$$R_1 = \frac{R_a R_b + R_b R_c + R_a R_c}{R_c}$$

$$= \frac{(16)(20) + (20)(28) + (16)(28)}{28} = \frac{1,328}{28} = 47.43 \ \Omega$$

$$R_2 = \frac{R_a R_b + R_b R_c + R_a R_c}{R_a}$$

$$= \frac{(16)(20) + (20)(28) + (16)(28)}{16} = \frac{1,328}{16} = 83 \ \Omega$$

$$R_3 = \frac{R_a R_b + R_b R_c + R_a R_c}{R_b}$$

$$= \frac{(16)(20) + (20)(28) + (16)(28)}{20} = \frac{1,328}{20} = 66.4 \ \Omega$$

example 22–7 Using the π–T conversion, determine the total circuit resistance between points ① and ② in Figure 22–17.

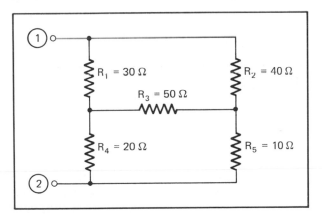

FIGURE 22–17
Circuit for Example 22–7

solution: Examination of Figure 22–17 shows a π circuit composed of the 50-Ω, 20-Ω, and 10-Ω resistances, which may be converted to T circuit to simplify the solution. In Figure 22–18, for convenience the circuit is relabeled so that the π segment is labeled in the same manner that was used in setting up our mathematical relationships. Within the π configuration, the placement of the T circuit that will replace it is shown. The values obtained for the equivalent T circuit are calculated as

$$R_a = \frac{R_1 R_3}{R_1 + R_2 + R_3} = \frac{(50)(20)}{50 + 10 + 20} = \frac{1,000}{80} = 12.5 \ \Omega$$

$$R_b = \frac{R_1 R_2}{R_1 + R_2 + R_3} = \frac{(50)(10)}{50 + 10 + 20} = \frac{500}{80} = 6.25 \ \Omega$$

$$R_c = \frac{R_2 R_3}{R_1 + R_2 + R_3} = \frac{(10)(20)}{50 + 10 + 20} = \frac{200}{80} = 2.5 \ \Omega$$

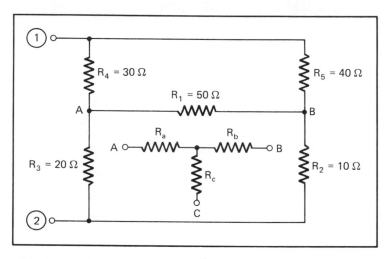

FIGURE 22–18
Circuit of Example 22–7 Showing π-to-T Replacement

The replacement of the π circuit and subsequent circuit simplifications are shown in Figure 22–19. Part (a) shows the π portion of the original circuit replaced with its equivalent T circuit. Part (b) shows a rearrangement of (a) for simplicity. In (c) the total resistance of each parallel branch is shown. In (d) the equivalent resistance of the parallel branches is shown. In (e) the total circuit resistance is shown.

EXERCISE 22–2

1. Convert the π circuit of Figure 22–20a to its equivalent T circuit if $R_1 = 20 \ \Omega$, $R_2 = 30 \ \Omega$, and $R_3 = 40 \ \Omega$.

2. If the π circuit of Figure 22–20a has values of $R_1 = 36 \ \Omega$, $R_2 = 72 \ \Omega$, and $R_3 = 156 \ \Omega$, determine the T equivalent.

3. Convert the T circuit of Figure 22–20b to its equivalent π circuit if $R_a = 25 \ \Omega$, $R_b = 16 \ \Omega$, and $R_c = 25 \ \Omega$.

4. If the T circuit of Figure 22–20b has values of $R_a = 58 \ \Omega$, $R_b = 76 \ \Omega$, and $R_c = 66 \ \Omega$, determine the equivalent π circuit.

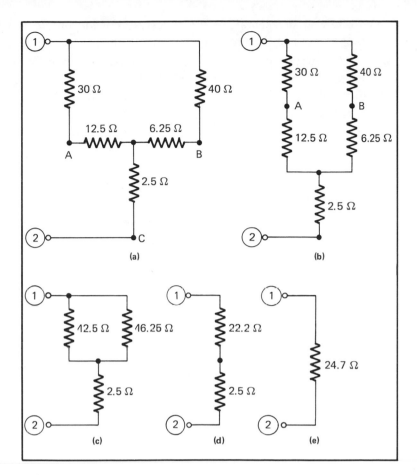

FIGURE   22–19
Circuit Simplification, Example 22–7

FIGURE   20–20
Circuits for Problems 1–4

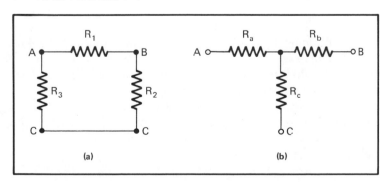

In the following problems use the necessary conversions to simplify the circuit and obtain the required answer.

5. In the circuit of Figure 22–21, determine the total circuit resistance if $R_1 = 50\ \Omega$, $R_2 = 60\ \Omega$, $R_3 = 80\ \Omega$, $R_4 = 40\ \Omega$, and $R_5 = 100\ \Omega$.

6. If 100 V was applied to terminals ① and ② of the circuit of Figure 22–21, what would be the line current in the circuit of problem 5?

7. In the circuit of Figure 22–21, if $R_1 = 160\ \Omega$, $R_2 = 120\ \Omega$, $R_3 = 100\ \Omega$, $R_4 = 200\ \Omega$, and $R_5 = 400\ \Omega$, what is the resistance between terminals ① and ②?

8. If 100 V was applied to terminals ① and ② of problem 7, what would be the current flow through R_4 and R_5?

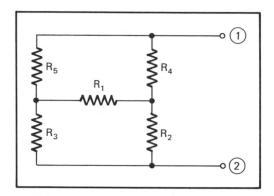

FIGURE 22–21
Circuit for Problems 5–8

22–6 THE SUPERPOSITION THEOREM

In Section 22–3, we saw how Kirchhoff's laws were applied to circuits containing two voltage sources. Example 22–3 involved such a circuit, which is shown again in Figure 22–22. The problem required the current flow through each resistor to be determined. The solution involved simultaneous equations.

In circuits containing more than one voltage source, as in Figure 22–22, a simpler method of solution may be used. This solution will not require the use of simultaneous equations. This method is called the *Superposition Theorem*.

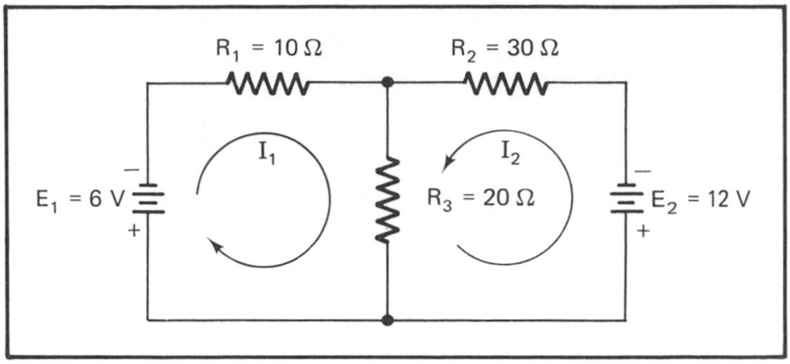

FIGURE 22-22
Circuit Containing Two Voltage Sources

The Superposition Theorem is stated as:

THE CURRENT OR VOLTAGE OF ANY COMPONENT OF A NETWORK
WITH TWO OR MORE VOLTAGE SOURCES IS THE ALGEBRAIC SUM OF
THE CURRENT OR VOLTAGE CAUSED BY EACH SOURCE ACTING
INDEPENDENTLY.

This means that in the circuit of Figure 22-22, the current or voltage
of R_3 is the result of each voltage source acting separately. In this
process, the effect of one voltage source would be obtained with the
other replaced with a short circuit. Then this process would be reversed. Let us see how this theorem is used in the circuit of Figure
22-22.

example 22-8 Determine the current flow through R_3 in Figure 22-22.

solution: The current flow through R_3 is first obtained with the
6-V source replaced with a short circuit. This is shown
in Figure 22-23a. This is seen to be a series-parallel
circuit with R_2 in series with the parallel combination
of R_1 and R_3. The resistance of the parallel combination
is found as

$$R_{par} = \frac{R_1 R_3}{R_1 + R_3} = \frac{(10)(20)}{10 + 20} = \frac{200}{30} = 6.66 \ \Omega$$

The total resistance is

$$R_T = R_{par} + R_2 = 6.66 + 30 = 36.66 \ \Omega$$

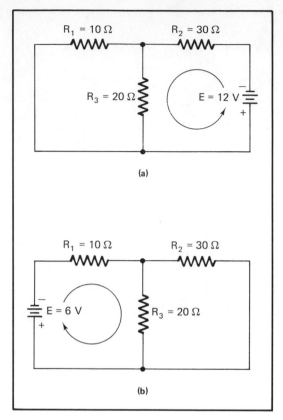

(a)

(b)

FIGURE 22–23
Circuit of Example 22–8

The total current is

$$I_T = \frac{E}{R_T} = \frac{12}{36.66} = 0.327 \text{ A}$$

as $I_T = I_{R_2}$, the voltage drop across R_2, is

$$E_{R_2} = I_T R_2 = 0.327 \times 30 = 9.81 \text{ V}$$

The voltage across the parallel combination is

$$E_{\text{par}} = E - E_{R_2} = 12 - 9.81 = 2.19 \text{ V}$$

The current through R_3 is

$$I_{R_3} = \frac{E_{\text{par}}}{R_3} = \frac{2.19}{20} = 0.110 \text{ A}$$

In a similar manner, the current flow through R_3 is obtained with the 12-V source replaced with a short circuit. This is shown in Figure 22-23b.

$$R_{\text{par}} = \frac{R_2 R_3}{R_2 + R_3} = \frac{(30)(20)}{30 + 20} = \frac{600}{50} = 12 \ \Omega$$

$$R_T = R_1 + R_{\text{par}} = 10 + 12 = 22 \ \Omega$$

$$I_T = \frac{E}{R_T} = \frac{6}{22} = 0.273 \text{ A}$$

$$E_{R_1} = I_T R_1 = 0.273 \times 10 = 2.73 \text{ V}$$

$$E_{\text{par}} = E - E_{R_1} = 6 - 2.73 = 3.27 \text{ V}$$

$$I_{R_3} = \frac{E_{\text{par}}}{R_3} = \frac{3.27}{20} = 0.163 \text{ A}$$

The direction of the current flow through R_3, as the result of each voltage source acting separately is as shown in Figure 22-23a and b. The current through R_3 is then

$$I_{R_3} = 0.110 + 0.163 - 0.273 \text{ A}$$

This is the same current that was obtained in Example 22-3.

A limitation of the Superposition Theorem is that it enables us to obtain the current or voltage for one component of a network, as I_{R_3} in Example 22-8. Often, however, this information will permit us to obtain other circuit values.

22-7 THÉVENIN'S THEOREM

Thévenin's theorem provides another means of simplifying voltage networks. In many instances we are not concerned with the inner operations of a device, only its external effects. This is often referred to as the *black-box* concept. For example, a complicated voltage supply could be replaced with a black box with only two external terminals. This voltage supply could contain any number of elements, with any manner of interconnection. However, the entire complicated voltage source could be replaced by this black box.

Thévenin's theorem permits the replacement of any complex voltage network of which we may or may not know the nature, with a single constant voltage voltage, E_{oc}, and a single series resistance, R_{TH}.

The voltage, E_{oc}, is the open-circuit voltage obtained at the terminals of the device. The resistance, R_{TH}, is obtained at the terminals of the device, with all the voltage sources of the device replaced with short circuits. This is shown in Figure 22–24.

The application of Thévenin's theorem is shown in the following example.

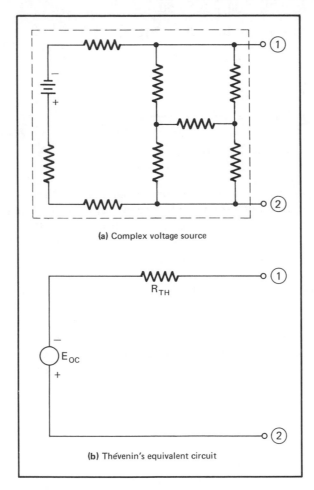

(a) Complex voltage source

(b) Thévenin's equivalent circuit

FIGURE   22–24
Thévenin's Equivalent of Complex Network

example 22–9   Replace the voltage source shown in Figure 22–25 with the Thévenin's equivalent circuit.

solution: As noted, such a circuit may be replaced with E_{oc} and R_{TH}. The voltage that would exist between ① and ② if there were no load connected across these terminals

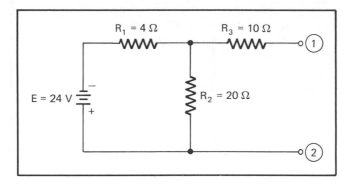

FIGURE 22–25
Circuit of Example 22–9

would be equal to the voltage that would exist across R_2. That is,

$$E_{oc} = V_{R_2}$$

This voltage may be calculated as

$$I_{R_2} = \frac{E}{R_1 + R_2} = \frac{24}{4 + 20} = \frac{24}{24} = 1 \text{ A}$$

$$V_{R_2} = I_{R_2}R_2 = 1 \times 20 = 20 \text{ V}$$

$$E_{oc} = V_{R_2} = 20 \text{ V}$$

The value of R_{TH} may be obtained by calculating the resistance across ① and ② with the voltage source replaced with a short circuit. This is shown in Figure 22–26. The value of the resistance between terminals ① and ② is seen to be R_3 in series with the parallel combination of R_1 and R_2. As this resistance is R_{TH}, we have

$$R_{TH} = R_3 + \frac{R_1 R_2}{R_1 + R_2}$$

$$= 10 + \frac{(4)(20)}{4 + 20} = 10 + \frac{80}{24} + 10 + 3.33 = 13.33 \text{ } \Omega$$

Thévenin's equivalent of this circuit is shown in Figure 22–27.

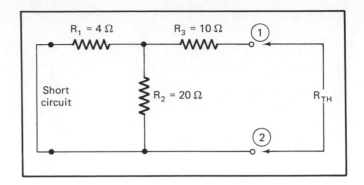

FIGURE 22–26
Circuit of Example 22–9 with *E* Replaced
with Short Circuit

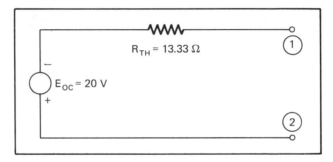

FIGURE 22–27
Thévenin's Equivalent of the Circuit
of Figure 22–25

Let us satisfy ourselves that the circuit of Figure 22–27 *is* the equivalent of the original circuit of Figure 22–25. This will be shown in the following example.

example 22–10   Establish that the circuit of Figure 22–28b is equivalent to the circuit of Figure 22–28a. Determine I_{RL} and E_{RL} in each circuit to prove this equivalence.

solution: First we will determine the current flow through R_1 in the original circuit. The total circuit resistance is seen to be

$$R_T = R_1 + \frac{R_2(R_3 + R_L)}{R_2 + (R_3 + R_L)} \quad 4 + \frac{20(10 + 100)}{20 + (10 + 100)}$$

$$= 4 + \frac{(20)(110)}{20 + 110}$$

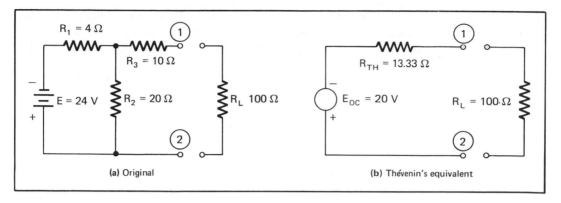

FIGURE 22-28
Circuit for Example 22-10

$$= 4 + \frac{2,200}{130} = 4 + 16.92$$

$$= 20.92 \ \Omega$$

$$I_T = \frac{E}{R_T} = \frac{24}{20.92} = 1.147 \text{ A}$$

$$E_{R_1} = I_T R_1 = 1.147 \times 4 = 4.59 \text{ V}$$

$$E_{R_2} = E - E_{R_1} = 24 - 4.59 = 19.41 \text{ V}$$

$$I_{R_2} = \frac{E_{R_2}}{R_2} = \frac{19.41}{20} = 0.971 \text{ A}$$

Using Kirchhoff's current law, we have

$$I_{R_3} = I_{RL} = I_T - I_{R_2} = 1.147 - 0.971 = 0.176 \text{ A}$$

$$E_{RL} = I_{RL} R_L = 0.176 \times 100 = 17.6 \text{ V}$$

For Thévenin's equivalent circuit, we have

$$R_T = R_{TH} + R_L = 13.33 + 100 = 113.33 \ \Omega$$

$$I_{RL} = \frac{E_{oc}}{R_T} = \frac{20}{113.33} = 0.176 \text{ A}$$

$$E_{RL} = I_{RL} R_L = 0.176 \times 100 = 17.6 \text{ V}$$

The circuits are seen to be equivalent.

The example shown is a relatively simple one. The question will arise as to how the voltage sources may be short-circuited if the net-

321

work is enclosed in a black box with only two terminals extending outside. This question will be answered when Norton's theorem is examined and the equivalence between Thévenin's and Norton's theorems is developed.

22-8 NORTON'S THEOREM

Like Thévenin's theorem, Norton's theorem provides a means of simplifying voltage networks. Similarly, with this theorem we are only concerned with the external effects of a network and not with the internal components or their arrangements.

Norton's theorem permits the replacement of any complicated voltage network, of which we may or may not know the nature, with a constant-current source, I_{sc}, and a single parallel resistance, R_N.

The constant-current source, I_{sc}, is equivalent to the current that would flow between the output terminals of the network if these terminals were short-circuited. The resistance, R_N, is obtained in the identical manner as R_{TH}, that is, by replacing all voltage sources with short circuits and by determining the resistance across the output terminals: $R_N = R_{TH}$. Norton's equivalent circuit is shown in Figure 22-29.

The application of Norton's theorem is shown in the following example.

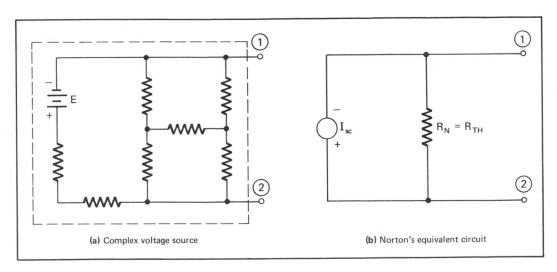

(a) Complex voltage source   (b) Norton's equivalent circuit

FIGURE 22-29
Norton's Equivalent of a Complex Network

example 22-11 Using the circuit of Example 22-10 (Figure 22-30), determine Norton's equivalent circuit.

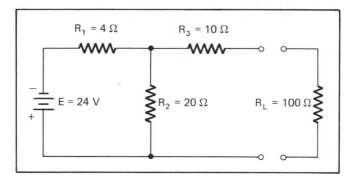

FIGURE 22–30
Circuit of Example 22–11

solution: The current that would flow between terminals ① and ②, if these terminals were short-circuited, is determined first. The circuit that we would then have is shown in Figure 22–31.

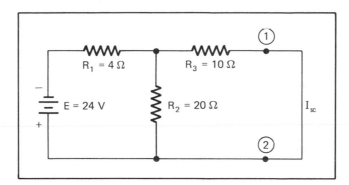

FIGURE 22–31
Circuit of Example 22–11, with a Short Circuit
Across ① and ②

The total circuit resistance, R_T, is seen to be

$$R_T = R_1 + \frac{R_2 R_3}{R_2 + R_3} = 4 + \frac{(20)(10)}{20 + 10}$$

$$= 4 + \frac{200}{30} = 4 + 6.67 = 10.67 \ \Omega$$

$$I_T = \frac{E}{R_T} = \frac{24}{10.67} = 2.25 \ \text{A}$$

$$E_{R_2} = E_{R_3} = E - I_T R_1 = 24 - 2.25 \times 4 = 24 - 9 = 15 \ \text{V}$$

$$I_{sc} = I_{R_3} = \frac{E_{R_3}}{R_3} = \frac{15}{10} = 1.5 \text{ A}$$

As $R_N = R_{TH}$, we have

$$R_N = 13.33 \ \Omega$$

Norton's equivalent of this circuit is shown in Figure 22–32.

As with Thévenin's equivalent circuit, let us satisfy outselves that the circuit of Figure 22–30 is the same as Norton's equivalent circuit of Figure 22–32. This will be shown in the following example.

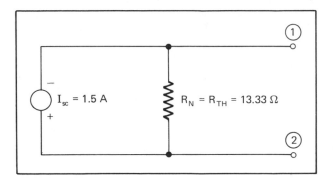

FIGURE 22–32
Norton's Equivalent of the Circuit of Figure
22–28

example 22–12   Establish that the circuit of Figure 22–33b is the equivalent of Figure 22–33a. Determine I_{RL} and E_{RL} in each circuit.

FIGURE 22–33
Circuit of Example 22–12

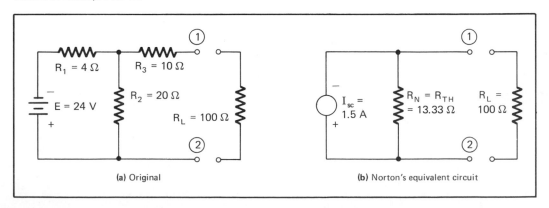

solution: The circuit of Figure 22–33a is identical to that of Example 22–10, in which

$$I_L = 0.176 \text{ A}$$

$$E_{RL} = 17.6 \text{ V}$$

325

Sec. 22–9
EQUIVALENCE OF
THÉVENIN'S AND
NORTON'S
CIRCUIT

For Norton's equivalent circuit of Figure 22–33b, we have

$$R_T = \frac{(R_N)(R_L)}{R_N + R_L} = \frac{(13.33)(100)}{13.33 + 100} = \frac{1,333}{113.33} = 11.76 \ \Omega$$

$$E_{RN} = E_{RL} = I_{sc} \times R_T = 1.5 \times 11.76 = 17.6 \text{ V}$$

$$I_{RL} = \frac{E_{RL}}{R_L} = \frac{17.6}{100} = 0.176 \text{ A}$$

These circuits are seen to be equivalent.

22-9 EQUIVALENCE OF THÉVENIN'S AND NORTON'S CIRCUIT

In the previous sections we developed Thévenin's and Norton's circuits. Using the same original network, we set up Thévenin's and Norton's equivalent circuits in Examples 22–9 and 22–11. We then established the validity of these equivalent circuits in Examples 22–10 and 22–12. The resultant equivalent circuits are shown in Figure 22–34. Examination of these circuits shows, as we have previously

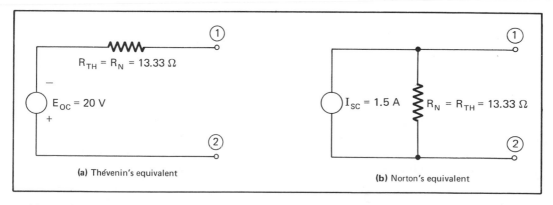

FIGURE   22–34
Equivalent Circuits Obtained in Examples 22–10
and 22–12

established, that

$$R_{TH} = R_N$$

In addition, it will be seen that using Thévenin's equivalent, we may obtain I_{sc}:

$$I_{sc} = \frac{E_{oc}}{R_{TH}} = \frac{20}{13.33} = 1.5 \text{ A}$$

Also, from Norton's equivalent we may obtain E_{oc}:

$$E_{oc} = I_{sc} \times R_N = 1.5 \times 13.33 = 20 \text{ V}$$

From this equivalence, it is seen that we may easily convert from one equivalent circuit to another.

In Section 22–7 the question was raised as to how the voltage sources could be short-circuited in order to calculate R_{TH}, if only two terminals of a black box were available. This will now be explained.

In previous sections, examples were used to establish the validity of our procedures. In practice, only two measurements are required to set up Thévenin's and Norton's circuits. These are

1. The open circuit voltage, E_{oc}, of the network. This is measured with a high-resistance voltmeter.
2. The short-circuit current, I_{sc}, that flows between the short-circuited output terminals, is measured with an ammeter of appropriate size.

Once E_{oc} and I_{sc} have been determined, the value of $R_{TH} = R_N$ may be calculated as

$$R_{TH} = R_N = \frac{E_{oc}}{I_{sc}}$$

The complex circuit may now be replaced by its equivalent in the form of either Thévenin's or Norton's circuit. Either equivalent circuit may be used interchangably to represent the network involved. In our work with transistor equivalent circuits, we will often use Thévenin's equivalent to represent the transistor input while Norton's equivalent is used to represent the transistor output circuit.

EXERCISE 22–3

1. Using the Superposition Theorem, determine the current through and voltage across R_3 in Figure 22–22, if $R_1 = 300 \ \Omega$, $R_2 = 600 \ \Omega$, and $R_3 = 2,000 \ \Omega$.

327
Sec. 22-9
EQUIVALENCE OF
THÉVENIN'S AND
NORTON'S
CIRCUIT

2. Using the Superposition Theorem, determine the current through and the voltage across R_3 in Figure 22–22 if the 6-V battery is replaced with a 24-V battery of the same polarity.

3. Repeat problem 2, except that the 24-V battery has its polarity reversed.

4. In Figure 22–35, determine Thévenin's equivalent circuit.

5. In Figure 22–35, determine Norton's equivalent.

6. The 12-V battery in Figure 22–35 has been replaced with a 24-V battery, with the polarity reversed. Determine Thévenin's and Norton's equivalent circuits.

7. A complex voltage source has an open-circuit voltage of 15.1 V. When the output terminals are short-circuited, a current of 1.31 A is measured. Show Thévenin's and Norton's equivalent circuits.

8. If $R_{TH} = 25$ Ω and $I_{sc} = 1.37$ A, what would be the voltage measured with a high-resistance voltmeter that would be obtained across the output terminals of a complex voltage source?

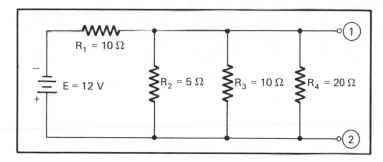

FIGURE 22–35
Circuit for Problems 4, 5, and 6

23

ANGLES AND TRIANGLES

In this chapter we will develop some concepts of angles and triangles. Triangles, as the name indicates, have three angles. The study of triangles is called *trigonometry*, a word of Greek origin, meaning "measurement of triangles." This subject is an extremely important one for the electronics technician in the study of alternating current.

When two lines meet at a point, an *angle* is formed. This is shown in Figure 23-1. The angle, θ, is formed when lines *AB* and *BC* intersect at point *B*. The point of intersection is called the *vertex*, and the two lines are called the *sides* of the angle.

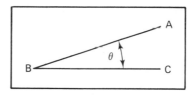

FIGURE 23-1
The Angle

The symbol for angle is ∠. In Figure 23-1 ∠θ may be referred to as ∠*ABC*, where the second letter indicates the vertex and the first and second letters and second and third letters designate the sides. Often the angle formed by the intersection of the two lines is designated by the letter of the vertex. That is, the angle formed by the two lines intersecting at the vertex *B* would be designated as ∠*B*.

Angles are often measured in *degrees*. If a circle is divided into 360 equal parts by lines or rays projecting from the center, the angle formed by adjacent rays is designated as 1 degree. A circle, then, contains 360 degrees.

A degree may be divided into 60 parts, called *minutes*, where 1 degree equals 60 minutes ($1° = 60'$). A minute may be further divided into 60 parts called *seconds*, where 1 minute equals 60 seconds ($1' = 60''$). This method of measurement, with its divisions in 60 parts, is called the *sexagesimal system*.

In navigation and astronomical measurements, minutes and seconds are used. In engineering, fractional parts of a degree are normally expressed decimally. Prior to the advent of the hand calculator, most engineering technicians and engineers used "deci-trig" slide rules. These slide rules had scales that gave fractional degrees in decimals. Modern hand calculators provide fractional angular measurements in decimal form.

It is often necessary to convert from one system to the other. The following examples show such conversions.

example 23–1   Convert $36°15'20''$ to decimal form.

---

solution: As $1' = \dfrac{1°}{60}$ and $1'' = \dfrac{1'}{60} = \dfrac{1}{60} \times \dfrac{1}{60} = \dfrac{1°}{3,600}$,

$$36°15'20'' = 36° + \frac{15°}{60} + \frac{20°}{3,600}$$

$$= 36 + 0.25 + 0.0055 = 36.2555°$$

example 23–2   Convert $46.25°$ to sexagesimal form.

---

solution: As $1° = 60'$, then

$$0.25° = 0.25 \times 60' = 15'$$

Then

$$46.26° = 46°15'$$

23–3 TYPES OF ANGLES

Angles are typed according to the size of the angle. Usually the right angle is used as a reference. The *right angle* is produced when the intersection of two lines produces four equal angles. When this occurs, the lines that produced the right angles are said to be *perpendicular*. This is designated by the symbol $\perp$. The formation of right angles is shown in Figure 23–2, where $\theta_1 = \theta_2 = \theta_3 = \theta_4$. Various types of angles are shown in Figure 23–3.

The following definitions describe the above angles:

The *acute angle* is less than $90°$.
The *right angle* is equal to $90°$.
The *obtuse angle* is greater than $90°$ but less than $180°$.
The *straight angle* is equal to $180°$.
The *reflex angle* is greater than $180°$.

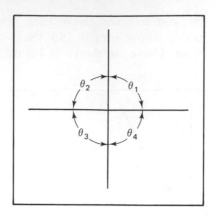

FIGURE 23–2
Right Angles

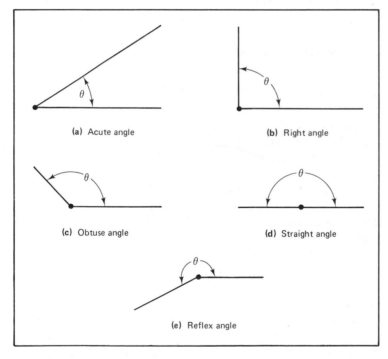

(a) Acute angle

(b) Right angle

(c) Obtuse angle

(d) Straight angle

(e) Reflex angle

FIGURE 23–3
Types of Angles

There are two further designations for angles in addition to those given above. These are complementary angles and supplementary angles. *Complementary angles* are two angles whose sum is 90°. Such angles

are said to *complement* each other. *Supplementary angles* are two angles whose sum is 180°. Such angles are said to *supplement* each other. These are shown in Figure 23–4.

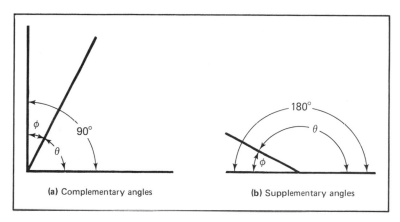

(a) Complementary angles   (b) Supplementary angles

FIGURE 23–4
Complementary and Supplementary Angles

23–4 GENERATION OF ANGLES

In previous sections, we have presented the angle as the opening that exists between two intersecting lines. This concept limits our study of trigonometry. Accordingly, we shall consider that an angle is the result of a line segment rotated about a pivot point or vertex. The starting position of rotation forms one side of the angle, called the *initial side*. The final position of rotation forms the second side of the angle, called the *terminal side*. The generation of an angle is shown in Figure 23–5. When an angle has its vertex at the origin and the initial side of the angles lies along the positive *x* axis, the angle is considered to be in *standard position*. The angle shown in Figure 23–5 is in standard position. This angle, θ, has been generated by the rotation of the line segment, *OA*, from an initial position on the positive *x* axis to the terminal position shown. This rotation was in a counterclockwise (CCW) direction, and an angle generated by rotation in this direction is considered a *positive angle*. An angle generated by rotation in a clockwise (CW) direction is considered a *negative angle*. The generation of positive and negative angles is shown in Figure 23–6. All such angles are in the standard position. The positive angles θ and φ in Figure 23–6a are generated by the CCW rotation of *OA* and *OB*, respectively. In Figure 23–6b the negative angles α and β are generated by the CW rotation of *OC* and *OD*, respectively.

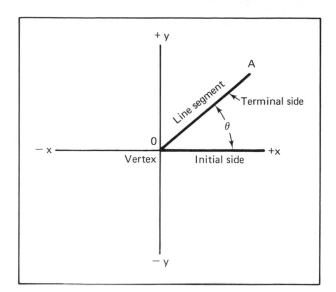

FIGURE 23–5
Generation of an Angle in Standard Position

FIGURE 23–6
Generation of Positive and Negative Angles

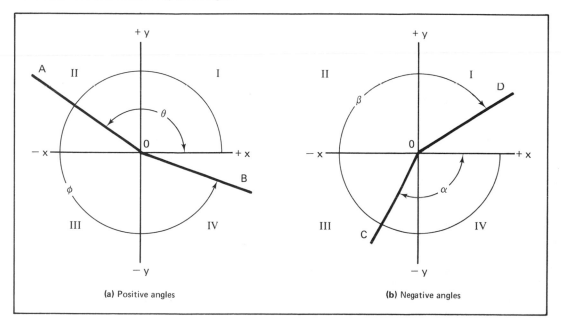

(a) Positive angles   **(b)** Negative angles

The terminal side of a standard position angle determines the quadrant of the angle. Thus

θ is a second quadrant positive angle

ϕ is a fourth quadrant positive angle

α is a third quadrant negative angle

β is a first quadrant negative angle

This method of generation permits angles greater than 360° to be generated. Figure 23–7a shows a positive 420° angle while Figure 23–7b shows a negative 390° angle. Notice that in Figure 23–7a the resultant angle is the same as that produced by rotating *OA* through +60°. That is, 420° − 360° = 60°. In Figure 23–7b the resultant angle is the same as rotating *OB* through −30°, or 390° − 360° = 30°. In our work with angles greater than 360° we will work with the angle resulting from the subtraction of the largest multiple of 360° possible. For example, an angle of +800° would contain two 360° multiples or 720°. This would be subtracted from +800° to produce a standard position, positive first quadrant angle of 80°, with which we would work.

FIGURE 23–7
Generation of Angles Greater Than 360°

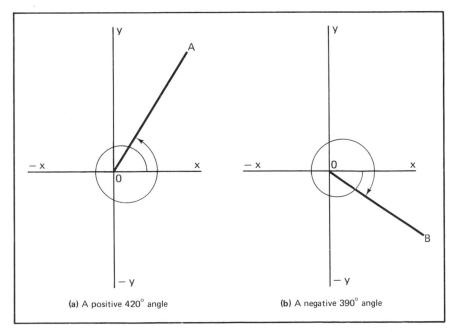

(a) A positive 420° angle   (b) A negative 390° angle

The *circular* or *natural system* is another method of angular measurement. The unit of measurement in the system is called the *radian*. A radian is equal to the angle formed with its vertex at the center of a circle and whose sides intercept an arc equal to the radius of the circle. This is shown in Figure 23–8. The circumference of a circle is equal to

$$C = 2\pi r$$

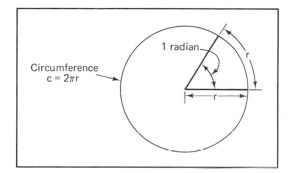

FIGURE 23–8
The Radian

The radius of the circle has a relation to the circumference of

$$r = \frac{C}{2\pi}$$

If the arc length of a radian is equal to the radius, r, then there are 2π radians in the circumference of a circle. As a circle has 360°, a radian has

$$1 \text{ radian} = \frac{360°}{2\pi} = \frac{360°}{6.28} = 57.29578°$$

or, more commonly,

$$1 \text{ radian} = 57.3°$$

The radian is abbreviated "rad." It may also be designated by the letter "r" used as a superscript, in a manner similar to the degree symbol "°," also used for angular measure. This is shown as

$$1 \text{ radian} = 1 \text{ rad} = 1^r = 57.3°$$

335

The above relationships show that there are $2\pi^r$ or 6.28^r in 360°, with each radian equal to approximately 57.3°. This means that there are 6 radians plus 0.28 radian in 360°. This is shown in Figure 23–9.

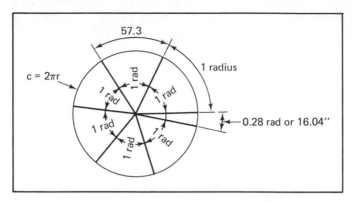

FIGURE 23–9
Circle Divided into Radians

It should be noted at this point that angles may be drawn and measured using a protractor. The reader is most likely familiar with this device from his previous courses in math and mechanical drafting. While geometric construction and other procedures may also be used for these purposes, the protractor will provide the degree of accuracy sufficient for our work.

Many of the modern hand calculators provide for conversion between radians and degrees. The mathematical process involved in such conversions is shown in the following examples.

example 23–3 Convert 32.1° to radians.

solution: As 57.3° = 1 rad, then 1° = 0.01745 rad. Then

$$32.1° = 32.1 \times 0.01745$$
$$= 0.56 \text{ rad}$$

example 23–4 Convert 1.56 radians to degrees.

solution: As 1 rad = 57.3°, then

$$1.56 \text{ rad} = 1.56 \times 57.3$$
$$= 89.39°$$

1. Convert the following to decimal form:
   25°30',   67°5',   5°32'

2. Convert the following to sexagesimal form:
   35.62°,   57.15°,   16.77°

3. What is the type of angle represented by the following?
   −32°,   350°,   −316°

4. What is the complement of the following?
   56°,   32°,   16°

5. What is the supplement of the following?
   56°,   32°,   116°

6. In what quadrants do the following angles fall?
   −16°,   255°,   −260°

7. Convert the following to radians:
   36.45°,   157.6°,   271.2°

8. Convert the following to degrees:
   1.67 rad,   4.78 rad, 3π rad

23–6 TRIANGLES

The triangle, as noted, has three angles. A triangle is formed when three lines intersect as shown in Figure 23–10. The points of intersection are usually labeled with capital letters with the sides opposite these points labeled with the appropriate lower-case letters. The angles formed are often designated with the Greek letter equivalent to the capital letter at the intersection point. These are also shown in Figure 23–10.

FIGURE 23–10
Triangle

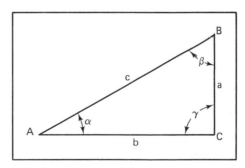

There are various types of triangles. These are shown in Figure 23–11. The four types of triangles shown *all* have the same three common characteristics. These are

1. The sum of the three angles is equal to 180°.
2. The sum of the lengths of any two sides is greater than the length of the remaining side.
3. The angles of a triangle are related to the length of the opposite side. The larger the angle, the longer the opposite side. The smaller the angle, the shorter the opposite side.

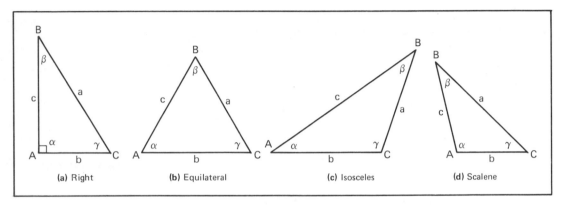

    (a) Right   (b) Equilateral   (c) Isosceles   (d) Scalene

FIGURE 23–11
Types of Triangles

A description of the types of triangles shown in Figure 23–11 follows.

Right Triangle: One angle is 90°; this is called a right angle and is usually designated with the symbol ∟, as shown above. As the sum of the three angles is equal to 180°, the sum of the angles other than the right angle must total 90°.

Equilateral Triangle: The three sides of this triangle are equal, and the three angles are also equal, or 60°.

Isosceles Triangle: Two of the sides of this triangle are equal, and the angles opposite the equal sides a and b are equal. That is, $a = b$ and $\alpha = \beta$.

Scalene Triangle: This triangle has three sides of unequal length, so none of the angles can equal another angle.

Note in the above descriptions and the appropriate figure how each of the three common characteristics apply to each of the triangles. Triangles of differing size but with equal corresponding angles are designated as similar triangles. Similar triangles are shown in Figure

23–12. In this figure the corresponding angles are seen to be identical, although the triangles differ in size. The sides opposite corresponding angles are proportional:

$$\frac{a}{a'} = \frac{b}{b'} = \frac{c}{c'}$$

Triangles with all three corresponding angles and sides identical are designated as congruent triangles. The symbol $\cong$ indicates identical or congruent triangles.

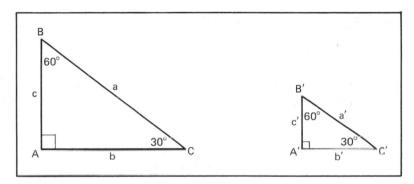

FIGURE 23–12
Similar Triangles

23–7 RIGHT TRIANGLES

In our previous discussions, a right triangle was seen to be a triangle with one of its angles a right angle. A right triangle, in the standard position, is shown in Figure 23–13. It should be observed that the side opposite the right angle is designated as the *hypotenuse*.

FIGURE 23–13
Right Triangle

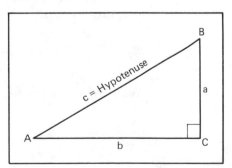

We have seen that the sum of the three angles of a triangle must equal 180°. A right triangle has one of its angles, the right angle, equal to 90°. This means, of course, that the sum of the remaining two angles must total 90°. This is an important concept, and it led to the discovery by the early Greek mathematician Pythagoras of a common characteristic of right triangles. This relationship, called the *Pythagorean theorem*, is stated:

THE SQUARE OF THE HYPOTENUSE OF A RIGHT TRIANGLE IS EQUAL TO THE SUM OF THE SQUARES OF THE OTHER TWO SIDES.

Using Figure 23–13, we may write

$$c^2 = a^2 + b^2$$

Such a relationship is of great importance in a wide range of engineering applications, for it permits the length of one side of a right triangle to be determined if the lengths of the other two are known.

example 23–5 What is the length of the hypotenuse of a right triangle if the two sides are 6 ft and 8 ft?

solution: Using the Pythagorean theorem, we have

$$c^2 = a^2 + b^2$$
$$= (6)^2 + (8)^2 = 36 + 64 = 100$$
$$c = 10 \text{ ft}$$

example 23–6 A television tower casts a shadow of 200 ft while a vertically held pole 10 ft long casts a shadow of 25 ft. What is the height of the television tower?

solution: Similar right triangles are created by the sun, causing shadows of the tower and the pole. These are shown in Figure 23–14. As the triangles are similar, the following proportions exist:

$$\frac{a}{a'} = \frac{b}{b'} \quad \text{as } b' = 10,\ a' = 2.5,\ a = 200$$

We may obtain the height b:

$$\frac{200}{2.5} = \frac{b}{10}$$

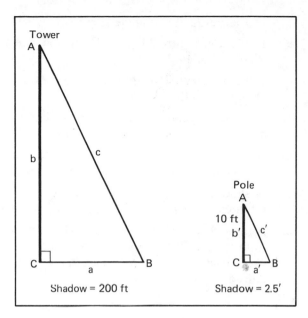

FIGURE 23–14
Figure for Example 23–6

$$2.5b = 2,000$$
$$b = 800 \text{ ft}$$

EXERCISE 23–2

1.　In Figure 23–15, if sides $c = 42$ and $b = 28$, determine the length of side a.

FIGURE 23–15
Triangle for Problems 1–4

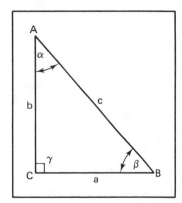

2. In Figure 23–15, if angle $\beta = 56.2°$, what is the size of angle α?

3. If side a in Figure 23–15 is 13.5 ft and side b is 19.7 ft, what is the length of side c?

4. If the hypotenuse of Figure 23–15 is 60 ft long, what is the length of side b if side $a = 27$ ft?

5. A church steeple 212 ft tall casts a shadow of 115 ft. What is the distance from the end of the shadow to the top of the steeple?

6. What length of shadow would a 200-ft chimney cast if a vertically held pole 12 ft long casts a shadow of 5.2 ft?

7. A shadow of 45.7 ft is cast by a flagpole. An adjacent pole 15.2 ft tall casts a shadow of 4.72 ft. What is the height of the flagpole?

8. A radio tower 90 ft tall has guy wires attached to the top and 30 ft from the top. If the guy wires were attached to a common anchor, 57 ft from the base, what are the lengths of the guy wires required?

24

TRIGONOMETRIC FUNCTIONS

In Chapter 23, a number of characteristics of the right triangle were developed. In this chapter, these relationships will be expanded. This will permit procedures to be developed that will enable us to work more effectively with the right triangle.

24–1 TRIANGLE TERMINOLOGY

Our work with triangles will involve relationships between the sides and angles of the right triangle. In order that confusion does not occur in this work, certain conventions for the designation of the sides and angles of a triangle have been established. This terminology is shown for a right triangle in the standard position in Figure 24–1. These interelationships will be extremely important in our future work. It is strongly recommended that this terminology be firmly established in the reader's memory.

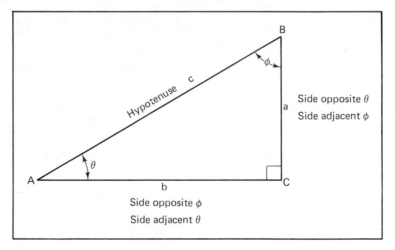

FIGURE 24–1
Conventional Side–Angle Designations

24–2 TRIGONOMETRIC RATIOS

In Chapter 23, corresponding sides of similar triangles were seen to be proportional. In other words, a ratio existed between the relative lengths of the corresponding sides. In this chapter, other ratios will be found to exist in the right triangle. To establish these ratios, the 45°–45°–90° triangle and the 30°–60°–90° triangle will be examined.

A 45°–45°–90° triangle is shown in Figure 24–2. In Chapter 23, it was seen that equal angles establish that the opposite sides are equal.

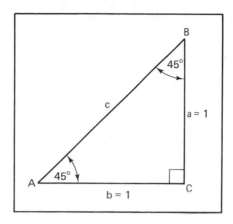

FIGURE 24–2
A 45°–45°–90° Triangle

As we have two equal angles, the two opposite sides are equal, and the 45°-45°-90° triangle is an isosceles triangle. As shown in Figure 24–2, these equal sides have been assigned a length equal to 1. It follows, then, that

$$c^2 = a^2 + b^2 = (1)^2 + (1)^2 = 1 + 1 = 2$$

$$c = \sqrt{2} = 1.414$$

Using these relationships, it is seen that the following ratio exists:

$$\frac{\text{side opposite 45° angle}}{\text{hypotenuse}} = \frac{1}{\sqrt{2}} = \frac{1}{1.414} = 0.707$$

This ratio applies to *all* 45°–45°–90° triangles. This ratio does not depend upon the size nor the particular orientation of the triangle. This is shown in the following example.

example 24–1 Determine the ratio $\dfrac{\text{side opposite 45° angle}}{\text{hypotenuse}}$ for the triangle shown in Figure 24–3.

solution: The hypotenuse, c, is first calculated as

$$c^2 = a^2 + b^2 = (6)^2 + (6)^2 = 36 + 36 = 72$$

$$c = \sqrt{72} = 8.485$$

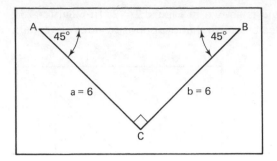

FIGURE 24–3
Triangle for Example 24–1

The ratio is now calculated

$$\frac{\text{side opposite } 45° \text{ angle}}{\text{hypotenuse}} = \frac{6}{8.485} = 0.707$$

As shown in the example above, the ratio is the same for a triangle of different size and orientation. This, then, establishes the validity of one more ratio for the right triangle. This is for the 45°–45°–90° right triangle.

The relationships of a 30′–60°–90° triangle will now be examined. We will start with the equilateral triangle shown in Figure 24–4a. In this figure the sides $a = b = c = 2$, as shown. If angle B is bisected with a line drawn perpendicular to side b, we have Figure 24–4b. In effect, this procedure has resulted in dividing angle $B = 60°$ and side $b = 2$ in half. Two 30°–60°–90° triangles have now been formed. These are shown in separated form in Figure 24–4c. In Figure 24–4c the length of

FIGURE 24–4
Development of Ratios for 30°–60°–90° Triangle

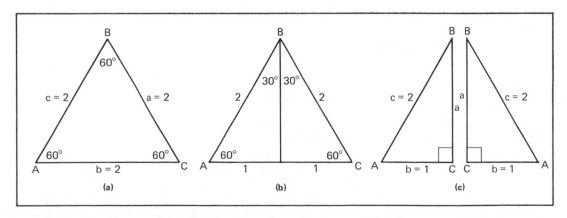

sides, a, may now be calculated. Note that the sides of these triangles have been relabeled to conform to the two triangles that now exist:

$$a^2 + b^2 = c^2$$

$$a^2 = c^2 - b^2 = (2)^2 - (1)^2 = 4 - 1 = 3$$

$$\therefore \quad a = \sqrt{3} = 1.732$$

The ratio for the sides, $b:a:c$ of the 30°–60°–90° triangle is seen to be $1:\sqrt{3}:2$, or $1:1.732:2$. This ratio applies to *all* 30°–60°–90° triangles. It does not depend upon the size or orientation of the triangle. This is shown in the following example.

example 24–2 Determine the ratio of the sides, $b:a:c$, in the triangle shown in Figure 24–5.

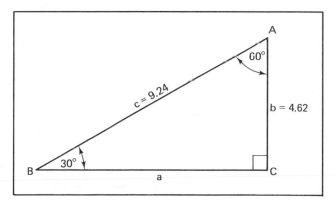

FIGURE 24–5
Diagram for Example 24–2

solution: Side a is first calculated as

$$a^2 + b^2 = c^2$$

$$a^2 = c^2 - b^2 = (9.24)^2 - (4.62)^2 = 85.34 - 21.34 = 64$$

$$a = 8.0$$

The ratio $b:a:c$ is $4.62:8.0:9.24$. To obtain b as the reference or as 1, all three quantities are divided by 4.62. This is shown as

$$\frac{4.62}{4.62} : \frac{8.0}{4.62} : \frac{9.24}{4.62}$$

which produces

$$1 : 1.732 : 2$$

As shown in the example above, the ratio of $1 : 1.732 : 2$ is valid for any orientation of any $30°-60°-90°$ triangle.

24-3 TRIGONOMETRIC FUNCTIONS

The ratios for the $45°-45°-90°$ and the $30°-60°-90°$ triangles are summarized in Figure 24-6. Examining Figure 24-6b for the $30°-60°-90°$

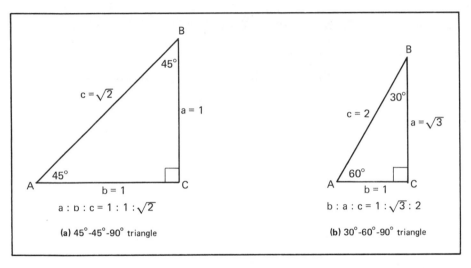

FIGURE 24-6
Triangle Ratios

triangle it is seen that additional ratios could be established between the sides and angles. These ratios would also apply to *all* $30°-60°-90°$ triangles regardless of size or orientation. These ratios are

$$\frac{\text{side opposite } 60° \text{ angle}}{\text{hypotenuse}} = \frac{a}{c} = \frac{\sqrt{3}}{2} = 0.866$$

$$\frac{\text{side adjacent } 60° \text{ angle}}{\text{hypotenuse}} = \frac{b}{c} = \frac{1}{2} = 0.50$$

$$\frac{\text{side opposite } 60° \text{ angle}}{\text{side adjacent } 60° \text{ angle}} = \frac{a}{b} = \frac{\sqrt{3}}{1} = 1.732$$

$$\frac{\text{side opposite } 30° \text{ angle}}{\text{hypotenuse}} = \frac{b}{c} = \frac{1}{2} = 0.50$$

$$\frac{\text{side adjacent }30^\circ \text{ angle}}{\text{hypotenuse}} = \frac{a}{c} = \frac{\sqrt{3}}{2} = 0.866$$

$$\frac{\text{side opposite }30^\circ \text{ angle}}{\text{side adjacent }30^\circ \text{ angle}} = \frac{b}{a} = \frac{1}{\sqrt{3}} = 0.577$$

Similar ratios could be established for the 45°–45°–90° triangle or, for that matter, for any right triangle of whatever size of configuration chosen. Of course the numerical values of the ratios will be different depending on the relative lengths of the sides of the triangle involved.

The ratios as designed in the form above are difficult to work with, so suitable mathematical names have been established for these ratios. The ratios, or *trigonometric functions*, for the 30°–60°–90° triangle of Figure 24–6b are

$$\text{sine } 60^\circ = \frac{\text{opp}}{\text{hyp}} = \frac{a}{c} = \frac{\sqrt{3}}{2} = 0.866$$

$$\text{cosine } 60^\circ = \frac{\text{adj}}{\text{hyp}} = \frac{b}{c} = \frac{1}{2} = 0.50$$

$$\text{tangent } 60^\circ = \frac{\text{opp}}{\text{adj}} = \frac{a}{b} = \frac{\sqrt{3}}{1} = 1.732$$

These trigonometric functions or ratios may be determined in the same manner for the 30° angle of Figure 24–6b. As noted above, they may be determined for *any* right triangle. These trigonometric functions, as well as reciprocal functions, are set up in general form for the right triangle of Figure 24–7. Using the abbreviations for the trigonometric

FIGURE 24–7
Right Triangle in General
Form

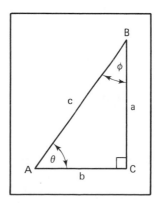

functions, we have

$$\sin \theta = \frac{\text{opp}}{\text{hyp}} = \frac{a}{c}$$

$$\cos \theta = \frac{\text{adj}}{\text{hyp}} = \frac{b}{c}$$

$$\tan \theta = \frac{\text{opp}}{\text{adj}} = \frac{a}{b}$$

In addition, reciprocals of these ratios are often used. These are called the *cosecant*, *secant*, and *cotangent*, abbreviated csc, sec, and cot. For angle θ in Figure 24–7 these functions are

$$\csc \theta = \frac{1}{\sin \theta} = \frac{1}{\dfrac{\text{opp}}{\text{hyp}}} = \frac{\text{hyp}}{\text{opp}} = \frac{c}{a}$$

$$\sec \theta = \frac{1}{\cos \theta} = \frac{1}{\dfrac{\text{adj}}{\text{hyp}}} = \frac{\text{hyp}}{\text{adj}} = \frac{c}{b}$$

$$\cot \theta = \frac{1}{\tan \theta} = \frac{1}{\dfrac{\text{opp}}{\text{adj}}} = \frac{\text{adj}}{\text{opp}} = \frac{b}{a}$$

These ratios may be set up in an identical manner for angle ϕ in Figure 24–7.

The above ratios may be applied to any right triangle. These trigonometric functions are now shown in summary form, using angle θ for convenience, remembering that they apply to any angle.

$$\sin \theta = \frac{\text{opp}}{\text{hyp}}, \qquad \csc \theta = \frac{\text{hyp}}{\text{opp}}$$

$$\cos \theta = \frac{\text{adj}}{\text{hyp}}, \qquad \sec \theta = \frac{\text{hyp}}{\text{adj}}$$

$$\tan \theta = \frac{\text{opp}}{\text{adj}}, \qquad \cot \theta = \frac{\text{adj}}{\text{opp}}$$

The above trigonometric ratios are absolutely essential for our future work. Comitting these ratios to memory is vital. The student should become so familiar with them that they may be used with the same ease as the multiplication tables of basic arithmetic.

The procedure of determining various trigonometric functions for any right triangle is shown in the following example.

example 24–3 Determine the following trigonometric functions for the triangle shown in Figure 24–8: sin α, cos β, tan α, sec β, cot α, and csc β.

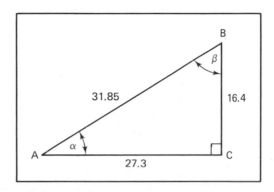

FIGURE 24–8
Diagram for Example 24–3

solution: The trigonometric functions are found as follows:

$$\sin \alpha = \frac{\text{opp}}{\text{hyp}} = \frac{16.4}{31.85} = 0.515$$

$$\cos \beta = \frac{\text{adj}}{\text{hyp}} = \frac{16.4}{31.85} = 0.515$$

$$\tan \alpha = \frac{\text{opp}}{\text{adj}} = \frac{16.4}{27.3} = 0.601$$

$$\sec \beta = \frac{\text{hyp}}{\text{adj}} = \frac{31.85}{16.4} = 1.942$$

$$\cot \alpha = \frac{\text{adj}}{\text{opp}} = \frac{27.3}{16.4} = 1.665$$

$$\csc \beta = \frac{\text{hyp}}{\text{opp}} = \frac{31.85}{27.3} = 1.167$$

24–4 COMPARISON OF TRIGONOMETRIC FUNCTIONS

The trigonometric functions in Section 24–3 were determined only for angle θ in Figure 24–7. If they were found for angle φ as well, an interesting fact would become apparent. The functions for both angle θ and angle ϕ are shown in tabular form as follows:

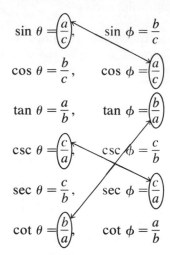

$$\sin \theta = \left(\frac{a}{c}\right), \qquad \sin \phi = \frac{b}{c}$$

$$\cos \theta = \frac{b}{c}, \qquad \cos \phi = \left(\frac{a}{c}\right)$$

$$\tan \theta = \frac{a}{b}, \qquad \tan \phi = \left(\frac{b}{a}\right)$$

$$\csc \theta = \left(\frac{c}{a}\right), \qquad \csc \phi = \frac{c}{b}$$

$$\sec \theta = \frac{c}{b}, \qquad \sec \phi = \left(\frac{c}{a}\right)$$

$$\cot \theta = \left(\frac{b}{a}\right), \qquad \cot \phi = \frac{a}{b}$$

Examination of these functions shows that an interrelation exists between them. It is seen that the function of one angle is equal to the cofunction of the other angle. For example, as shown above, $\sin \theta = \cos \phi$, $\tan \phi = \cot \theta$, $\csc \theta = \sec \phi$, etc. As angles θ and ϕ are complementary angles, that is, $\theta + \phi = 90°$, we see that $\theta = 90° - \phi$ and $\phi = 90° - \theta$. The above relationships are used to establish the following:

$$\sin \phi = \sin (90° - \theta) = \cos \theta$$

$$\cos \phi = \cos (90° - \theta) = \sin \theta$$

$$\tan \phi = \tan (90° - \theta) = \cot \theta$$

$$\csc \phi = \csc (90° - \theta) = \sec \theta$$

$$\sec \phi = \sec (90° - \theta) = \csc \theta$$

$$\cot \phi = \cot (90° - \theta) = \tan \theta$$

This interrelationship of functions, as shown above, is often very useful. For example, if the $\sin 30° = 0.5$, then $\sin (90° - 60°) = \cos 60° = 0.5$. Similarly, if the $\cos 30° = 0.866$, then $\cos (90° - 60°) = \sin 60° = 0.866$. In short, *knowing the function of any angle smaller than 90° immediately provides us with the cofunction of its complementary angle.*

EXERCISE 24-1

Using the triangle of Figure 24-9:

1.   Determine $\sin \alpha$, $\cot \beta$, and $\csc \alpha$.

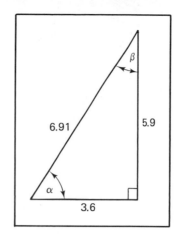

FIGURE 24–9
Triangle for Problems 1–3

2. Determine sin β, tan α, and sec β.

3. Determine cos α, tan β, and cot α.

Using the triangle of Figure 24–10:

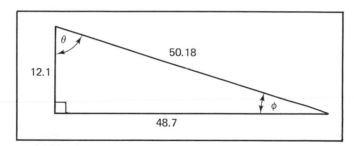

FIGURE 24–10
Triangle for Problems 4–6

4. Determine cos θ, sin φ, and tan θ.

5. Determine sin θ, sec φ, and cot θ.

6. Determine cot φ, csc θ, and sec θ.

Using the triangle of Figure 24–11:

7. Determine sin α, cot β, and tan β.

8. Determine cos β, sec α, and sin β.

9. Determine tan α, csc β, and cos α.

Using the triangle of Figure 24–12:

10. If $a = 16$, $b = 12$, find tan α, csc β, and cot α.

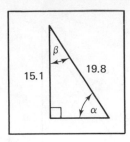

FIGURE 24–11
Triangle for Problems 7–9

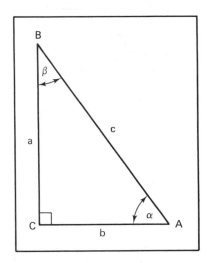

FIGURE 24–12
Triangle for Problems 10–13

11. If $c = 15.1$ and $a = 12.2$, find $\sin \beta$, $\cot \beta$, and $\sec \alpha$.

12. If $b = 27.1$ and $c = 56.5$, find $\cos \alpha$, $\cot \beta$, and $\sin \alpha$.

13. If $a = 124$ and $b = 182$, find $\csc \alpha$, $\sec \beta$, and $\cot \alpha$.

14. If $\sin \theta = 0.617$, what is $\csc \theta$?

15. If $\cot \beta = 1.76$, what is $\tan \beta$?

16. If $\cos \alpha = 0.317$, what is $\sec \alpha$?

24–5 FUNCTIONS OF POSITIVE ANGLES GREATER THAN 90°

In previous sections, we have discussed only angles in the standard position in the first quadrant, or from 0 to 90°. It will be seen that the *functions of any angle* are a logical extension of this basic knowledge.

355
Sec. 24–5
FUNCTIONS OF
POSITIVE
ANGLES
GREATER
THAN 90°

In Chapter 23, we saw how a rotating radius could be used to represent any angle. When the rotation was CCW, a positive angle was generated, while CW rotation generated a negative angle.

In Figure 24–13, positive angles of 160°, 210°, and 300° are shown generated by a rotating radius of length, r. In each figure a perpendicular is dropped to the x axis. From our work with Cartesian coordinates, it is remembered that this establishes the x, y position of the outer point of the radius. More important, however, is that we now have right triangles in which *all three sides are known*. The value of y represents the opposite side of the angle formed with the x axis, while the value of x represents the adjacent side. The radius represents the hypotenuse of the triangles.

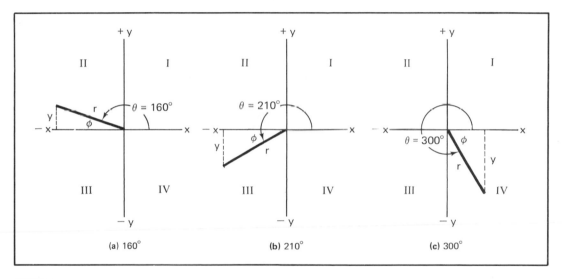

FIGURE 24–13
Angles Greater than 90°

The functions of angles greater than 90° are determined in a similar manner to those less than 90°. All the functions in quadrant I were positive, while the various functions in quadrants II, III, and IV may be either positive or negative. This is determined by the sign of the x and y coordinates representing the sides of the triangle. For example, in Figure 24–13a, the opposite side of the triangle is represented by a $+y$ value, while the adjacent side is represented by a $-x$ value. The functions will reflect this as

$$\sin 160° = \frac{\text{opp}}{\text{hyp}} = \frac{y}{r} \quad \text{while the} \quad \cos 160° = \frac{\text{adj}}{\text{hyp}} = \frac{-x}{r}$$

The sine is seen to have a positive value, in that both y and r are positive. The cosine will be negative, however, in that the value of x has a negative value and the value of r is positive. In a similar manner, the sign of any function may be determined.

In Figure 24–14 the signs of the functions in each quadrant are shown. A simple method of remembering the signs of these functions

II		I
sin +		sin +
cos −		cos +
tan −		tan +
sin −		sin −
cos −		cos +
tan +		tan −
III		IV

FIGURE 24–14
Signs of Functions
in Each Quadrant

is shown in Figure 24–15. In Figure 24–14 it is noted that only the sine is positive in the second quadrant. In the third quadrant only the tangent is positive. In the fourth quadrant only the remaining function or the cosine is positive. In the first quadrant all functions are positive.

Second (II)		First (I)
sin +		all +
tan +		cos +
Third (III)		Fourth (IV)

FIGURE 24–15
Simplified Method
for Determining Signs

Once the signs of the functions in each quadrant have been mastered, the signs of the reciprocal functions are easily determined. The result of division into 1 does not result in a change of sign; hence the reciprocal functions have the *same* sign as the function involved. For example, the tangent in the third quadrant is positive, resulting in a positive cotangent. Similarly, the cosine is negative in the second quadrant; hence the secant would be negative. Although it is helpful to have such memory aids as the figures shown, it is much more important for the reader to establish firmly the basic principles involved. In this manner, the signs of the functions in any quadrant can easily be established.

If an angle greater than 360° is involved, the procedure is identical with that used in Chapter 23. This involves subtracting the largest 360° multiple from the angle involved. This would leave an angle between 0 and 360°. This angle would be treated in exactly the same manner as those above.

example 24–4 Determine the sign of the sine and tangent of an angle of +870°.

solution: It is seen that there are two multiples of 360°, or 720°, in this angle. Therefore,

$$870° - 720° = 150°$$

The angle of 150° is in quadrant II, where the sin 150° is + and the tan 150° is −.

24–6 FUNCTIONS OF NEGATIVE ANGLES

A negative angle is generated by the CW rotation of a radius, *r*. A negative angle of −250° is depicted in Figure 24–16. This figure shows a −250° angle and a +110° angle form the same angle ϕ with the −*x* axis. The functions of a positive angle are determined as shown in previous sections.

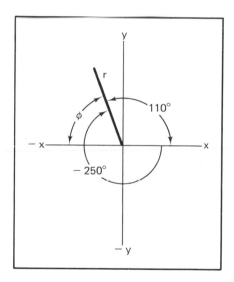

FIGURE 24–16
Diagram of an Angle of −250°

example 24–5 Determine the sign of the sine and tangent of −200°.

solution: An angle of −200° is seen to be equivalent to an angle of $360° - 200° = +160°$. A +160° angle falls in quadrant II, where

sin + 160°   is +

cos + 160°   is −

example 24-6 Determine the sign of the cosine and tangent of $-390°$.

solution: It is seen that there is one $360°$ multiple in $-390°$. Hence $-390°$ is equivalent to $-30°$. A $-30°$ angle is equivalent to an angle of $360° - 30° = +330°$. The $+330°$ angle falls in quadrant IV, where

$$\cos + 330° \text{ is } +$$

$$\tan + 330° \text{ is } -$$

24-7 TRIGONOMETRIC FUNCTIONS OF 0° AND 90°

In Section 24-3, the trigonometric functions for the 45°–45°–90° and the 30°–60°–90° triangles were found. The functions for 0° and 90° were, however, not discussed.

In Figure 24–17a, the angle θ, represented by θ_1 and θ_2, is shown to be decreasing toward 0°. The functions of the angle θ are, as $\theta_1 \to \theta_2 \to 0°$:

$$\sin \theta = \frac{a}{c}: \quad \text{as } a \to 0; \text{ then } \sin 0° = \frac{0}{c} = 0$$

$$\cos \theta = \frac{b}{c}: \quad \text{as } c \to b; \text{ then } \cos 0° = \frac{b = c}{c} = 1$$

$$\tan \theta = \frac{a}{b}: \quad \text{as } a \to 0; \text{ then } \tan 0° = \frac{0}{b} = 0$$

FIGURE 24–17
Diagrams for Developing Functions of 0° and 90°

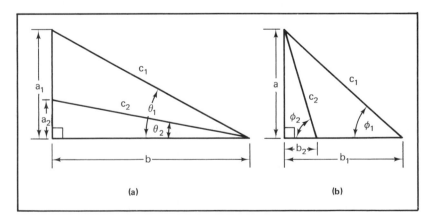

(a)　　　　　　　　(b)

In Figure 24–17b, angle ϕ, represented by ϕ_1 and ϕ_2, is seen to be increasing toward 90°. The functions of the angle ϕ are, as

$$\phi_1 \to \phi_2 \to 90°$$

$$\sin \phi = \frac{a}{c}; \quad b \to 0, c \to a; \text{ then } \sin 90° = \frac{a = c}{c} = 1$$

$$\cos \phi = \frac{b}{c}; \quad b \to 0; \text{ then } \cos 90° = \frac{0}{c} = 0$$

$$\tan \phi = \frac{a}{b}; \quad b \to 0; \text{ then } \tan 90° = \frac{c}{0} = \infty$$

Note that division by zero is impossible. However as $b \to 0$, $\tan \phi$ becomes infinitely large. This is designated by ∞.

The above values of the functions, as well as those previously obtained, are shown in Table 24–1. In the table, the values of the

TABLE 24–1 Selected Trigonometric Functions

ANGLE	SIN	COS	TAN
0°	0	1	0
30°	0.500	0.866	0.577
45°	0.707	0.707	1
60°	0.866	0.500	1.732
90°	1	0	∞

trignometric functions of a few common angles have been tabulated. For these tables to be consistently useful, such data would have to be available for all angles between 0° and 90°. Fortunately, these trigonometric tables are available, and individual calculations are not necessary. Such trigonometric tables are found in Table B in the Appendix. The use of the tables will be discussed in Chapter 25.

EXERCISE 24–2

Determine the sign of the sine, cosine, and tangents of the following angles:

1. 95°   2. 190°   3. −190°

4. 280°   5. −300°   6. −5°

7. −365°   8. 952°   9. −604°

Determine the quadrants in the following.

10. $\sin \theta$ is $+$, $\cos \theta$ is $+$ **11.** $\tan \theta$ is $-$

12. $\cot \theta$ is $+$ **13.** $\csc \theta$ is $+$

14. If the CCW rotation of radius, r, shown in Figure 24–18 generates angle θ and point A has coordinates (6, 8), what are the sine, cosine, and tangent of θ?

15. Repeat problem 14, with point A coordinates $(-8, -10)$.

16. Repeat problem 14, with point A coordinates $(-9, 4)$.

FIGURE   24–18
Diagram for Problems 14–16

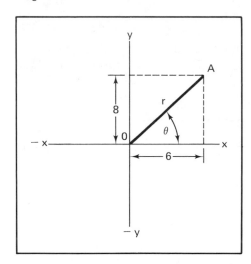

25

TRIGONOMETRIC OPERATIONS

In Chapter 24, a simple trigonometric table was developed. It was noted that accurate tables of trigonometric functions for angles from 0 to 90° have been developed. Table B in the Appendix is an example of such a table. In this chapter, these tables will be used in a number of trigonometric operations involving the right triangle.

25–1 TRIGONOMETRIC TABLES

Various types of tables of trigonometric functions are available. Some tables provide the functions for angles in degrees and minutes while others have the angles with decimal divisions.

The tables that we will be using are called *natural trigonometric functions*. Table B in the Appendix provides the functions of angles in 0.1° increments from 0–90°. A segment of Table B is shown in Table 25–1. This shows the cosine function for 25°–26.9°.

TABLE 25–1 Segment of Cosine Functions Table: Appendix Table B

DEG-REE	0.0°	0.1°	0.2°	0.3°	0.4°	0.5°	0.6°	0.7°	0.8°	0.9°
25°	0.9063	0.9056	0.9048	0.9041	0.9033	0.9026	0.9018	0.9011	0.9033	0.8996
26°	0.8988	0.8980	0.8973	0.8965	0.8957	0.8949	0.8942	0.8934	0.8926	0.8918

25–2 FINDING THE FUNCTIONS OF A GIVEN ANGLE

Examination of Table 25–1 shows that any cosine function between 25° and 26.9° may be determined. For example,

$$\cos 25.0° = 0.9063$$

$$\cos 25.8° = 0.9003$$

$$\cos 26.6° = 0.8942$$

This procedure is a straightforward one, requiring only the selection from the table of the value of the function for the angle involved. The sine, cosine, or tangent function of any angle between 0° and 90° may be similarly obtained by using the appropriate table in the Appendix.

The question will arise as to how the cosine of an angle of 25.26° is determined. The divisions in Table 25–1 show only the functions for 25.2° and 25.3°. The process of "proportioning" the difference between the two angles to determine the function of the angle required is called *interpolation*. This is shown as follows:

	Angle	Cosine Function
	25.2°	0.9048
	25.3°	0.9041
Difference	+0.1°	−0.0007

This shows that a 0.1° increase in the angle causes a 0.0007 decrease in the function. The required angle, 25.26°, is 0.06° above the function value for 25.2°. Setting up a proportion, we see that

$$\frac{0.1°}{0.0007} = \frac{0.06}{x} \quad \text{or} \quad x = \frac{0.06}{0.1}(0.0007)$$

$$x = \frac{0.06}{0.1}(0.0007) = 0.6(0.0007) = 0.00042$$

Then the cosine function of 25.26° is:

function 25.2° − the 0.06° increment   or

0.9048 − 0.00042

0.90438

This calculation with the five-place results shown implies an accuracy that is not present in our four-place function tables. The proper procedure is to "round off" the interpolation results to four places. Then

cos 25.26° = 0.9044

example 25–1 Determine tan 56.25°.

solution:

	tan 56.2° =	1.494
	tan 56.3° =	1.499
Difference	+0.1°	+0.005

Using a proportional relation, as before, results in

$$x = \frac{0.05}{0.1}(0.005)$$

$$= 0.5(0.005) = 0.0025$$

$$\tan 56.25° = \text{function } 56.2° + 0.05° \text{ increment}$$

$$= 1.494 + 0.0025$$

$$= 1.4965 \quad \text{or (rounding)}$$

$$= 1.497$$

example 25-2   Determine $\sin 18.78°$.

solution:

$$\sin 18.7° = \quad 0.3206$$
$$\sin 18.8° = \quad 0.3223$$
$$\text{Difference} \quad +0.1° \quad +0.0017$$

$$x = \frac{0.08}{0.1}(0.0017)$$

$$= 0.8(0.0017) = 0.00136$$

$$\sin 18.78° = \text{function } 18.7° + 0.08° \text{ increment}$$

$$= 0.3206 + 0.00136$$

$$= 0.32196$$

$$= 0.3220$$

EXERCISE   25-1   Find the sine, cosine, and tangent of the following angles.

1.	(a) 52°	(b) 38°	(c) 89°
2.	(a) 5.3°	(b) 16.7°	(c) 21.2°
3.	(a) 23.2°	(b) 33.3°	(c) 15.5°
4.	(a) 62.75°	(b) 9.63°	(c) 77.77°

25-3   FINDING THE ANGLE OF A GIVEN FUNCTION

The process of finding the angle of a given function is an inverse procedure of that used in Section 25-2. A system of notation has evolved to provide a more convenient method of saying

----

"find the angle whose sine is"   or
"find the angle whose tangent is"   etc.

This is done in the following manner:

$$\theta = \arcsin x \quad \text{or}$$

$$\theta = \sin^{-1} x$$

In each case we are saying

"θ is the angle whose sine is . . ."

To avoid confusion with exponential notation, the form $\theta = \text{arcsin } x$ will be used in this text.

example 25–3   Find $\theta = \text{arcsin } 0.5906$.

solution: This involves a search of the sine tables for a value equal to 0.5906. It is often helpful to use values for common angles with which we are familiar. For example, we know from our previous work that sin 30° = 0.5 and sin 45° is 0.707. This tells us that the angle we are looking for is between 30° and 45°. This narrows our search considerably. From the tables.

$\theta = \text{arcsin } 0.5906 = 36.2°$

example 25–4   Find $\theta = \text{arctan } 2.660$.

solution: We know that tan 45° = 1 and tan 60° = 1.732. The search is thus narrowed to an angle between 60° and 90°. From the tables,

$\theta = \text{arctan } 2.660 = 69.4°$

example 25–5   Find $\theta = \text{arccos } 0.6775$.

solution: We know that cos 60° = 0.50 and cos 45° = 0.707. Our search is thus narrowed to an angle between 45° and 60°. From the tables it is seen that interpolation is required:

	Angle	Cosine Function
	47.4°	0.6769
	47.3°	0.6782
Difference	−0.1°	+0.0013

The data show that a decrease of 0.1° causes an increase in the cosine function of 0.0013. The required function is

$0.6675 - 0.6769 = 0.0006 \text{ unit}$

above the 47.4° function or is located

$$\frac{0.0006}{0.0013} = 0.46 \text{ of the distance between the two angles,}$$

$47.4°$ and $47.3°$ or

$$0.1° \times 0.46 = 0.046° \text{ below } 47.4°$$

$$47.4° - 0.046° = 47.354° \quad \text{or}$$

$$\theta = \arccos 0.6775 = 47.35°$$

example 25–6   Find $\theta = \arctan 0.1850$.

solution: As $\tan 0° = 0$ and $\tan 30° = 0.577$, θ will be found in this range. From the tables it is found that interpolation is necessary.

	Angle	Tangent Function
	10.4°	0.1835
	10.5°	0.1853
Difference	+0.1°	+0.0018

The required function is seen to be $0.1850 - 0.1835 = 0.0015$ unit above the 10.4° function, or is located

$$\frac{0.0015}{0.0018} = 0.833 \text{ of the distance between } 10.4° \text{ and}$$

$10.5°$ or

$$0.1° \times 0.833 = 0.0833° \text{ above } 10.4° \quad \text{or}$$

$$10.4° + 0.0833° = 10.4833° \quad \text{or}$$

$$\theta = \arctan 0.1850 = 10.48°$$

     The above examples have provided an exposure to operations that require determination of the angle of a given function. In Section 25–2, experience was obtained in determining the functions of a given angle. In both these operations, tables were used and interpolations performed with far greater accuracy than often required. These procedures did, however, provide experience in the methods involved which are of considerable importance.

     It has been pointed out previously that circuit components, voltage variations, temperature effects, component aging, and so on, are practical considerations involved in electronic circuit operations. These factors are some of the reasons why great accuracy in our calculations is often unnecessary. For most circuit work, accuracy such as is used in the previous examples is unneeded. Most of you will probably use the small integrated-circuit hand calculators. Many of these will provide accuracies far greater than practical considerations require. As indicated in an earlier chapter, accuracy to three places is suitable for our purposes unless otherwise required.

EXERCISE 25–2 Find the angle of the following given functions.

1. $\theta = \arcsin 0.672$
2. $\beta = \arctan 1.627$

3. $\phi = \arccos 0.027$
4. $\theta = \arcsin 0.058$

5. $\alpha = \arcsin 0.465$
6. $\phi = \arccos 0.167$

7. $\beta = \arctan 0.292$
8. $\alpha = \arcsin 0.278$

25–4 OPERATIONS WITH ANGLES GREATER THAN 90°

In Section 24–5, procedures were developed for determining the functions of angles greater than 90°. This work was valid and created no problems until it was found that the tables of trigonometric functions only include angles between 0° and 90°. It becomes obvious, then, that at this point we must reexamine our previous work to cope with this situation. Accordingly, Figure 24–13, which dealt with angles greater than 90°, is repeated here as Figure 25–1. In Figure 25–1a, an angle $\theta = 160°$ in the second quadrant was created by the rotation

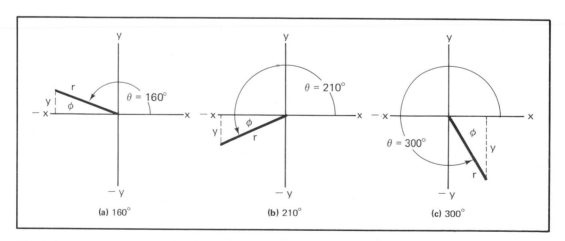

FIGURE 25–1
Angles Greater than 90°

of a radius, r. The functions of θ were determined using the x and y coordinates of the terminal point of radius, r, which were obtained by dropping a perpendicular to the x axis. Examination of this triangle, or similar triangles in other quadrants, have the general functions of

$$\sin \theta = \frac{y}{r}, \qquad \cos \theta = \frac{x}{r}, \qquad \tan \theta = \frac{y}{x}$$

However, these functions are equivalent to the absolute values of the functions of the angle ϕ, in that the acute angle ϕ is bounded by the sides x, y, and r. We may then relate angle θ and angle ϕ:

$$\sin (180° - \theta) = \frac{y}{r} = \sin \phi$$

$$\cos (180° - \theta) = \frac{-x}{r} = -\cos \phi$$

$$\tan (180° - \theta) = \frac{y}{-x} = -\tan \phi$$

As $\phi = (180° - \theta)$, we have an angle between 0° and 90°, and the tables of trigonometric functions may be used. For example, in Figure 25–1a where $\theta = 160°$,

$$\sin 160° = \sin (180° - 160°) = \sin 20° = 0.342$$

In Figure 25–1b we see that

$$\sin \phi = \frac{-y}{r}, \qquad \cos \phi = \frac{-x}{r}, \qquad \tan \phi = \frac{-y}{-x}$$

As these are equivalent to the absolute values of the functions of angle θ, we may write

$$\sin (\theta - 180°) = \frac{-y}{r} = -\sin \phi$$

$$\cos (\theta - 180°) = \frac{-x}{r} = -\cos \phi$$

$$\tan (\theta - 180°) = \frac{-y}{-x} = \tan \phi$$

As $\phi = (\theta - 180°)$, we are again working with an angle between 0° and 90°. For example, in Figure 25–1b where $\theta = 210°$,

$$\cos 210° = -\cos (210° - 180°) = -\cos 30° = -0.866$$

In Figure 25–1c, we may write

$$\sin \phi = \frac{-y}{r}, \qquad \cos \phi = \frac{x}{r}, \qquad \tan \phi = \frac{-y}{x}$$

Again, as these are equivalent to the absolute values of the functions of angle θ, we have

$$\sin (360° - \theta) = \frac{-y}{r} = -\sin \phi$$

$$\cos (360° - \theta) = \frac{x}{r} = \cos \phi$$

$$\tan (360° - \theta) = \frac{-y}{x} = -\tan \phi$$

Again we have an angle in the 0° to 90° range. For example, in Figure 25–1c where $\theta = 300°$

$$\tan 300° = -\tan (360° - 300°) = -\tan 60° = -1.732$$

Angles above 360° are handled in a manner outlined in Chapter 24. The largest multiple of 360° is subtracted from the angle. This leaves an angle between 0° and 360°. This is then treated as above, depending on the size of the angle, which of course determines its quadrant and the method of handling.

Negative angles are handled in a similar manner. The CW rotation of a radius stops in a particular quadrant. A perpendicular dropped to the x axis permits the functions of θ and ϕ to be determined as before. The only difference in a positive and negative angle is in the direction in which the radius is rotated. For example, the functions of a 30° angle are identical with those of a $-330°$ angle. The resultant angle with the x axis is the same, the only difference being in the direction of radius rotation.

In summary, the functions of any angle θ, positive or negative, are obtained from the acute angle ϕ which the rotating radius forms with the x axis. The appropriate sign for the particular function, in the particular quadrant involved, must then be designated.

example 25–7 Determine the sine, cosine, and tangent of $\theta = 100°$.

solution: This angle is shown in Figure 25–2. Angle $\theta = 100°$ forms the acute angle $\phi = 180° - \theta = 180° - 100° = 80°$ with the x axis, as shown. This is a second quadrant angle, and hence the signs of the functions are determined using the $+y$ and $-x$ coordinates.

$$\sin 100° = \sin 80° = 0.985$$

$$\cos 100° = -\cos 80° = -0.174$$

$$\tan 100° = -\tan 80° = -5.671$$

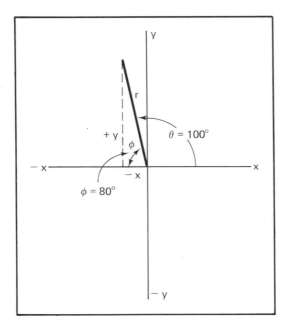

FIGURE 25–2
Diagram for Example 25–7

example 25–8 Determine the sine, cosine, and tangent of $\theta = 200°$.

solution: As shown in Figure 25–3,

$$\phi = \theta - 180° = 200° - 180° = 20°$$

$$\sin 200° = -\sin 20° = -0.342$$

$$\cos 200° = -\cos 20° = -0.940$$

$$\tan 200° = \tan 20° = 0.364$$

example 25–9 Determine the sine, cosine, and tangent of $\theta = 300°$.

solution: As shown in Figure 25–4,

$$\phi = 360° - \theta = 360° - 300° = 60°$$

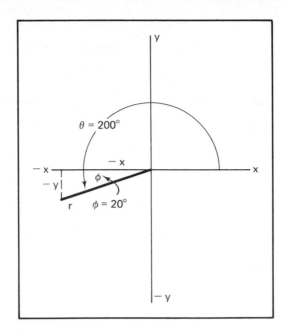

FIGURE 25–3
Diagram for Example 25–8

FIGURE 25–4
Diagram for Example 25–9

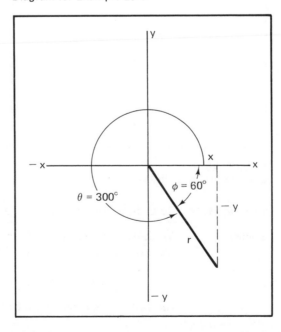

$$\sin 300° = -\sin 60° = -0.866$$

$$\cos 300° = \cos 60° = 0.500$$

$$\tan 300° = -\tan 60° = -1.732$$

example 25-10 Determine the sine, cosine, and tangent for $\theta = -206°$.

solution: As shown in Figure 25–5,

$$\phi = \theta - 180° = 206 - 180 = 26°$$

$$\sin - 206° = \sin 26° = 0.438$$

$$\cos - 206° = -\cos 26° = -0.899$$

$$\tan - 206° = -\tan 26° = -0.488$$

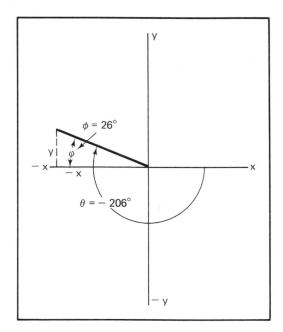

FIGURE 25–5
Diagram for Example 25–10

example 25-11 Determine the sine, cosine, and tangent of 600°.

solution: As shown in Figure 25–6, there is one 360° multiple in 600°, resulting in an angle of $600° - 360° = 240°$:

$$\phi = 240° - 180° = 60°$$

$$\sin 240° = -\sin 60° = -0.866$$

$$\cos 240° = -\cos 60° = -0.500$$

$$\tan 240° = \tan 60° = 1.732$$

Note the comparison with Example 25–9, where $\phi = 60°$ (but in the fourth quadrant).

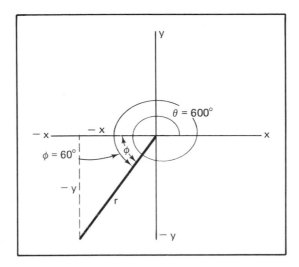

FIGURE 25–6
Diagram for Example 25–11

EXERCISE 25–3

1. Determine the sine, cosine, and tangent of 165°.

2. Determine the sine, cosine, and tangent of 235°.

3. Determine the sine, cosine, and tangent of −65°.

4. Determine the sine, cosine, and tangent of 660° and −420°.

25–5 RIGHT-TRIANGLE OPERATIONS

This section will provide the reader with some helpful suggestions for the solution of problems involving the right triangle. These are of a general nature and apply to all work with right triangles in subsequent sections.

Solution of problems involving the right triangle may be made using graphical methods or trigonometry. The accuracy and convenience of trigonometric procedures are far superior to graphical methods. Trigonometry will therefore be the method used in the solution of problems involving the right triangle.

In previous work a number of facts regarding triangles have been developed. These will now be summarized. The facts that can be stated about the triangle shown in Figure 25–7 follows:

$$\alpha + \beta + \gamma = 180°$$

$$\alpha + \beta = 90°$$

$$a^2 + b^2 = c^2$$

$$\sin \alpha = \cos \beta = \frac{a}{c}, \qquad \sin \beta = \cos \alpha = \frac{b}{c}$$

$$\cos \alpha = \sin \beta = \frac{b}{c}, \qquad \cos \beta = \sin \alpha = \frac{a}{c}$$

$$\tan \alpha = \cot \beta = \frac{a}{b}, \qquad \tan \beta = \cot \alpha = \frac{b}{a}$$

$$\alpha = \arcsin \frac{a}{c}, \qquad \alpha = \arccos \frac{b}{c}, \qquad \alpha = \arctan \frac{a}{b}$$

$$\beta = \arcsin \frac{b}{c}, \qquad \beta = \arccos \frac{a}{c}, \qquad \beta = \arctan \frac{b}{a}$$

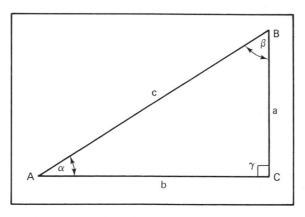

FIGURE 25–7
Triangle in Standard Position

The above information when properly applied is all that is necessary to solve problems involving the right triangle. In any solution, a systematic approach is essential. This takes the following form:

1. Sketch the triangle to a convenient scale. This procedure will permit a visual check of the results of your calculations.

2. Label the known parts. There are six parts of the triangle involved. These are the sides, a, b, and c and the angles α, β, and γ.

3. Carefully analyze the problem—what is known and unknown, and what is required—and then determine the procedures necessary to obtain the solution.

4. Perform the necessary calculations carefully, rounding out results when possible.

5. Check your computations using the scale triangle. Sketch to visually confirm the results. Where possible, use the newly acquired calculated data to confirm results, using another of the triangle facts listed in the summary.

375
Sec. 25–6
TRIANGLE
SOLUTIONS—ONE
SIDE AND AN
ACUTE ANGLE
KNOWN

The above procedures should provide the reader with some assistance in the solution of problems involving the right triangle. They provide a logical and systematic problem approach which should produce results that are correct with a minimum amount of time and effort.

In subsequent sections a wide variety of examples involving the right triangle will be presented. A thorough familiarity of the solution methods, along with experience in the solution of problems provided in the exercises, will be of great assistance in the ac circuit work that follows.

25–6 TRIANGLE SOLUTIONS—ONE SIDE AND AN ACUTE ANGLE KNOWN

example 25–12 Given $\theta = 37°$, $a = 18$, find b, c, and ϕ.

solution: Figure 25–8 is drawn with the known parts labeled.

$$\theta + \phi = 90°,$$

$$37° + \phi = 90°,$$

$$\phi = 90° - 37° = 53°$$

We now have the two acute angles plus one side. We may now choose any function in which two of the three quantities are known and obtain the unknown value. For example,

$$\tan \theta = \frac{a}{b}, \qquad \sin \theta = \frac{a}{c}$$

$$\tan \phi = \frac{b}{a}, \qquad \cos \phi = \frac{a}{c}$$

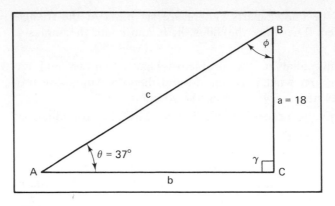

FIGURE 25–8
Diagram for Example 25–12

In each of the above there is one unknown. Choosing at random,

$$\cos \phi = \frac{a}{c}$$

$$c = \frac{a}{\cos \phi} = \frac{18}{\cos 53} = \frac{18}{0.602} = 29.9$$

The following relationship may be used to solve for b, the remaining unknown:

$$\tan \theta = \frac{a}{b}$$

$$b = \frac{a}{\tan} = \frac{18}{\tan 37°} = \frac{18}{0.754} = 23.88$$

to check:

$$a^2 + b^2 = c^2$$

$$(18)^2 + (23.88)^2 = (29.9)^2$$

$$324 + 570 = 894$$

$$894 = 894$$

The calculations are correct.

example 25–13 Given $\phi = 67°$ and $b = 26$, find θ, c, and a.

solution: Figure 25–9 is shown with known parts labeled. Selecting any convenient function with two known quantities,

377
Sec. 25–6
TRIANGLE
SOLUTIONS—ONE
SIDE AND AN
ACUTE ANGLE
KNOWN

$$\sin \phi = \frac{b}{c}$$

$$c = \frac{b}{\sin \phi} = \frac{26}{\sin 67°} = \frac{26}{0.921} = 28.24$$

$$\tan \phi = \frac{b}{a}$$

$$a = \frac{b}{\tan \phi} = \frac{26}{\tan 67°} = \frac{26}{2.36} = 11.02$$

$$\theta + \phi = 90°, \qquad \theta = 90° - \phi = 90° - 67° = 23°$$

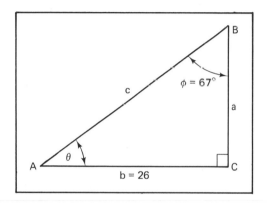

FIGURE 25–9
Diagram for Example 25–13

to check:

$$a^2 + b^2 = c^2$$

$$(11.02)^2 + (26)^2 = (28.24)^2$$

$$121.4 + 676 = 797.4$$

$$797.4 = 797.4$$

The solution is correct.

---

example 25–14 Given $c = 28$ $\phi = 39.2°$, find a, b, and θ.

solution: Figure 25–10 is drawn with known parts labeled.

$$\theta + \phi = 90° \qquad \theta = 90° - \phi = 90° - 39.2° = 50.8°$$

$$\cos \theta = \frac{b}{c}$$

$$b = c \cos \theta = 28 \cos 50.8° = 28 \times 0.632$$

$$= 17.70$$

$$\sin \theta = \frac{a}{c}$$

$$a = c \sin \theta = 28 \sin 50.8° = 28 \times 0.775$$

$$= 21.70$$

to check: $a^2 + b^2 = c^2$ $(21.7)^2 + (17.7)^2 = (28)^2$

$$784 = 784$$

The answer is correct.

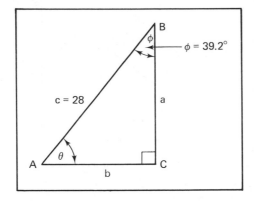

FIGURE 25–10
Diagram for Example 25–14

example 25–15 Given $c = 67.3$ and $\theta = 48.9°$, find ϕ, a, and b.

solution: Figure 25–11 is drawn with known parts labeled.

$$\cos \theta = \frac{b}{c}$$

$$b = c \cos \theta = 67.3 \cos 48.9° = 67.3 \times 0.657$$

$$= 44.24$$

$$\tan \theta = \frac{a}{b}$$

$$a = b \tan \theta = 44.24 \tan 48.9° = 44.24 \times 1.146$$

$$= 50.71$$

$$\theta + \phi = 90°, \qquad 48.9° + \phi = 90°$$
$$\phi = 41.1°$$

to check: $\qquad a^2 + b^2 = c^2 \qquad (50.71)^2 + (44.24)^2 = (67.3)^2$

$$4{,}529 = 4{,}529$$

The answer is correct.

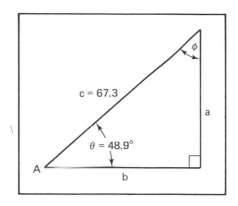

FIGURE 25–11
Diagram for Example 25–15

25-7 TRIANGLE SOLUTIONS—TWO SIDES KNOWN

example 25-16 Given $c = 40.75$ and $b = 25.3$, find a, θ, and ϕ.

solution: Figure 25–12 is drawn with parts labeled.

$$\cos \theta = \frac{b}{c} = \frac{25.3}{40.75} = 0.621$$

$$\theta = \arccos 0.621$$

$$\theta = 51.62°$$

$$\theta + \phi = 90°, \qquad 51.62° + \phi = 90°$$

$$\phi = 38.38°$$

$$\tan \theta = \frac{a}{b}$$

$$a = b \tan \theta = 25.3 \tan 51.62° = 25.3 \times 1.263$$

$$= 31.94$$

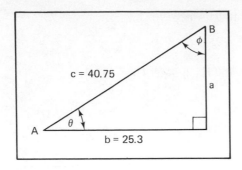

FIGURE   25–12
Diagram for Example 25–16

to check: $a^2 + b^2 = c^2$ $(31.94)^2 + (25.3)^2 = (40.75)^2$

$1660 = 1660$

The answer is correct.

example 25–17   Given $a = 12.5$ and $b = 30.2$, find θ, ϕ, and c.

solution: Figure 25–13 is drawn with parts labeled.

$$\tan \theta = \frac{a}{b} = \frac{12.5}{30.2} = 0.414$$

$$\theta = \arctan 0.414$$

$$= 22.49°$$

$$\theta + \phi = 90°$$

$$\phi = 90° - \theta = 90° - 22.49°$$

$$= 67.51°$$

$$\cos \theta = \frac{b}{c}$$

$$c = \frac{b}{\cos \theta} = \frac{30.2}{\cos 22.49°} = \frac{30.2}{0.924}$$

$$= 32.68$$

to check: $a^2 + b^2 = c^2$

$$(12.5)^2 + (30.2)^2 = (32.68)^2$$

$$1,068 = 1,068$$

The answer is correct.

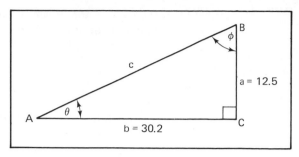

FIGURE 25-13
Diagram for Exercise 25-17

381
Sec. 25-8
PRACTICAL
PROBLEMS
INVOLVING
TRIANGLES

EXERCISE 25-4 In the following problems, solve for the unknown
parts of the triangle of a, b, c, θ, and ϕ.

1. $a = 16.7$,　$\theta = 32.5°$
2. $b = 32.7$,　$\theta = 5.9°$
3. $c = 66.5$,　$\theta = 71°$
4. $a = 48.7$,　$\phi = 21.2°$
5. $b - 55.9$,　$\phi = 36.7°$
6. $c = 41.6$,　$\phi = 55.2°$
7. $a = 16.7$,　$b = 27.2$
8. $a = 27.2$,　$b = 7.25$
9. $a = 71.4$,　$b = 32.7$
10. $a = 36.5$,　$c = 56.9$
11. $a = 44.5$,　$c = 66.8$
12. $b = 56.7$,　$c = 77.1$
13. $b = 61.2$,　$c = 82.3$
14. $\phi = 9.71°$,　$a = 13.2$
15. $\theta = 52.6°$,　$b = 56.4$
16. $\theta = 31.4°$,　$c = 107.2$

25-8 PRACTICAL PROBLEMS INVOLVING TRIANGLES

The work in previous sections of this chapter involved no practical
applications of the use of triangles and trigonometry. In this section, a
number of practical examples of the use of trigonometry will be shown.

example 25-18 A faulty aircraft warning light on a television trans-
mitting tower had to be replaced. At a distance of 1,000

ft from the base of the tower, a line of sight taken to the faulty light indicated an angle of 30.2° with the horizontal. At what level is the faulty light?

solution:

Figure 25–14 is drawn showing the tower and what is known in the problem. Examination shows that a right triangle exists, in which one side, the base, and the acute angle made with the ground is known. The distance x is unknown. Further examination shows that the adjacent side of the known angle is given and the side opposite, x, is the unknown. We may use the tangent function as

$$\tan 30.2° = \frac{\text{opposite side } (x)}{\text{adjacent side (base} = 1{,}000 \text{ ft)}}$$

$$x = 1{,}000 \tan 30.2°$$

$$= (1{,}000)(0.582)$$

$$= 582 \text{ ft} = \text{height of faulty light}$$

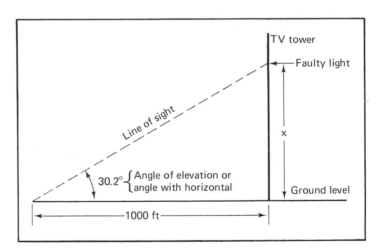

FIGURE 25–14
Diagram for Example 25–18

example 25–19 A 90-ft radio tower requires three guy wires at each of three levels, 90 ft, 60 ft, and 30 ft. The guy wires from each level will be connected to a common anchor, located 60 ft from the tower base. There will be three sets of guys around the tower 120° apart. Neglecting connections, what is the length of each guy wire and the total length of guy wire required for the tower? What angle does the wire make with the ground?

solution:

383

Sec. 25–8
PRACTICAL
PROBLEMS
INVOLVING
TRIANGLES

The tower is first drawn and labeled as shown in Figure 25–15. It is seen that we have three triangles formed, each with the base and the vertical side known. For each triangle, the angle the guy wire makes with the ground is determined as follows:

$$\tan \theta_1 = \frac{opp}{adj} = \frac{30}{60} = 0.500, \quad \theta_1 = \arctan 0.500 = 26.56°$$

$$\tan \theta_2 = \frac{opp}{adj} = \frac{60}{60} = 1.00, \quad \theta_2 = \arctan 1.00 = 45°$$

$$\tan \theta_3 = \frac{opp}{adj} = \frac{90}{60} = 1.50, \quad \theta_3 = \arctan 1.50 = 56.31°$$

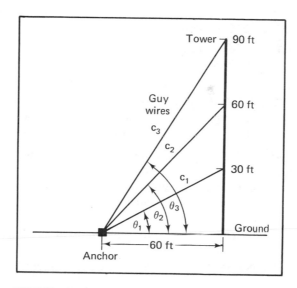

FIGURE 25–15
Diagram for Example 25–19

The guy wires are seen to be the hypotenuse of the triangles, which may now be determined as follows:

$$\cos \theta_1 = \frac{adj}{hyp} \quad or$$

$$c_1 = \frac{60}{\cos \theta_1} = \frac{60}{\cos 26.56°} = \frac{60}{0.894} = 67.1 \text{ ft}$$

$$\cos \theta_2 = \frac{adj}{hyp} \quad or$$

$$c_2 = \frac{60}{\cos \theta_2} = \frac{60}{\cos 45°} = \frac{60}{0.707} = 84.9 \text{ ft}$$

$$\cos \theta_3 = \frac{\text{adj}}{\text{hyp}} \quad \text{or}$$

$$c_3 = \frac{60}{\cos \theta_3} = \frac{60}{\cos 56.31°} = \frac{60}{0.555} = 108.1 \text{ ft}$$

The total length of guy wire per side is

$$c_1 + c_2 + c_3 = 67.1 + 84.9 + 108.1 = 260.1 \text{ ft}$$

As the tower has guys on three sides, the total wire is

$$L_T = 260.1 \times 3 = 780.3 \text{ ft}$$

EXERCISE 25-5

1. A 28-ft ladder is placed against the side of a building. The top of the ladder is 22 ft from the ground. Determine the distance the base of the ladder is from the building.

2. A metal brace 25 ft long is to be placed against a radio tower at a 45° angle. How far away from tower will be the base of the brace? How far above the ground will the top of the brace be placed?

3. A 180-ft vertical radio tower, similar to that of Example 25–19, is to be similarly guyed at three levels and at 120° intervals around the tower. Guys are to be placed at the top of the tower, 120 ft and 60 ft. The length of the longest guy is 204 ft. Determine the distance the common anchor is from the base, the lengths of the other two guys, the total length of guy wire required for the three sets of guys, and the angle that each guy makes with the ground. Neglect the length of wire for connections.

25-9 THE LAW OF SINES

Our work so far has involved only right triangles. As there are many triangles without a right angle, often called nonright triangles, it is necessary that we develop relationships to work with triangles of this type.

In Figure 25–16 a nonright triangle is shown. Note in this figure that while there is no hypotenuse, there are several characteristics in common with the right triangle. The sum of the three angles is 180°, and the longest side is opposite the largest angle. In addition, as with the right triangle, the sum of any two sides is larger than the remaining side.

To develop relationships that apply to nonright triangles, the triangle in Figure 25–16b is used. In this triangle, from point B a per-

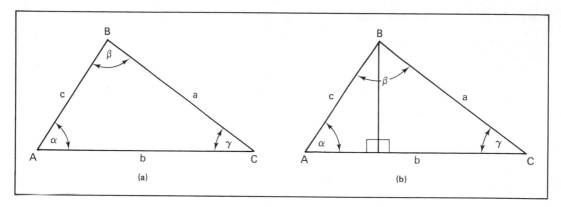

FIGURE 25–16
Nonright Triangles

pendicular, h, has been dropped to side b. This converts the nonright triangle into two right triangles. Using the common side, we may write

$$\sin \alpha = \frac{h}{c}, \qquad \sin \gamma = \frac{h}{a}$$

or

$$h = c \sin \alpha, \qquad h = a \sin \gamma$$

As both equations are equal to the same quantity, h, they are equal to each other. We may now write

$$c \sin \alpha = a \sin \gamma$$

This equation may be rewritten

$$\frac{a}{\sin \alpha} = \frac{c}{\sin \gamma}$$

A similar relationship may be developed using angle B. This results in the following equation, which is called the *Law of Sines*:

$$\frac{a}{\sin \alpha} = \frac{b}{\sin \beta} = \frac{c}{\sin \gamma}$$

This relationship permits solution of nonright triangles when at least three of four appropriate quantities are known: for example, two angles and one opposite side, or one side and any two angles.

example 25-20 Determine the unknowns for a triangle with $a = 16$, $\alpha = 80°$, and $\beta = 60°$.

solution: The triangle is sketched and parts labeled as shown in Figure 25-17. As $\alpha + \beta + \gamma = 180°$ and $\gamma = (180° - 80° - 60°) = 40°$, we may write

$$\frac{a}{\sin \alpha} = \frac{b}{\sin \beta} = \frac{c}{\sin \gamma}$$

$$\frac{16}{\sin 80°} = \frac{b}{\sin 60°} = \frac{c}{\sin 40°}$$

$$\frac{16}{0.985} = \frac{b}{0.866} = \frac{c}{0.643}$$

from which

$$b = 14.07 \quad \text{and} \quad c = 10.44$$

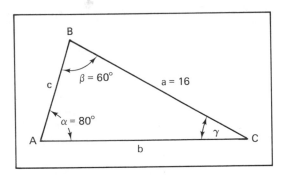

FIGURE 25-17
Diagram for Example 25-20

25-10 THE LAW OF COSINES

Another useful relationship is the law of cosines. It is developed in a manner similar to that used for the law of sines. A nonright triangle is shown in Figure 25-18, with a perpendicular, h, dropped from point B to side b. With the two right triangles thus formed, we may write

$$h^2 + x^2 = c^2 \quad \text{or} \quad h^2 = c^2 - x^2$$

and

$$h^2 + (b - x)^2 = a^2 \quad \text{or} \quad h^2 = a^2 - (b - x)^2$$

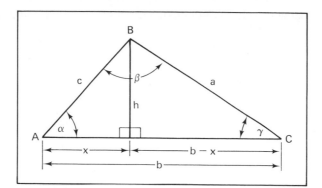

FIGURE 25–18
Triangle Used for Development of Law of
Cosines

As both equations are equal to h^2, we may now write

$$c^2 - x^2 = a^2 - (b - x)^2 \quad \text{or}$$

$$c^2 - x^2 = a^2 - b^2 + 2bx - x^2 \quad \text{or}$$

$$a^2 = b^2 + c^2 - 2bx$$

and as $x = c \cos \alpha$, we have

$$a^2 = b^2 + c^2 - 2bc \cos \alpha$$

This is known as the *Law of Cosines.*

Individually considering each remaining side as the base of the
triangle, the following two equations result, using an analysis as above:

$$b^2 = a^2 + c^2 - 2ac \cos \beta$$

$$c^2 = a^2 + b^2 - 2ab \cos \gamma$$

These are the three forms of the Law of Cosines. The application of
this law permits the solution of a nonright triangle if

1. All three sides are known.
2. Any two sides and the angle between are known.

It should be observed that if one angle of the triangle, for example β,
is a right triangle, the term

$$-2ac \cos \beta = 0$$

because the cos 90° = 0. This leaves the equation in the form

$$b^2 = a^2 + c^2$$

which is, of course, the Pythagorean theorem for the right triangle.

example 25-21 Solve the triangle shown in Figure 25–19.

solution: It is seen that all three sides are known. Using the Law of Cosines, we have, solving for α,

$$a^2 = b^2 + c^2 - 2bc \cos \alpha$$

$$(18)^2 = (26)^2 + (40)^2 - (2)(26)(40) \cos \alpha$$

$$324 = 676 + 1,600 - 2,080 \cos \alpha$$

$$2,080 \cos \alpha = 1,952$$

$$\cos \alpha = 0.938$$

$$\alpha = \arccos 0.938 = 20.2°$$

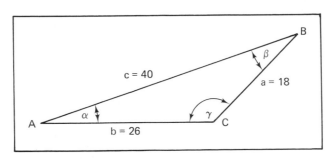

FIGURE 25–19
Diagram for Example 25–21

As we now have one angle and all three sides, the less involved equation, the Law of Sines, may be used:

$$\frac{18}{\sin \alpha} = \frac{26}{\sin \beta} = \frac{40}{\sin \gamma}$$

$$\frac{18}{\sin 20.2°} = \frac{26}{\sin \beta} = \frac{40}{\sin \gamma}$$

$$\frac{18}{0.345} = \frac{26}{\sin \beta} = \frac{40}{\sin \gamma}$$

$$52.17 = \frac{26}{\sin \beta} = \frac{40}{\sin \gamma}$$

$$\sin \beta = \frac{26}{52.17} = 0.498$$

$$\beta = \arcsin 0.498 = 29.9°$$

$$\sin \gamma = \frac{40}{52.17} = 0.766$$

$$\gamma = \arcsin 0.766 = 50.1°$$

to check:
$$\alpha + \beta + \gamma = 180°$$

$$20.2 + 29.9 + 50.1° = 100.2°$$

$$100.2° \neq 180°$$

Examination of the triangle shows that γ is $> 90°$. Then, as $\gamma = \arcsin 0.766$, we will try the supplement of γ:

$$\gamma = 180 - 50.1° = 129.9°$$

testing:
$$\alpha + \beta + \gamma = 180°$$

$$20.2 + 29.9 + 129.9 = 180°$$

$$180° = 180°$$

The solution is correct.

25–11 AREA OF TRIANGLES

Using the relationships of this chapter, we may develop a method for determining the area of any triangle. Using the triangle of Figure 25–20, we may write

$$A = \tfrac{1}{2}ab$$

As $b = c \sin \beta$, we may write

$$A = \tfrac{1}{2}ac \sin \beta$$

and as $a = c \sin \alpha$, we have

$$A = \tfrac{1}{2}bc \sin \alpha$$

A similar relation may be established for γ. These expressions apply to nonright triangles as well as the right triangle, as will be shown in the following example.

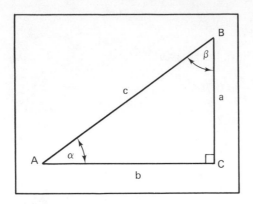

FIGURE 25–20
Triangle for Area Calculations

example 25–22 Determine the area of the triangle in Figure 25–21.

solution: $A = \frac{1}{2}bc \sin \alpha = \frac{1}{2}(28)(22) \sin 30°$

$= 308 \sin 30° = (308)(0.5)$

$= 154 \text{ ft}^2$

To check, the remaining two angles may be determined using the Law of Cosines and the Law of Sines. Side a may be determined as

$a^2 = (28)^2 + (22)^2 - (2)(28)(22) \cos 30°$

$= 201.1$

$a = 14.18 \text{ ft}$

Using the Law of Sines,

$$\frac{a}{\sin \alpha} = \frac{b}{\sin \beta} = \frac{c}{\sin \gamma}$$

$$\frac{14.18}{\sin 30°} = \frac{28}{\sin \beta} = \frac{22}{\sin \gamma}$$

$$\beta = 99.14°$$

$$\gamma = 50.8°$$

to check: $\alpha + \beta + \gamma = 180° = 30° + 118.2° + 50.8° = 179.9°$

Using the calculated side and angles to check area calculations,

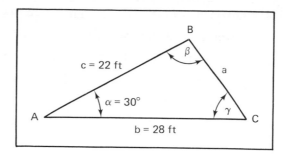

FIGURE 25–21
Triangle for Example 25–22

$$A = \tfrac{1}{2}ab \, \sin \gamma = \tfrac{1}{2}(14.18)(28) \, \sin 50.8° = 154 \text{ ft}^2$$

$$A = \tfrac{1}{2}ac \, \sin \beta = \tfrac{1}{2}(14.18)(22) \, \sin 99.14° = 154 \text{ ft}^2$$

The original area calculations are therefore correct.

If it is desired to check the correctness of original area relationships, the triangle of Figure 25–21 may be divided into two right triangles by dropping a perpendicular from B to side b. The necessary sides and angles of these right triangles may be determined and their areas added. This may then be compared with the area calculated above.

EXERCISE 25–6 In the following problems, use the triangle shown in Figure 25–22.

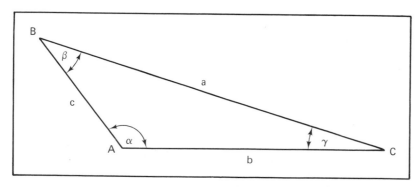

FIGURE 25–22
Triangle for Problems 1–10

1. Given $c = 20$, $b = 38$, and $\gamma = 30°$, find α, β, and a.

2. Given $\alpha = 95°$, $a = 50$, and $b = 39$, find c, β, and γ.

3. Given $\beta = 41.2°$, $b = 22$, and $c = 14$, find a, α, and γ.

4. Given $a = 71$, $b = 50$, and $c = 32$, find α, β, and γ.

5. Given $b = 66$, $c = 38$, and $\alpha = 96.2°$, find a, β, and γ.

6. Given $a = 75$, $c = 22$, and $\beta = 36°$, find b, α, and γ.

7. Given $a = 46$, $b = 28$, and $\gamma = 21.2°$, find c, α, and β.

8. Given $a = 52$, $b = 39$, and $c = 28$, find α, β, and γ.

9. Given $c = 27$ ft, $b = 19.8$ ft, and $\alpha = 21.4°$, find the area of the triangle.

10. Given $a = 54.1$, $c = 20.2$, and $\beta = 30.6°$, find the area of the triangle.

26

VECTORS, PHASORS, AND PERIODIC FUNCTIONS

Certain quantities, such as oranges, pounds, and gallons, have magnitude only. The magnitude is represented by a number, such as 5 resistors, 10 capacitors, and so on. These are called *scalar quantities*. Other quantities have both a magnitude and a direction indicated. A wind velocity of 25 mi/h from the northeast is an example. Such a quantity is called a *vector quantity*. In this chapter, the uses and applications of vector quantities will be developed.

26-1 VECTORS

The vector quantity, representing both magnitude and direction, is usually depicted as an arrow, which is called a *vector*. The length of the vector represents magnitude and its orientation represents direction.

In Figure 26–1, a force of 200 lb in a southwestern direction is shown acting on an object. This force and direction is represented by vector *OA*. The length of the vector *OA* represents the 200-lb force; the orientation of the vector, between the south and west, represents the direction.

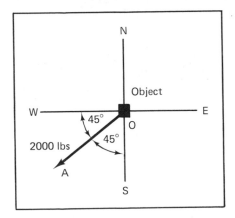

FIGURE 26–1
Vector Representing Force
and Direction

There are several methods of designating a vector. In Figure 26–1 the vector was indicated as *OA*. This vector could be also designated as $\overrightarrow{OA}$. Other common methods of designation include **A** printed in bold-face type, $\overline{A}$ and $\dot{A}$. In this text we shall use the form $\overrightarrow{OA}$ to designate vectors in written form.

In Figure 26–1, a single force represented by vector $\overrightarrow{OA}$ is shown acting on the object. In Figure 26–2, an object is shown being acted upon by two forces, represented by vectors $\overrightarrow{OA}$ and $\overrightarrow{OB}$. The motion of the object will be the result of the effects of the magnitude and direction of the two forces represented by the two vectors. The effect of these forces is obtained by "adding" the vectors. The result of the "addition" is called the *resultant*.

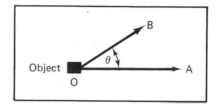

FIGURE 26–2
Two Forces Acting on an
Object

When scalar quantities are involved, the addition involves only a simple algebraic addition, such as 6 resistors plus 4 resistors equal 10 resistors. The addition of vector quantities is a little more involved because of the direction as well as the magnitude being involved. Vector addition may be performed using graphical or algebraic methods.

In Figure 26–3, the graphical addition of the vectors $\overrightarrow{OA}$ and $\overrightarrow{OB}$ is shown. This is called a *parallelogram of forces*. The vector addition is performed by completing the parallelogram, as shown. This construction has side AC equal and parallel to $\overrightarrow{OB}$ and side BC equal and parallel to $\overrightarrow{OA}$. The resultant vector $\overrightarrow{OC}$ is drawn, as shown.

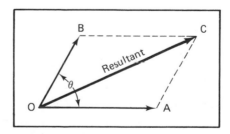

FIGURE 26–3
Graphical Addition of
Vectors

In Figure 26–4, another method of graphical addition is shown. Here two forces, $\overrightarrow{OA}$ and $\overrightarrow{AB}$, are acting at right angles to each other.

396

Ch. 26
VECTORS,
PHASORS,
AND PERIODIC
FUNCTIONS

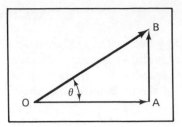

FIGURE 26–4
Graphical Addition of
Vectors

The result of the action of the two forces is determined by connecting points O and B to form the resultant, $\overrightarrow{OB}$.

The magnitude and direction of the resultant, as in Figure 26–3, may be measured using a scale and a protractor. Such graphical processes, while useful, are time consuming and often do not provide the degree of accuracy required.

In Figure 26–4, the drawing of vector $\overrightarrow{OB}$ is seen to form a right triangle. Trigonometric methods of solution may therefore be used. For example, if vector $\overrightarrow{OA}$ represents a force of 40 lb and vector $\overrightarrow{AB}$ a force of 25 lb, it is seen that

$$(40)^2 + (25)^2 = (OB)^2$$

$$OB = 47.12 \text{ lb}$$

Note that the resultant OB is not designated as a vector because the direction is not designated. This may be found as

$$\tan \theta = \frac{AB}{OA} = \frac{25}{40} = 0.625$$

$$\theta = \arctan 0.625 = 32°$$

Therefore,

$$\overrightarrow{OB} = 47.12 \text{ lb at } 32°$$

26–3 VECTOR REPRESENTATION

In Section 26–2, it was seen that a vector could be represented as shown in Figure 26–5a. This is called the *polar-notation form* of representation. The vector is designated as

$$\overrightarrow{OA} = 100\underline{|26.5°}$$

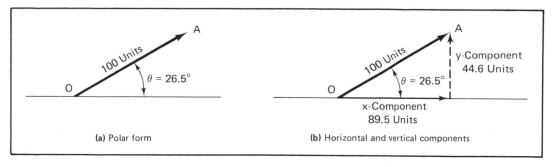

FIGURE 26–5
Vector Representation

It is seen that any vector could be so represented using as a degree reference the conventional quadrant system: that is,

$$42.5\underline{|104°}, \qquad 56.5\underline{|-68°}, \qquad 6\underline{|268°}$$

In Figure 26–4 it was shown that the two vectors $\overrightarrow{OA}$ and $\overrightarrow{AB}$ at right angles to each other formed a resultant $\overrightarrow{OB}$. The vector $\overrightarrow{OA}$ was the horizontal component of the resultant $\overrightarrow{OB}$, while the vector $\overrightarrow{AB}$ was the vertical component. In a similar manner, the vector shown in Figure 26–5a in polar-notation form could be considered to have a horizontal and a vertical component. This is the basis of the second method of vector notation, called *rectangular coordinate notation*.

Examination of Figure 26–5a shows the vector

$$\overrightarrow{OA} = 100\underline{|26.5°}$$

It is seen that

$$100 \cos 26.5° = 89.5\text{—horizontal component of } \overrightarrow{OA}$$

$$100 \sin 26.5° = 44.6\text{—vertical component of } \overrightarrow{OA}$$

This means that a vector represented in polar rotation as $100\underline{|26.5°}$ may be converted to a rectangular form, composed of a horizontal component of 89.5 and a vertical component of 44.6. This is shown in Figure 26–5b. It is, of course, inconvenient to have to designate these horizontal and vertical components in this manner. A review of Section 20–16 provides us with a method of vector representation. In this section, it was shown that the j operator was used to indicate a rotation through 90°. Following this, the horizontal and vertical component of the vector $100\underline{|26.5°}$ in Figure 26–5b could be represented as

$$89.5 + j44.6$$

398

Ch. 26
VECTORS,
PHASORS,
AND PERIODIC
FUNCTIONS

These, then, are the polar and rectangular notation methods of vector representation.

$$100\underline{|26.5°} = 89.5 + j44.6$$

Polar form   Rectangular form

A review of Section 20–16 shows that a $+j$ represents a 90° CCW notation and $-j$ represents 90° CW rotation. Accordingly, rectangular notation may be used with Cartesian coordinates to represent any vector in polar rotation.

A vector in polar form may easily be converted to rectangular form. Similarly, a vector in rectangular form may easily be converted to polar form. This is shown in the following example.

example 26–1   Convert (a) $67\underline{|25°}$ to rectangular form, and (b) $36 + j46$ to polar form.

solution: The two vectors are drawn as shown in Figure 26–6.

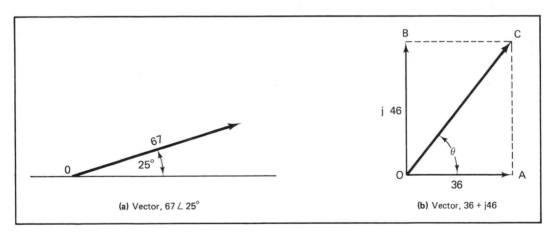

(a) Vector, 67 ∠ 25°

(b) Vector, 36 + j46

FIGURE 26–6
Diagrams for Example 26–1

(a) $67\underline{|25°}$ is seen to have horizontal and vertical components of

67 cos 25° = 67 × 0.906 = 60.7 horizontal component

67 sin 25° = 67 × 0.423 = 28.3 vertical component

Written in rectangular form, $60.7 + j28.3$.

(b) $36 + j46$ may be converted to polar form in the following manner. Note in Figure 26–6b that the vertical component OB is equal to the vertical side AC, which forms the triangle OAC. We know the two sides of this right triangle, so we may determine its hypotenuse, which will be OC. As $AC = OB$, then

399
Sec. 26–4
VECTOR
REPRESENTATION
IN EACH
QUADRANT

$$\tan \theta = \frac{AC = OB}{OA} = \frac{46}{36} = 1.28$$

$$\theta = \arctan 1.28 = 52°$$

$$OC \cos \theta = OA \quad \text{or} \quad OC = \frac{OA}{\cos \theta}$$

$$OC = \frac{36}{\cos 52°} = \frac{36}{0.616} = 58.4$$

Written in polar form $58.4\underline{|52°}$

26–4 VECTOR REPRESENTATION IN EACH QUADRANT

In this section, vector representation in each quadrant will be examined. As vectors in quadrant I were examined in Section 26–3, they will not be presented again.

example 26–2 Convert $122\underline{|125°}$ to rectangular notation.

solution: This vector is shown in Figure 26–7. The horizontal component of $122\underline{|125°}$ is seen to be

FIGURE 26–7
Diagram for Example 26–2

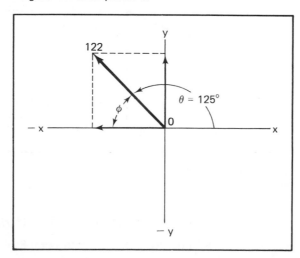

400

Ch. 26
VECTORS,
PHASORS,
AND PERIODIC
FUNCTIONS

$122 \cos \phi,$ where $\phi = 180° - \theta = 180° - 125° = 55°$

$122 \cos 55° = 122 \times 0.574 = 70.0$

The vertical component of $122\underline{|125°}$ is seen to be

$122 \sin \phi$

$122 \sin 55° = 122 \times 0.819 = 99.9$

To write this in rectangular form, the signs of the horizontal and vertical components must be examined. The horizontal component lies along the $-x$ axis and the vertical component lies along the $+y$ axis. In rectangular form, then, we have

$-70 + j99.9$

example 26–3 Convert $86\underline{|-160°}$ to rectangular notation.

solution: This vector is shown in Figure 26–8. The x component of this vector is

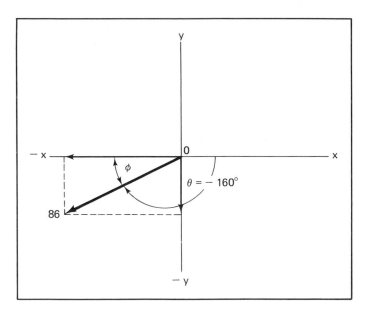

FIGURE 26–8
Diagram for Example 26–3

$86 \cos \phi,$ where $\phi = 180° - 160° = 20°$

$86 \cos 20° = 86 \times 0.940 = 80.8$

The y component of this vector is

$$86 \sin \phi = 86 \sin 20° = 86 \times 0.342 = 29.4$$

401
Sec. 26–4
VECTOR
REPRESENTATION
IN EACH
QUADRANT

In this quadrant both the x and y components are negative. Then

$$-80.8 - j29.4$$

example 26–4 Convert $56\underline{|310°}$ to rectangular notation.

solution: This vector is shown in Figure 26–9. The x component is

$$56 \cos \phi, \quad \text{where } \phi = 360° - 310° = 50°$$
$$56 \cos 50° = 56 \times 0.643 = 36$$

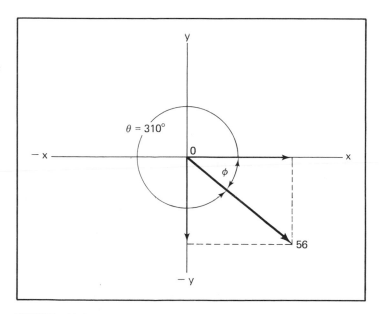

FIGURE 26–9
Diagram for Example 26–4

The y component is

$$56 \sin \phi = 56 \sin 50° = 56 \times 0.766 = 42.9$$

A vector in this quadrant has a $+x$ component and a $-y$ component. Then

$$36 - j42.9$$

402
Ch. 26
VECTORS,
PHASORS,
AND PERIODIC
FUNCTIONS

example 26-5 Convert the vector $16\underline{|470°}$.

solution: This vector is shown in Figure 26–10. As in previous work, the largest possible 360° multiple is subtracted from the angle involved. Here the largest multiple is 1.

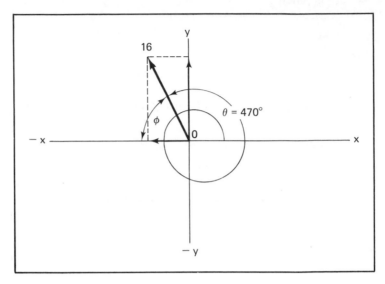

FIGURE 26–10
Diagram for Example 26–5

$$470° - 360° = 110°$$

The $\underline{|470°}$ is equivalent to $\underline{|110°}$:

$$\phi = 180° - 110° = 70°$$

The x component is

$$16 \cos \phi = 16 \cos 70° = 16 \times 0.342 = 5.47$$

The y component is

$$16 \sin \phi = 16 \sin 70° = 16 \times 0.940 = 15.04$$

In quadrant II, the x component is $-$, while the y component is $+$. Then

$$-5.47 + j15.04$$

example 26-6 Convert $-30 - j43$ to polar notation.

solution: Both the x and y components are negative. This represents a vector in quadrant **III**. This is shown in Figure 26-11. The magnitude of the polar vector, A, is found as

$$A^2 = (30)^2 + (43)^2 = 2,748.9$$

$$A = 52.4$$

The angle ϕ is found as

$$\cos \phi = \frac{30}{52.4} = 0.572$$

$$\phi = \arccos 0.572 = 55.1°$$

$$\theta = \phi + 180° = 55.1° + 180° = 235.1°$$

In polar notation the vector is

$$52.4 \underline{|235°}$$

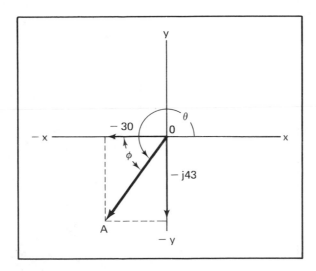

FIGURE 26-11
Diagram for Example 26-6

26-5 VECTOR ADDITION

The process of vector addition consists of adding, algebraically, the x and y components of individual vectors. The individual vectors must

404

Ch. 26

VECTORS,
PHASORS,
AND PERIODIC
FUNCTIONS

be expressed in rectangular notation. This procedure is shown in the following examples.

example 26–7 Add the vectors $4 + j8$ and $6 - j12$.

solution: The two vectors are shown in Figure 26–12. Adding the x and y components algebraically,

$$
\begin{aligned}
\vec{A} &= 4 + j8 \\
\vec{B} &= 6 - j12 \\
\hline
\vec{C} &= 10 - j4
\end{aligned}
$$

The position of $\vec{C}$ is sketched in Figure 26–12 to show the addition of $\vec{A}$ and $\vec{B}$ graphically. This, of course, agrees with the position of $\vec{C}$, resulting from the addition of the rectangular notation components above.

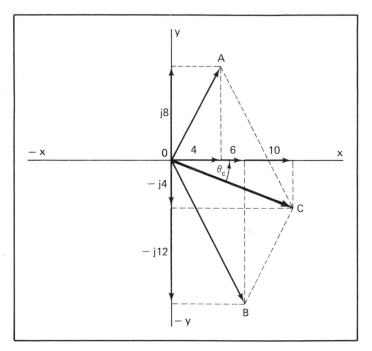

FIGURE 26–12
Diagram for Example 26–7

To convert $\vec{C}$ to polar form,

$$\tan \theta_c = \frac{4}{10} = 0.40$$

$$\theta_c = \arctan 0.40 = -21.8°$$

$$C \cos \theta_c = 10$$

$$C = \frac{10}{\cos \theta_c} = \frac{10}{0.928} = 10.78$$

The result of the addition in polar form is

$$10.78 \underline{|-21.8°}$$

example 26–8 Add the vectors $26.7\underline{|37°}$ and $8 - j6$.

---

solution: The vectors $\vec{A}$ and $\vec{B}$ are shown in Figure 26–13. The vector $\vec{A}$ is converted to rectangular notation as

$$\vec{A} = 26.7\underline{|37°} = 26.7 \cos 37° + j26.7 \sin 37°$$
$$= 21.3 + j16.07$$

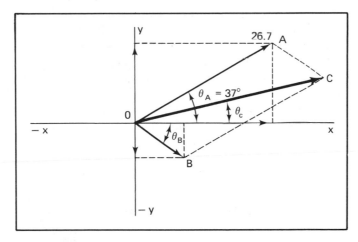

FIGURE 26–13
Diagram for Example 26–8

Adding $\vec{A} + \vec{B}$,

$$\vec{A} = 21.3 + j16.1$$
$$\underline{\vec{B} = 8 - j6}$$
$$\vec{C} = 29.3 + j10.1$$

$$\tan \theta_c = \frac{10.1}{29.3} = 0.345$$

$$\theta_c = \arctan 0.345$$
$$= 19°$$

$$C \cos \theta_c = 29.3$$

$$C = \frac{29.3}{\cos \theta_c} = \frac{29.3}{\cos 19°} = \frac{29.3}{0.945} = 31$$

$$\vec{C} = 31 \underline{|19°}$$

26–6 PHASORS

In our study of alternating current, it will be found that we will be working with quantities that are continually changing in magnitude and periodically changing in direction. In addition, there are often angular differences between ac quantities such as voltage and current. The representation of ac quantities with vectors is, therefore, not completely accurate.

The angular difference between ac quantities represents a time *lag* or a time *lead*. This time relationship is referred to as a *phase difference*. In essence, then, the representation of these quantities graphically could be called *phase vectors*. This is shortened to *phasors*.

In our electronics work we shall use the term "phasors" to graphically depict quantities in ac circuits. On paper, all the operations involving vectors that were developed in previous sections apply to phasors. The rectangular and polar notation and the representation of vectors, as well as the addition of vectors, apply to phasors.

Phasors will be used in our work in ac circuits, which follows. With the preceding background in vectors, this change will be seen to require only a slight adjustment in our thinking.

EXERCISE 26–1

Express the following in rectangular notation.

1. $50 \underline{|36°}$
2. $26 \underline{|135°}$
3. $16 \underline{|290°}$
4. $5 \underline{|200°}$
5. $77 \underline{|330°}$
6. $15 \underline{|-45°}$
7. $36 \underline{|-120°}$
8. $43 \underline{|390°}$
9. $27 \underline{|-180°}$
10. $43 \underline{|-390°}$

Express the following in polar notation.

11. $3 + j4$
12. $-6 + j7$
13. $15 - j12$
14. $-20 - j30$
15. $15 + j20$
16. $25 - j16$
17. $-152 + j152$
18. $-60 + j120$
19. $-50 + j50$
20. $7.25 - j8.72$

Add the following vectors.

21. $3 + j4,\ 6 + j8$ 22. $3 - j5,\ 6 + j9$

23. $-13 - j13,\ -12 - j12$ 24. $15 - j15,\ 16 + j15$

25. $16 - j12,\ -16 + j12$ 26. $15\underline{|30°},\ 20\underline{|60°}$

27. $28\underline{|-45°},\ 28\underline{|45°}$ 28. $327\underline{|20°},\ 300\underline{|-20°}$

29. $100\underline{|30°},\ 200\underline{|60°}$ 30. $2\underline{|60°},\ 3 + j4$

26–7 ROTATING VECTORS

In Figure 26–14, the vector $\overrightarrow{OA}$ is shown. If the vector $O\overset{\textstyle.}{A}$ has a magnitude of 1, it would have a horizontal component of

$$1 \cos \theta = 1 \cos 30° = 1 \times 0.866 = 0.866$$

and a vertical component of

$$1 \sin \theta = 1 \sin 30° = 1 \times 0.500 = 0.500$$

If $\overrightarrow{OA}$ were rotated in a CCW direction to the 60° position shown in Figure 26–14, it would have a horizontal component of

$$1 \cos 60° = 1 \times 0.500 = 0.500$$

and a vertical component of

$$1 \sin 60° = 1 \times 0.866 = 0.866$$

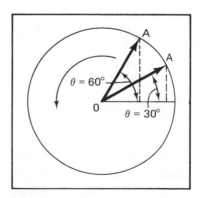

FIGURE 26–14
Rotating Vector

It is seen that the vector $\overrightarrow{OA}$ could be rotated through 360°. At any point in its rotation, the horizontal and vertical components of the vector could be determined. In Figure 26–15 the vertical-component values of vector $\overrightarrow{OA}$ are plotted for every 30° as the vector is rotated through 360°. As in Figure 26–14, the vector $\overrightarrow{OA}$ has a magnitude of 1.

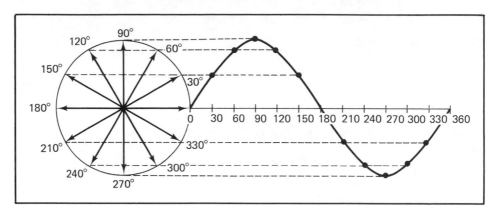

FIGURE 26–15
Vector Rotation Through 360°

As shown in Figure 26–14, the vertical component of the vector $\overrightarrow{OA}$ is

1 sin θ

At each 30° increment, the vertical component of the vector would be a function of the sine of the angle at that point. If these points were connected, the curve shown in Figure 26–15 would result. As the points on this curve reflect the sine functions of the angle involved, the resultant curve is called the *sine curve*.

In effect, the curve of Figure 26–15 represents a plot of the vertical component, y, of the vector $\overrightarrow{OA}$ for various values of θ. This may be stated algebraically as

$y = 1 \sin \theta$

In a similar manner, the horizontal component of the vector $\overrightarrow{OA}$ could be plotted for each point of rotation. At each point the horizontal component would be a function of the cos θ. If this value were to be plotted on a vertical plane, as with the sine curve, we may write

$y = 1 \cos \theta$

This curve is called the *cosine curve* and is shown plotted in Figure 26–16.

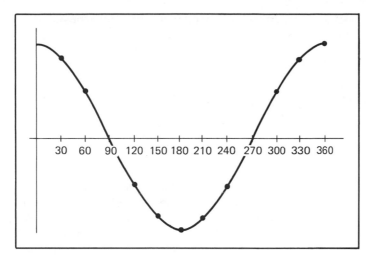

FIGURE 26–16
Cosine Curve

26–8 PERIODIC FUNCTIONS

The sine and cosine curves shown in Figures 26–15 and 26–16 are plotted from 0° to 360°. If these curves were plotted for larger degree values, the curves would be seen to repeat. The individual curves would exhibit the same characteristics of magnitude and direction on a periodic basis. The equations for the sine and cosine curves are referred to as *periodic functions*.

In Chapter 27, the generation of an ac waveform will be discussed. It will be seen that such a waveform is a periodic function. The ac waveform, like the sine and cosine curves, are continually changing in magnitude and periodically changing in direction.

26–9 ANGULAR MEASURE

The rotating vectors shown in Figures 26–14 and 26–15 repeat the periodic functions at a rate that depends upon the speed of rotation. The rate at which angle θ in Figure 26–14 is generated would be seen to vary as the speed of rotation of $\overrightarrow{OA}$ varies. The rate at which angle θ is generated is called the *angular velocity*. It is designated by the Greek letter omega ω.

The units of angular velocity may be expressed in

radians/second or degrees/second

In this text we shall use the radians/second (rad/s) units, most commonly used in practice. Normally, the angular velocity is expressed in terms of revolutions per second, which is designated with the letter f.

410

Ch. 26
VECTORS,
PHASORS,
AND PERIODIC
FUNCTIONS

As there are 2π radians per revolution, 360°, the angular velocity may be expressed as

$$\omega = 2\pi f \quad \text{rad/s}$$

example 26-9 A blade of a fan rotates at 2,400 revolutions/minute (r/min). Determine the angular velocity.

solution: $\omega = 2\pi f = 6.28 \times \dfrac{2,400}{60} = 251.2 \text{ rad/s}$

example 26-10 A spoke of a wheel has an angular velocity of 18,260 rad/min. Determine the size of angle θ that would be generated in 1.46 s. How many radians would be generated in this time period? How many revolutions would the wheel make in this time period?

solution: $18{,}260 \text{ rad/min} = \dfrac{18{,}260}{60} \text{ rad/s} = 304.3 \text{ rad/s}$

$$304.3 \text{ rad/s} \times 1.46 \text{ s} = 444.3 \text{ rad}$$

As there are 2π rad per revolution,

$$f = \frac{444.3}{2\pi} = 70.7 \text{ revolutions}$$

The angle that would be generated by a rotating vector with an angular velocity of ω would be a function of time. This would be expressed as

$$\omega = 2\pi ft = \omega t \quad \text{rad}$$

example 26-11 Determine in radians and degrees the angle that would be generated in 0.352 sec by a spoke on a wheel. The spoke is rotating at an $f = 60$ r/s.

solution: $\omega = 2\pi f = 6.28 \times 60 = 377 \text{ rad/s}$

$$\theta = \omega t = 377 \times 0.352 = 132.7 \text{ rad}$$

$$= 132.7 \times 57.3° = 7{,}603.9°$$

26-10 SINE-WAVE CHARACTERISTICS

Several characteristics of the sine wave should be examined. The understanding of these properties is essential for our work with ac circuits.

AMPLITUDE——*In previous sections, the sine waves that were examined had an amplitude of 1. In effect, then, the equation of the sine wave*

$$y = \sin \theta$$

had an understood coefficient of 1. In Figure 26–17, the sine wave of voltage represented by the equation

$$y = E \sin \theta$$

is plotted for $E_1 = 100$ V, $E_2 = 200$ V, $E_3 = 300$ V. From the curves of Figure 26–17 it is seen that the amplitude *of the sine wave is a function of the coefficient. In this case the coefficient was expressed in volts. It could have been in other units, such as microamperes or kilovolts.*

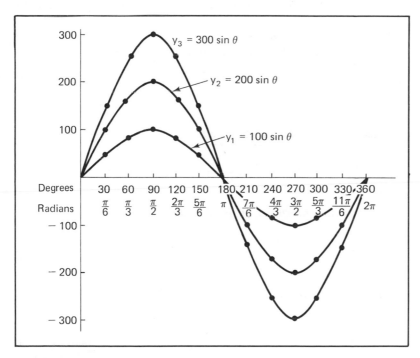

FIGURE 26–17
Sine Waves of Voltage

If these curves were generated by the rotation of a vector of length **E***, the amplitude of any point on a curve would be seen to be a function of*

$$y = E \sin \omega t$$

412

Ch. 26
VECTORS,
PHASORS,
AND PERIODIC
FUNCTIONS

As before, the value of ω would represent the angular velocity of the rotating vector and the time, t, would determine the value of the angle, θ, that would be generated.

CYCLE——*A* cycle *is the series of events in a sine wave that occurs in 360° These are the events generated by one complete revolution of the rotating vector. As seen, this results in a complete sine wave. This is called one cycle. Additional complete revolutions of the vector produce complete sine waves or cycles. A cycle, then, is one complete series of events.*

FREQUENCY—— *The* frequency *of a sine wave is the number of cycles that occur in a given period of time. The frequency is designated by the letter* f. *The units of frequency are cycles per second or hertz (Hz). Alternating current used for power purposes usually has a frequency of 60 Hz. It should be noted that each cycle is made up of a positive and negative segment called an* alternation.

PERIOD——*The time required for one complete event or cycle to occur is called the* period *of the wave. As the angular velocity of a rotating vector is expressed*

$$\omega = 2\pi f$$

then

$$f = \frac{\omega}{2\pi}, \quad \text{where } \omega = \text{rad/s and } f = \text{Hz}$$

From this relationship it is seen that as

$$f = \frac{\text{cycles}}{\text{s}}$$

the time, or period, T, *for one cycle to occur may be determined as*

$$T = \frac{1}{f} \quad \text{s}$$

example 26–12 Determine the period of waveform of 1,000 Hz.

solution: The waveform has 1,000 cycles occurring in 1 s. The time for each cycle, or the period, T, is found as

$$T = \frac{1}{f} = \frac{1}{1,000} = 0.001 \text{ s}$$

PHASE ANGLE—— *In Figure 26–18, two rotating vectors, $\vec{E}$ and $\vec{I}$, are shown. They have different amplitudes and there is an angular difference between the vectors. The angular difference between vectors E and I is seen to be*

$$\theta = \phi_1 - \phi_2$$

This is called the phase angle.

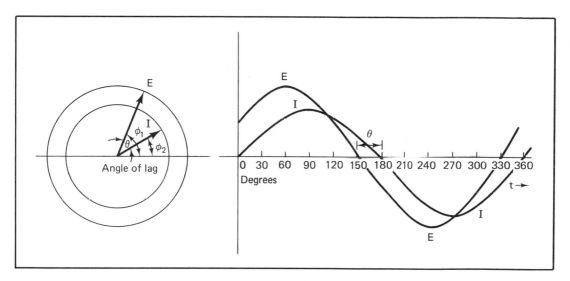

FIGURE 26–18
Phase Relationships, *I* Lagging *E, E* Leading *I*

In starting from the 0° position and rotating in a CCW direction, the vector $\vec{I}$ would generate the sine curve shown. The vector $\vec{E}$ is seen to be leading the vector $\vec{I}$ by θ^0. Thus the *E* curve crosses the 0° position θ^0 ahead of the *I* curve. The $\vec{E}$ vector would therefore generate the sine curve shown.

The vector $\vec{I}$ is seen to be lagging behind $\vec{E}$ by θ^0. This is, then, a lagging phase angle, or *angle of lag*. The amplitude of any point on the *I* curve would be represented as

$$y = I \sin \omega t$$

where ωt is in radians. The amplitude of any point on the *E* curve would be represented as

$$y = E \sin (\omega t + \theta)$$

414

Ch. 26
VECTORS,
PHASORS,
AND PERIODIC
FUNCTIONS

In Figure 26–19, the $\vec{I}$ vector is seen to be leading the $\vec{E}$ vector by θ^0, generating the sine curves as shown. As before, the amplitude of any point on the I curve would be represented as

$$y = I \sin \omega t$$

The amplitude of any point on the E curve would be represented as

$$y = E \sin (\omega t - \theta^0)$$

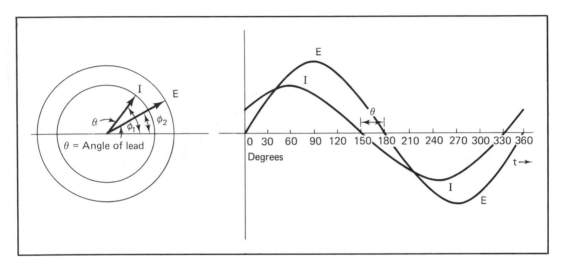

FIGURE 26–19
Phase Relationships, *E* Lagging *I*, *I* Leading *E*

In practice, the lagging or leading of a wave is a relative matter. For example, in Figure 26–19, waveform *I* may be considered to be leading waveform *E* by θ^0. However, waveform *E* may be considered lagging waveform *I* by θ^0. In effect, then, a waveform may be considered to have a lagging or leading phase angle, depending on the reference used. The amplitude of any point on a waveform will therefore depend upon the reference. The general relationship for this value may be written

$$y = A \sin (\omega t \pm \theta)$$

where *A* is the magnitude of the particular rotating vector involved.

26–11 SINE-WAVE ANALYSIS

In Section 26–10, the characteristics of sine waves were examined. In this section the equations of sine waves will be placed in practical perspective.

example 26–13 What are the characteristics of the sine wave represented by the equation

$$y = 30 \sin 2{,}512t?$$

solution: The general equation for the sine wave is

$$y = A \sin (\omega t + \theta)$$

the amplitude of the rotating vector, hence the sine wave represented by this equation, is seen to be

$$A = 30$$

Similarly, $\omega = 2{,}512$ rad/s. This is a single sine wave, hence $\theta = 0°$. The frequency is found as

$$\omega = 2\pi f$$

$$f = \frac{\omega}{2\pi} = \frac{2{,}512}{6.28} = 400 \text{ Hz}$$

The period of the sine wave is found as

$$T = \frac{1}{f} = \frac{1}{400} = 0.0025 \text{ s}$$

example 26–14 Determine the frequency, period, and amplitude at $t = 0$ and $t = 0.0075$ s, for the sine wave represented by the equation

$$y = 600 \sin (314t + 45°)$$

solution: The amplitude is seen to be

$$A = 600$$

The frequency is found as

$$f = \frac{\omega}{2\pi} = \frac{314}{6.28} = 50 \text{ Hz}$$

The period is determined as

$$T = \frac{1}{f} = \frac{1}{50} = 0.02 \text{ s}$$

416

Ch. 26
VECTORS,
PHASORS,
AND PERIODIC
FUNTIONS

It should be observed that the curve

$$y = 600 \sin 314t$$

represents a curve that would start at 0°, while the curve

$$y = 600 \sin (314t + 45°)$$

would represent a curve leading by 45°. This is shown in Figure 26–20.

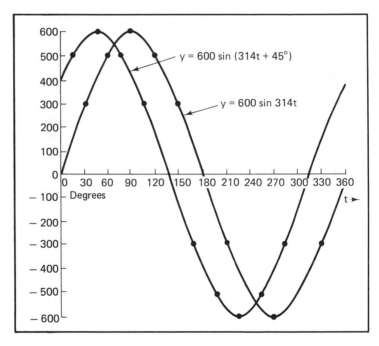

FIGURE 26–20
Diagram for Example 26–11

At $t = 0$ s, the equation becomes

$$y = 600 \sin (314 \times 0 + 45°)$$

$$= 600 \sin (0^r + 45°)$$

$$= 600 \sin 45°$$

$$= 424.3$$

At $t = 0.0075$ s,

$$y = 600 \sin (314 \times 0.0075 + 45°)$$
$$= 600 \sin (2.35^r + 45°)$$
$$= 600 \sin (2.35 \times 57.3 + 45°)$$
$$= 600 \sin (135° + 45°)$$
$$= 600 \sin 180°$$
$$= 600 \times 0$$
$$= 0$$

Examination of Figure 26–20 shows that the curve $y = 600 \sin (314t + 45°)$ has a value of zero at 135°. Note that the product, ωt is in radians and must be converted to degrees, as shown above, before it can be added to θ, which is in degrees.

EXERCISE 26–2

1. A fan blade rotates at 15,000 r/min. What is its angular velocity?

2. A radius drawn on a flywheel has an angular velocity of 306 rad/min. What angle would be generated in 3.5 s?

3. In problem 2, how many radians would be generated in 6.72 s? How many revolutions would the flywheel make in 14.24 s?

4. A wheel is rotating at 240 r/min. Determine the number of radians and degrees generated by a spoke on the wheel in 15.6 s.

5. Determine the period of a waveform of 24,000 Hz.

6. Determine the amplitude, period, and frequency of the sine wave represented by

$$y = 36 \sin 256t$$

7. Determine the amplitude of the waveform of problem 6 after 3.12 s.

In the curves represented by the equations given, determine the angular velocity, amplitude, frequency, and period.

8. $y = 600 \sin 377t$

9. $y = 24.6 \sin 167t$

10. $y = 300 \sin 1,307t$

11. $y = 15.5 \sin (4,678t + 30°)$

12. $y = 1,236 \sin (3.2t - 16°)$

13. $y = 26 \sin (12.56t + 0°)$

418
Ch. 26
VECTORS,
PHASORS,
AND PERIODIC
FUNCTIONS

14. $y = 371 \sin (436t + 6.2°)$

15. $y = 43.2 \sin (15.67t - 35°)$

16. $y = 127 \sin (207.8t + 21.2°)$

27

ALTERNATING-CURRENT CONCEPTS

In previous chapters, we have developed many mathematical principles. In this chapter, a number of concepts of alternating current will be presented. As our work progresses, it will be seen that the mathematics of alternating currents and related circuits will involve little more than the application of principles previously developed.

27-1 FUNDAMENTAL CONCEPTS

Michael Faraday, an English scientist, discovered in 1831 that an electric current would result if a conductor were moved through a magnetic field. This principle, when refined, forms the basis of the electric generator. A simple ac generator is shown in Figure 27–1.

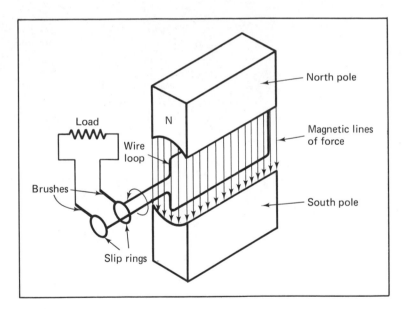

FIGURE 27-1
Simple Alternating-Current Generator

This consists of a CCW rotating wire loop situated between the north and south poles of a permanent magnet. The magnetic lines of force are shown leaving the north magnetic pole and entering the south magnetic pole. The wire ends are connected to slip rings in order that the generated voltage may be removed from the rotating loop. In Figure 27–2, the rotating wire loop is shown in positions 45° apart. This is for the purpose of showing how a sine wave of voltage is generated.

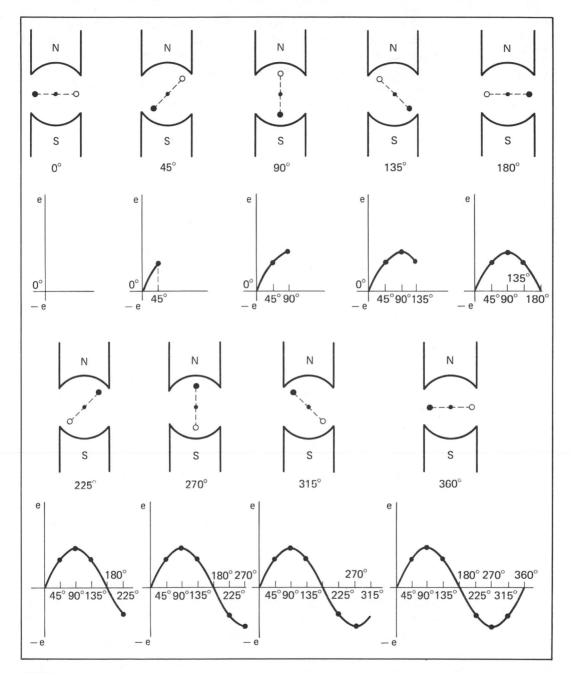

FIGURE 27–2
Sine-Wave Generation of Voltage

As each point is plotted, that portion of the sine wave is drawn. Thus when the coil has revolved through 360°, a complete sine wave is shown. As the wire loop is rotated, the magnetic field is cut. The level of the voltage generated is a function of the number of lines of magnetic force that are cut. The number of magnetic lines that are cut is a function of the horizontal component of the velocity of the wire loop at that particular instant. The horizontal component of velocity of the wire loop is a function of the sine of the angle of rotation, and so a sine wave of voltage, shown in Figure 27–2, is generated.

The generation of the sine wave in Figure 27–2 is explained in the following manner. When the wire loop is in the 0° position, there is no horizontal component of velocity, all magnetic lines pass through the loop, and no voltage is generated.

When the loop is in the 45° position, the horizontal component of velocity has a value such that the voltage shown at this point on the curve is developed.

At the 90° position, the horizontal component of velocity is at its maximum, resulting in the generation of the maximum value of voltage, as shown.

At the 135° position, the number of magnetic lines cut have decreased, resulting in the voltage represented.

At the 180° position, the horizontal component of velocity is zero. This results in no lines being cut, and thus zero voltage is shown at this point on the sine curve.

The individual sides of the loop have now reached a point opposite to their initial position. As these opposite sides of the loop cut magnetic lines of force, a voltage is developed which is opposite to that generated during the first 180° of rotation.

As the horizontal component of the velocity of the wire loop increases, the number of magnetic lines of force that are cut increases. This increases, *in a negative direction*, the voltage generated. When the loop reaches a vertical position, the maximum voltage is again developed.

As rotation continues, the number of magnetic lines of force cut decrease. As a result, the voltage developed decreases. This voltage continues to decrease until the horizontal position is again reached. At this point no lines of force are cut and no voltage is developed.

The loop has now been rotated through 360° and is back in its original position. One complete cycle of voltage has been generated. Further rotation continues this voltage-generation process, with one complete cycle of voltage generated for each 360° rotation.

27–2 PHASOR REPRESENTATION OF ELECTRICAL QUANTITIES

In Chapter 26, we saw how a rotating vector was used to generate a sine wave. In Section 27–1, it was shown how a sine wave was generated by mechanical rotation of a wire loop in a magnetic field. It follows, then, that a phasor may be used to represent the voltage thus generated. For example, the sine wave in Figure 27–3a has a maximum value of 300 V. The sine wave may be represented by a phasor with a length representing this maximum value of 300 V. This is shown in Figure 27–3b.

423
Sec. 27–2
PHASOR
REPRESENTATION
OF ELECTRICAL
QUANTITIES

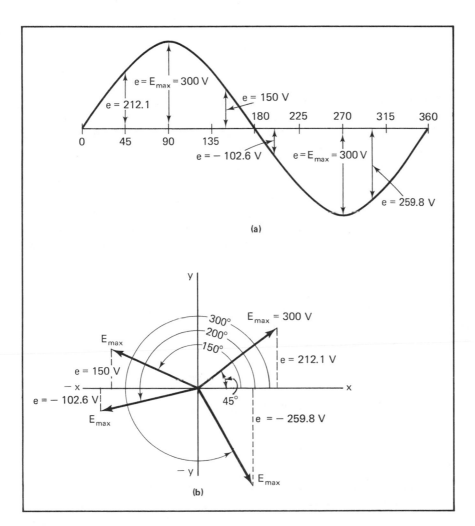

FIGURE 27–3
Phasor Representation of Sine-Wave Voltage

The phasor drawn in Figure 27–3b is shown in a 45° position. The vertical component of voltage at this point is

$$e_{45°} = E_{max} \sin 45° = 300 \times 0.707 = 212.1 \text{ V}$$

This represents the magnitude of voltage that exists at the 45° point on the sine wave, as shown in Figure 27–3a. In a similar manner, any point on the sine wave may be similarly represented. For example,

$$e_{150°} = E_{max} \sin (180° - 150°) = 300 \sin 30° = 300 \times 0.5 = 150 \text{ V}$$

$$e_{200°} = E_{max}[-\sin (200° - 180°)] = 300(-\sin 20°)$$

$$= 300 \times -0.342 = -102.6 \text{ V}$$

$$e_{300°} = E_{max}[-\sin (360° - 300°)] = 300(-\sin 60°)$$

$$= 300 \times -0.866 = -259.8 \text{ V}$$

These voltages represent the instantaneous values that occur at these degree positions. The phasor representations are shown in Figure 27–3b and the equivalent values of voltage at the particular degree positions are shown on the sine wave in Figure 27–3a.

Note that the sine of an angle in the third and fourth quadrants is negative. As a result, the instantaneous values of voltage thus obtained are negative. This, of course, agrees with the negative portion of the sine wave that exists between 180° and 360°.

In a similar manner, the instantaneous values at any point of a sine wave may be represented by phasors. This will be shown in the examples that follow.

In our work with Ohm's law it was seen that the current was directly proportional to the voltage. As such, a sine-wave variation in voltage will produce a directly proportional sine-wave variation in current. This being true, the instantaneous values of current may be represented with the general equation

$$i = I_{max} \sin \omega t \quad \text{A}$$

As with the instantaneous voltage relationships we may write this equation as

$$i = I_{max} \sin \theta \quad \text{A}$$

The application of these voltage and current relationships are shown in the following example.

example 27–1 In Figure 27–4, a sine wave of voltage and current is shown. Determine the instantaneous values of both at 52.6° and 290° of their cycle. Show the results in phasor form.

solution: The instantaneous values of e and i at 52.6° are found as

$$e_{52.6°} = E_{max} \sin 52.6° = 1,000 \times 0.794 = 794 \text{ V}$$

$$i_{52.6°} = I_{max} \sin 52.6° = 15.4 \times 0.794 = 12.23 \text{ A}$$

At 290° the instantaneous values are found as

$$e_{290°} = E_{max}[-\sin (360° - 290°)] = 1,000(-\sin 70°)$$
$$= 1,000 \times -0.940 = -940 \text{ V}$$

$$i_{290°} = I_{max}[-\sin (360° - 290°)] = 15.4(-\sin 70°)$$
$$= 15.4 \times -0.940 = -14.48 \text{ A}$$

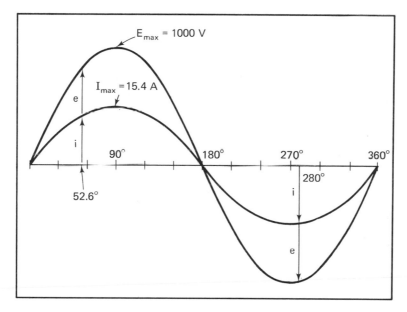

FIGURE 27–4
Diagram for Example 27–1

These values, shown in phasor form, are shown in
Figure 27–5.

27–3 MECHANICAL GENERATION OF AC VOLTAGE

In previous sections, it was seen that the wire loop rotated 360° to
generate one cycle of voltage. This simple ac generator, or alternator,
had a single pair of magnetic poles. Let us now examine what occurs
when additional pairs of magnetic poles are used. Such an arrangement is shown in Figure 27–6. As before, the wire loop is shown in
cross section. Examination of Figure 27–6a shows that with a four-
pole unit, a 360° rotation results in the loop passing under two pairs of
N-S magnetic poles. In this process two complete voltage cycles will
be generated.

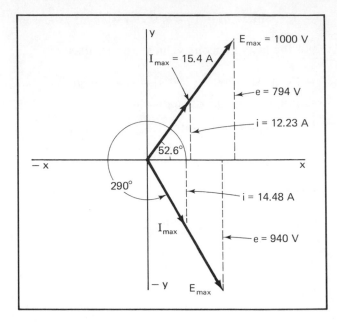

FIGURE 27-5
Phasor Diagram for Example 27-1

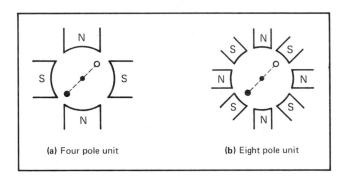

(a) Four pole unit   (b) Eight pole unit

FIGURE 27-6
Four-Pole and Eight-Pole Alternator

Often there is a comparison made between rotational degrees and electrical degrees. In the case of the four-pole alternator, 360 rotational degrees will result in two complete electrical cycles, or 720 electrical degrees, being generated.

In Figure 27-6b, a 360° rotation results in the wire loop passing under four pairs of N-S magnetic poles. This results in the generation of four complete voltage cycles. With this arrangement, 360 rotational degrees will result in four electrical cycles, or 1,440 electrical degrees, being generated.

In our alternating-current work we shall be more concerned with the time element of a cycle rather than the comparison of mechanical and electrical degrees. Time considerations were discussed in Section 26–5, where relationships among frequency, period, and phase were discussed.

At this point, it is desirable to point out that time factors are involved in the mechanical generation of an ac voltage. For example, if we wished to generate a 60-Hz voltage, using the two-pole alternator, the wire loop would have to revolve 60 times per second, or

$$60 \times 60 = 3,600 \text{ r/min}$$

Using the four-pole generator, a 60-Hz voltage would require a rotation of 30 times per second, or

$$30 \times 60 = 1,800 \text{ r/min}$$

The eight-pole alternator would have to revolve 15 times per second to produce 60 Hz, or

$$15 \times 60 = 900 \text{ r/min}$$

As a result, the following relationship may be written:

$$f = \frac{PS}{60} \quad \text{Hz,} \quad \text{where}$$

f = frequency, Hz

P = pairs of poles

S = r/min

The preceding relationships provides a very basic background in the procedures involved in the generation of an ac voltage. In other courses, a more thorough understanding of these principles will be provided.

27–4 AVERAGE VALUE OF A SINE WAVE

We have previously examined two characteristics of a sine wave, its maximum value and its instantaneous value, It is often desirable to describe a sine wave in terms of its average value in relation to its maximum value.

The average value of a complete cycle is seen to be zero, in that the positive alternation is equal to the negative alternation. Under such circumstances, the average value is considered the value for one alternation. No distinction is made for the negative or positive nature of the alternation. The average value of an alternation may be determined by several means. A mechanical method, involving a device called a *polar planimeter*, may be used. A mathematical method involving calculus may be used. In addition, a graphical method of "averaging" a number of small segments of the alternation may be used. The result is a value, expressed in terms of the maximum voltage of

$$E_{av} = \frac{2}{\pi} E_{max} \quad V, \quad \text{or using approximate values}$$

$$= 0.637 E_{max} \quad V$$

The average value of current may be expressed as

$$I_{av} = 0.637 I_{max} \quad A$$

The maximum value of a voltage or current may also be expressed in terms of its average value as

$$E_{av} = 0.637 E_{max} \quad V, \qquad E_{max} = \frac{E_{av}}{0.637} = 1.57 E_{av} \quad V$$

$$I_{av} = 0.637 I_{max} \quad A, \qquad I_{max} = \frac{I_{av}}{0.637} = 1.57 I_{av} \quad A$$

27–5 EFFECTIVE VALUE OF A SINE WAVE

In previous chapters, the power dissipated in a resistor was seen to be equal to

$$P = \frac{E^2}{R} \quad W \quad \text{or} \quad P = I^2 R \quad W$$

The use of these equations and the maximum values of the ac voltages or currents will not result in the same power dissipation as the same level of dc voltages or currents. This is because the ac power is the result of an infinite number of instantaneous voltages or currents along the sine wave during each cycle. Using the above equations, the instantaneous power at each instant is seen to be a function of the square of the voltage or the current at that instant.

The effective value of a voltage or current is determined by obtaining the square root of the mean, or average, of many equally spaced, squared values of the voltage or current, obtained during one cycle.

For example, for a sine wave of voltage this would involve dividing the sine wave into perhaps 50 equal segments. The instantaneous values of voltage at each of these points would be measured, squared, and then the total averaged. The square root of this average value is then taken to obtain the effective value of voltage. As a result of this procedure, the effective value of voltage or current is referred to as the *root-mean-square*, or *rms, value*. The determination of the rms value of voltage or current is represented by

$$E_{rms} = \sqrt{\frac{e_1^2 + e_2^2 + e_3^2 + e_4^2 + \ldots + e_n^2}{n}} \, E_{max} \qquad V$$

$$I_{rms} = \sqrt{\frac{i_1^2 + i_2^2 + i_3^2 + i_4^2 + \ldots + i_n^2}{n}} \, I_{max} \qquad A$$

These procedures result in the following:

$$E_{rms} = \frac{1}{\sqrt{2}} E_{max} \qquad V$$

$$I_{rms} = \frac{1}{\sqrt{2}} I_{max} \qquad A$$

which are rounded off to

$$E_{rms} = 0.707 E_{max} \qquad V$$
$$I_{rms} = 0.707 I_{max} \qquad A$$

The maximum value of a voltage or a current is often expressed in terms of the rms value as

$$E_{rms} = 0.707 E_{max} \qquad V, \qquad E_{max} = \frac{E_{rms}}{0.707} = 1.414 E_{rms} \qquad V$$

$$I_{rms} = 0.707 I_{max} \qquad A, \qquad I_{max} = \frac{I_{rms}}{0.707} = 1.414 I_{rms} \qquad A$$

Measuring instruments for ac voltages and currents are calibrated to read rms values. In nearly all our work we will be dealing with rms values. As such, a voltage or current without subscripts,

$$E \quad \text{and} \quad I$$

will be understood to mean *rms* values. Subscripts will be used to designate the maximum and average values:

$$E_{max}, I_{max} \quad \text{and} \quad E_{av}, I_{av}$$

EXERCISE 27-1

1. What is I if $I_{max} = 3.52$ A?

2. Determine E_{av} if $E_{max} = 56$ V.

3. Find the value of I_{max} if $I = 45.3$ mA.

4. What is the value of E_{max} if $E_{av} = 156$ mV?

5. What is the effective value of current in a circuit if the maximum value is 381.2 A?

6. Determine the average value of voltage if the effective value is 35.6 V.

7. If the average value of current in a circuit is 15.26 mA, what is its effective value?

8. What is I_{max} if $I_{av} = 353.4$ mA?

27-6 PHASE RELATIONSHIPS IN AC CIRCUITS

In Figure 27-7, a voltage and a current waveform are shown. These waves are in phase. They may be represented by rotating phasors and by waveforms as shown. Note that the positive and negative peaks and the points where the curves cross the *x* axis are the same for each curve. Also observe that the rotating phasors are in phase. Under such circumstances we have $\theta = 0°$, and the voltage and the resulting current that it produces in the circuit are said to be *in phase*.

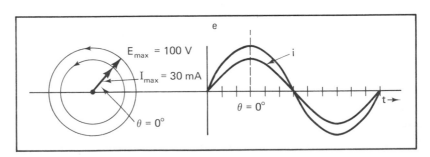

FIGURE 27-7
Voltage and Current in Phase

In Figure 27-8, rotating voltage and current phasors and waveforms are shown in which the current is "behind" the voltage by $\theta°$.

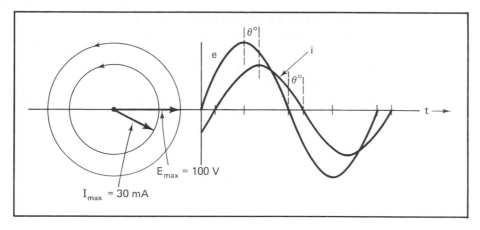

FIGURE 27-8
Current Lagging Voltage by $\theta°$

Notice that the rotating current phasor is $\theta°$ behind of the voltage phasor. This is normally expressed as: the current *lags* the voltage by $\theta°$.

Observe how the phase difference of the rotating phasors affects the waveform. The peak of the current wave is seen to lag the peak of the voltage by $\theta°$. Similarly, the point where the current wave crosses the x axis is seen to occur $\theta°$ after the voltage wave.

In Figure 27-9, rotating voltage and current phasors and waveforms are shown in which the current is "ahead" of the voltage by $\theta°$. This is normally expressed as: the current leads the voltage by $\theta°$. Note in the waveforms that the current peaks occur $\theta°$ before the voltage peak. Also observe that the current wave crosses the x axis $\theta°$ before the voltage wave.

FIGURE 27-9
Current Leading a Voltage by $\theta°$

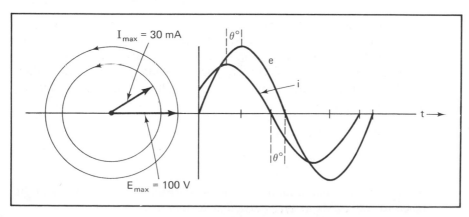

431

In Figures 27–8 and 27–9 the rotating voltage phasor is shown at the 0° position. The voltage and current phasors may also be shown at any other point in their rotation. In Figure 27–10 the phasors for Figure 27–9 are shown at an angle $\phi°$ from the 0° position. The angle ϕ is usually considered the voltage angle, that is the angle from the positive x-axis to the voltage phasor. The points that the voltage and current phasors represent at the angle $\phi°$ are shown on the waveforms. This is for the purpose of writing general equations that will permit us to determine the instantaneous values of voltage or current *at any point in the cycle for any angle $\phi°$*. Examination of Figure 27–10 shows that the instantaneous value of voltage may be written as

$$e = E_{max} \sin \phi \quad \text{V}$$

The instantaneous value of current for any angle of $\phi°$ is written

$$i = I_{max} \sin (\phi + \theta) \quad \text{A}$$

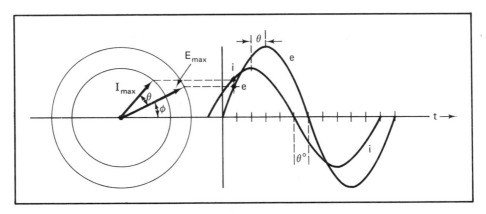

FIGURE 27–10
Phasor Positions at $\phi°$

In normal practice, the waveforms are not drawn. The phasor diagram is all that is necessary to describe the voltage and current phase relationship of a circuit. In Figure 27–11, a phasor diagram is drawn for a circuit in which the current lags the voltage by $\theta°$. Under these conditions, the instantaneous values of voltage and current for any angle may be written

$$e = E_{max} \sin \phi \quad \text{V}$$
$$i = I_{max} \sin (\phi - \theta) \quad \text{A}$$

Note that any instantaneous value is represented by the vertical distance to the x axis at that particular instant.

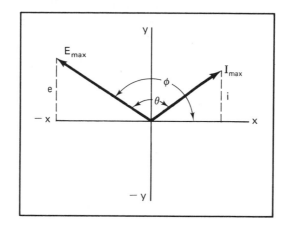

FIGURE 27–11
Phasor Diagram with Current Lagging Voltage

example 27–2 Determine the instantaneous values of voltage and current for the phasors shown in Figure 27–12 for $\phi = 36°$.

solution: $e = E_{max} \sin \phi = 100 \sin 36° = 100 \times 0.588 = 58.8$ V

$i = I_{max} \sin (\phi + \theta) = 5 \sin (36 + 42°)$

     $= 5 \sin 78° = 5 \times 0.978$

     $= 4.89$ A

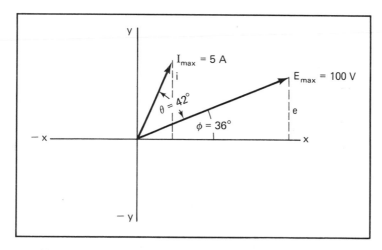

FIGURE 27–12
Phasor Diagram for Example 27–2

example 27–3 Determine the instantaneous values of voltage and current for the phasors shown in Figure 27–13 for $\phi = 335°$

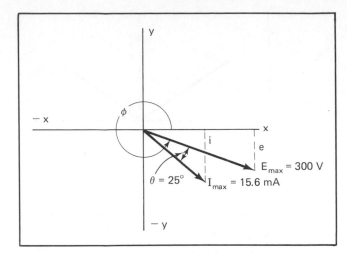

FIGURE 27–13
Phasor Diagram for Example 27–3

solution:

$$e = E_{max} \sin 335°$$

$$= E_{max} \sin (360° - 335°) = E_{max} \sin - 25°$$

$$= 300 \sin - 25° = 300 \times -0.423$$

$$= -126.78 \text{ V}$$

$$i = I_{max} \sin (\phi - \theta)$$

$$= 15.6 \sin (335° - 25°) = 300 \sin\ 310°$$

$$= 15.6 \sin (360° - 310°) = 15.6 \sin - 50°$$

$$= 15.6 \times (-0.766)$$

$$= -11.95 \text{ mA}$$

EXERCISES 17–2

1. In a 60-Hz ac circuit, the current lags the voltage by 52.6°. If $I_{max} = 30$ A, determine the instantaneous value of the current when the current has completed 98° of its cycle. At this point, what is the instantaneous value of voltage if $E_{max} = 300$ V?

2. In Figure 27–14, determine the instantaneous values of voltage and current for $\phi = 156°$.

3. If the value of ϕ in problem 2 was equal to $\phi = 260°$, what would be the instantaneous values of the voltage and current?

4. Determine the instantaneous values of voltage and current in problem 2 if $\phi = 360°$.

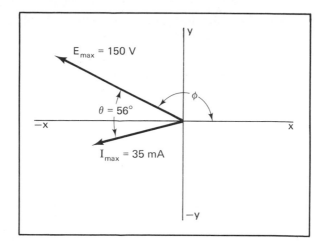

FIGURE 27–14
Phasor Diagram for Problems 2–4

5. In Figure 27–15, determine the instantaneous values of voltage and current if $\phi - 167°$.

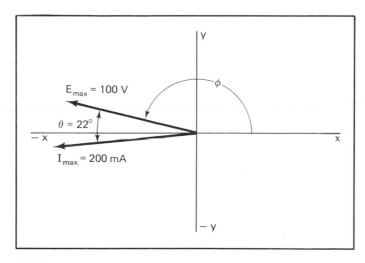

FIGURE 27–15
Phasor Diagram for Problems 5 and 6

6. Determine the instantaneous values of voltage and current in problem 5 if $\phi = 400°$.

7. In Figure 27–16, determine the instantaneous values of voltage and current if $\phi = 155°$.

8. What are the instantaneous values of voltage and current in problem 7 if $\phi = 90°$? If $\phi = 180°$?

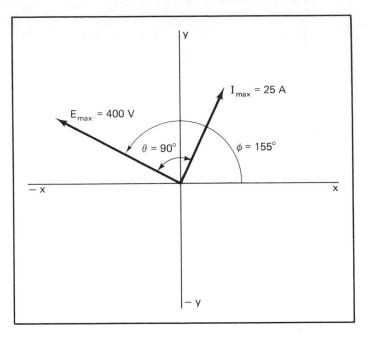

FIGURE   27–16
Phasor Diagram for Problems 7 and 8

28

ALTERNATING-CURRENT SERIES CIRCUIT

In this chapter, we shall investigate the characteristics of the alternating-current series circuit. The understanding of these circuits, and the parallel and complex circuits that will be discussed in Chapter 29, are vital to your work in electronics. Although these circuits are somewhat more difficult than the dc circuits with which you have worked, you will find, as most students do, that their behavior is much more interesting.

28-1 REACTANCE AND IMPEDANCE

In our studies of dc circuits, our work only involved resistance elements. It was found that Ohm's law always applied and that the power consumed in these circuits was the product of the voltage multiplied by the current.

In ac circuits, it will be necessary to adjust our thinking regarding Ohm's law. In addition, we will find that the power consumed in these circuits will normally not be equal to the product of the voltage and the current. We shall also discover that the sum of the ac voltages across circuit elements in series can exceed that of the voltage supply. Let us now examine briefly the reasons for behavior of this type in ac circuits. In ac circuits, in addition to resistance, we will be using inductive and capacitive devices. It is these devices that create the effects noted above.

Inductors and capacitors, like resistors, are devices that create an opposition to an electric current. The behavior of inductors and capacitors in ac circuits is quite different from that produced by resistors. If an ac voltage were applied to a resistor, an ammeter in the circuit would immediately indicate the current flow. This would not be true if the ac voltages were to be impressed across an inductor. The reason for this is the characteristic of an inductor called the *inductance*. Inductance is that property of an inductor that tends *to oppose any change in the circuit current*. When voltage is first impressed across an inductor, there is a delay in the current, reaching steady-state conditions. This is the result of a process in which the inductor converts a portion of energy applied to the circuit into magnetic energy. This magnetic energy is stored as a magnetic field by the inductor. This storing process occurs when the current in the circuit is increasing. At times when the current is decreasing, the magnetic energy is released. This is the result of the collapse of the magnetic field. The effect is such that the energy provided from this available magnetic energy tends *to oppose any change in the circuit current*. The properties of an inductor, composed of pure inductance, are such that the current flow through an inductor is found to "lag" the applied voltage by 90°.

A voltage impressed across a capacitor would similarly not establish instantaneous steady-state conditions. This is the result of the property of a capacitor called *capacitance*. Unlike the inductor, which stores energy in an electromagnetic form, the capacitor stores energy in an electrostatic form. This storing process in a capacitor occurs when the *voltage* applied to the circuit is increasing. This energy is released when the voltage of the circuit is decreasing. This effect, then, is such that the capacitance of a circuit tends *to oppose any change in the circuit voltage*. The properties of a capacitor, composed of pure capacitance, are such that the current flow through a capacitor is found to "lead" the applied voltage by 90°.

The opposition to changes in circuit current of inductance and the opposition to changes in circuit voltage of a capacitance is called *reactance*. The reactance caused by an inductor is termed *inductive reactance*, whereas the reactance caused by a capacitor is termed *capacitive reactance*.

The net effect of opposition to current and voltage flow in an ac circuit is called *impedance*. The circuit imepedance is composed of resistance, inductive reactance, and capacitive reactance. The amount of impedance in an ac circuit depends upon the amount of reactance created by any or all of these elements present and their arrangement. The arrangement may be in a series, parallel, or complex form. In this chapter we shall examine the characteristics and behavior of the ac series circuit.

28-2 AC CIRCUITS CONTAINING ONLY RESISTANCE

The behavior of an ac circuit, containing only resistance, is similar to that of a dc circuit containing only resistance. A simple resistive circuit, composed of three resistors in series, is shown in Figure 28-1. The

FIGURE 28-1
Series AC Circuit

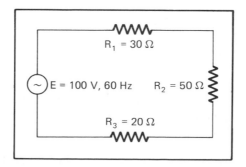

total circuit resistance is

$$R_T = R_1 + R_2 + R_3 = 30 + 50 + 20 = 100 \ \Omega$$

The current flowing in the circuit is

$$I = \frac{E}{R_T} = \frac{100}{100} = 1 \ A$$

The voltage drop across each resistor is

$$
\begin{aligned}
E_1 &= IR_1 = 1 \times 30 = & 30 \ V \cdot \\
E_2 &= IR_2 = 1 \times 50 = & 50 \ V \\
E_3 &= IR_3 = 1 \times 20 = & \underline{20 \ V} \\
E &= & 100 \ V
\end{aligned}
$$

It should be noted that to this point our operations are identical to that of a similar dc circuit. We are, however, dealing with an alternating voltage which necessitates some adjustment in our thinking. Keep in mind that the voltages and currents that we are working with above are effective values. In addition, the phase relationships must be considered.

In an ac circuit composed of only resistance, the voltage and current are in phase. This is shown in Figure 28–2. Observe that the voltage and current phasors, as shown, are in phase. The voltage and

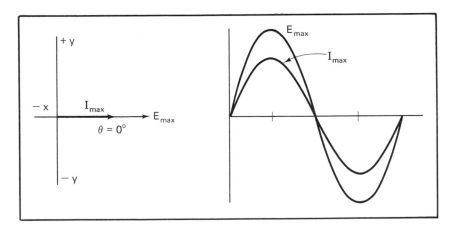

FIGURE 28–2
Voltage and Current Relationships

current waveforms reflect this, as the equations for the instantaneous values are

$$e = E_{max} \sin (\omega t + \theta) \quad \text{V}$$

$$i = I_{max} \sin (\omega t + \theta) \quad \text{A}$$

Using the maximum values of voltage and current calculated from the effective values given and for a frequency of 60 Hz, these equations become

$$e = 141.4 \sin (377t + 0°) = 141.4 \sin 377t \quad \text{V}$$

$$i = 1.414 \sin (377t + 0°) = 1.414 \sin 377t \quad \text{A}$$

Note that these equations differ only in amplitude. This is reflected in the waveforms shown in Figure 28–2. These phasors are drawn using maximum values. These are then used with the appropriate angular position to determine the instantaneous value of voltage or current at that particular instant.

The instantaneous power in an ac circuit consisting of only resistance is the product of the instantaneous values of voltage and current. This is shown as

$$p = ei$$

with this product expressed in units of VA (volt-amperes) or kVA (kilovolt-amperes) where appropriate. The power curve is shown in Figure 28–3. Note that this curve is positive for both halves of the

FIGURE 28–3
Power Curve for Text
Example

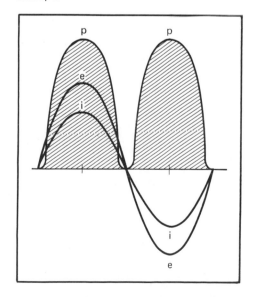

cycle, in that the product of e and i is positive when both are positive or both are negative. Observe further that as both sections of the curve are the same, the average value is equal to

$$P_{av} = \frac{E_{max}I_{max}}{2} \text{ W}$$

For our example, this becomes

$$P = \frac{141.4 \times 1.414}{2} = \frac{200}{2} = 100 \text{ W}$$

It is also seen that the product of the effective values of E and I also produce the same amount of power:

$$P = EI = 100 \times 1 = 100 \text{ W}$$

The average power for a series ac circuit containing only resistance, reflecting the above relationships, is obtained using the effective values of the circuit voltage and currents:

$$P = EI \quad \text{in W, or kW, where appropriate}$$

example 28–1 Determine the power dissipated by each resistor and the total circuit power for Figure 28–4.

---

solution: $R_T = R_1 + R_2 + R_3 + R_4 = 50 + 40 + 20 + 60 = 170 \ \Omega$

$$I_{cir} = \frac{E}{R_T} = \frac{115}{170} = 0.676 \text{ A}$$

The power consumed by each resistor is found using the relationship

$P = I^2 R$

$P_1 = I^2 R_1 = (0.676)^2 \times 50 = 22.9 \text{ W}$

$P_2 = I^2 R_2 = (0.676)^2 \times 40 = 18.3 \text{ W}$

$P_3 = I^2 R_3 = (0.676)^2 \times 20 = 9.1 \text{ W}$

$P_4 = I^2 R_4 = (0.676)^2 \times 60 = \underline{27.4 \text{ W}}$

Total circuit power   77.7 W

to check: Circuit power is also equal to

$$P = EI = 115 \times 0.676 = 77.7 \text{ W}$$

The power consumed by each resistor is

$$P_{R_1} = I^2 R_1 = (0.882)^2 \times 100 = \quad 77.8 \text{ W}$$

$$P_{R_2} = \frac{E_{par}^2}{R_2} = \frac{(211.8)^2}{600} \quad\quad = \quad 74.7 \text{ W}$$

$$P_{R_3} = \frac{E_{par}^2}{R_3} = \frac{(211.8)^2}{400} \quad\quad = 112.1 \text{ W}$$

Total circuit power $\quad$ 264.6 W

to check: $\qquad P_{clr} = EI = 300 \times 0.882 = 264.6 \text{ W}$

UITS CONTAINING ONLY INDUCTANCE

It was observed in Section 28–1 that an inductance has properties such that it opposes any change in the circuit current. This opposition is brought about through magnetic energy stored as a magnetic field around the inductor. During the first quarter and third quarter of the cycle when the current is increasing, energy would be stored. During the second quarter and fourth quarter of the cycle, stored energy would be released. This is shown in Figure 28–6. During quarters 1 and 3, the current flow establishes an emf in the process of storing magnetic energy that tends to oppose the current increase. In quarters 2 and 4, the release of magnetic energy through the collapse of the magnetic establishes an emf that opposes current changes during these periods.

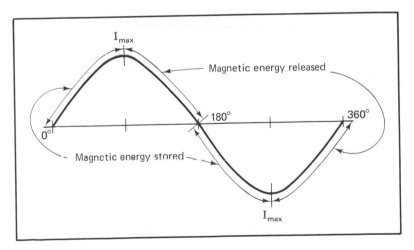

FIGURE 28–6
Storage and Release of Magnetic Energy

An inductance, L, of 1 H is present when a change of 1 A in 1 s induces a voltage of 1 V. This may be expressed in equation form as

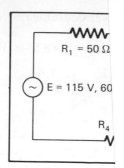

Figure   28–4
Circuit for Example 28

example 28–2   Determine the power consumed by e
circuit power for the circuit shown i

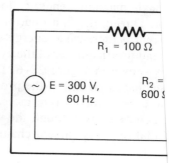

Figure   28–5
Circuit for Example 28–2

solution: The equivalent resistance of the parall
found as

$$R_{eq} = \frac{R_2 R_3}{R_2 + R_3} = \frac{600 \times 400}{600 + 400} = \frac{240,000}{1,000}$$

$$R_T = R_1 + R_{eq} = 100 + 240 = 340 \ \Omega$$

$$I = \frac{E}{R_T} = \frac{300}{340} = 0.882 \ \text{A}$$

The voltage drop across resistor R_1 is

$$E_{R_1} = IR_1 = 0.882 \times 100 = 88.2 \ \text{V}$$

The voltage across the parallel combinati

$$E_{par} = E - E_{R_1} = 300 - 88.2 = 211.8 \ \text{V}$$

$$E_{av} = L\frac{I}{t} \quad \text{V}, \quad \text{where}$$

1 V is produced by 1 H by a $\dfrac{\text{change of 1 A}}{\text{in 1 s}}$.

As there are four periods during one cycle when the storage and release of magnetic energy occurs, for a time period of $\frac{1}{4f}$ s we may write

$$E_{av} = L\frac{I_{max}}{\frac{1}{4f}} \quad \text{V} \quad \text{or}$$

$$= 4fLI_{max} \quad \text{V}$$

As $\quad E_{av} = \dfrac{2}{\pi} E_{max} \quad$ V, we may write

$$\frac{2}{\pi} E_{max} = 4fLI_{max} \quad \text{V}, \quad \text{or}$$

$$E_{max} = 2\,{}^{\pi}fLI_{max} \quad \text{V}$$

Dividing both sides by $\sqrt{2}$ to convert E_{max} and I_{max} to effective values, we may now write

$$E = 2\pi fLI \quad \text{V}$$

Rearranging we have

$$\frac{E}{I} = 2\pi fL \quad \Omega$$

Note that we have the $\frac{E}{I}$ factor in the form used to determine the value of R in Ohm's law. Here, however, it is the inductive reactance, X_L, which provides the opposition or reactance to the flow of current. In effect, then, we have developed Ohm's law for an ac circuit containing only inductance. We may now write

$$X_L = \frac{E}{I} = 2\pi fL \quad \Omega, \quad \text{or}$$

$$= \frac{E}{I} = \omega L \quad \Omega, \quad \text{where}$$

$$\omega = 2\pi f$$

$$L = \text{inductance, henrys}$$

It is seen then, that Ohm's law for an ac circuit containing only inductance is

$$X_L = \frac{E}{I} \quad \Omega, \quad \text{or, in the form above}$$

$$= \omega L \quad \Omega$$

An actual inductor contains some resistance. At this point in our studies we shall consider an inductor to have a negligible resistance. The voltage that is induced by the constantly changing current in an ac circuit provides a continual opposition to current changes. This opposition is represented in phasor form by a current phasor which *lags* the voltage phasor by 90°. This is shown in Figure 28–7. The instantaneous values of voltage and current may be written

$$e = E_{max} \sin \omega t = E_{max} \sin \phi \quad V$$

$$i = I_{max} \sin (\omega t - \theta) = I_{max} \sin (\phi - \theta) \quad A$$

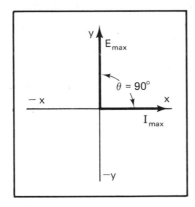

FIGURE 28–7
Circuit Containing Pure
Inductance

example 28–3 Determine the inductive reactance and the current of the circuit of Figure 28–8 and the instantaneous values of voltage and current when the voltage is at 150° of its cycle.

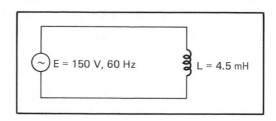

FIGURE 28–8
Circuit for Example 28–3

solution:

$$X_L = 2\pi fL = 6.28 \times 60 \times 4.5 \times 10^{-3}$$

$$= 1,696.5 \times 10^{-3}$$

$$= 1.696 \ \Omega$$

$$I = \frac{E}{X_L} = \frac{150}{1.696} = 88.4 \ \text{A}$$

At 150° of the voltage cycle, we have the phasor positions shown in Figure 28–9.

$$e = E_{\max} \sin \phi$$

$$= 1.414 \ E \sin 150° = 1.414 \times 150 \sin (180° - 150°)$$

$$= 212.1 \sin 30°$$

$$= 106.05 \ \text{V}$$

$$i = I_{max} \sin (\phi - \theta)$$

FIGURE 28–9
Phasor Positions in Example 28–3

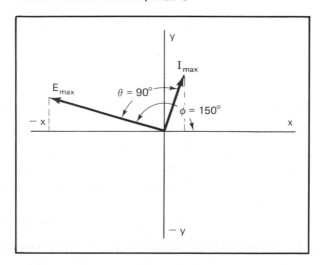

$$= 1.414 \, I \sin (150° - 90°) = 1.414 \times 88.4 \sin 60°$$

$$= 125 \sin 60°$$

$$= 108.25 \text{ A}$$

At this point it would be well to point out the effect of inductors in series. The inductances add in the same manner as resistances add in a series circuit. As a result, *the inductive reactances of series inductors are also added.*

example 28–4 Determine the inductive reactance of the circuit of Figure 28–10.

$$X_{L_1} = 2\pi f L_1 = 377 \times 5 \times 10^{-3} = 1.88 \ \Omega$$

$$X_{L_2} = 2\pi f L_2 = 377 \times 25 \times 10^{-3} = 9.43 \ \Omega$$

$$X_{L_T} = X_{L_1} + X_{L_2} = 1.88 + 9.43 = 11.3 \ \Omega$$

to check:
$$L_T = L_1 + L_2 = 5 \text{ mH} + 25 \text{ mH} = 30 \text{ mH}$$

$$X_{L_T} = 2\pi f L_T = 377 \times 30 \times 10^{-3} = 11.3 \ \Omega$$

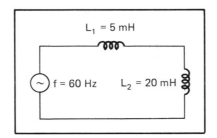

FIGURE 28–10
Circuit for Example 28–4

EXERCISE 28–1

1. Determine the reactance of a 35-mH inductor at 60 Hz.

2. What is the inductance of an inductor that has a reactance of 16.2 Ω at 60 Hz?

3. What is the reactance of the inductor of problem 1 at 400 Hz?

4. Determine the inductance that would produce a reactance of 47.6 Ω at 1.75 kHz.

5. What is the reactance of a 250-mH coil at 1.5 MHz?

6. Determine the reactance of a 35.2-μH coil at 27.6 MHz.

7. What effect does decreasing the frequency have on the inductive reactance? Decreasing the inductance?

8. In Example 28–3, what are the instantaneous values of voltage and current when the voltage is at 300° of its cycle?

28–4 POWER IN A CIRCUIT CONTAINING ONLY INDUCTANCE

In Figure 28–11, the waveforms of voltage, current, and power are shown for an ac circuit containing only inductance. The current is shown lagging the voltage by 90°. For explanation purposes, the current waveform is shown starting at 0°. The instantaneous values

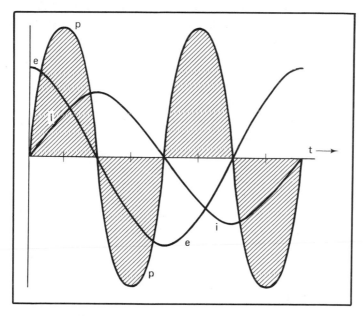

FIGURE 28–11
Waveforms for Circuit Containing Only *L*

of power are the product of the instantaneous values of voltage and current. The power curve, reflecting these instantaneous products, is shown in Figure 28–11. There are several interesting features of the power curve. These are

1. When both *e* and *i* have the same sign, the power curve is positive.
2. When the power curve is positive, the inductor is storing magnetic energy.
3. When the signs of *e* and *i* are not the same, the power curve is negative.

4. A negative power curve means that the magnetic field is collapsing, inducing a voltage that tends to oppose any change in the circuit current. During this period when the power curve is negative, stored magnetic energy is being supplied to the circuit.

5. Observe that energy is being stored during periods when the current is increasing toward its positive or negative maximum points. Stored magnetic energy, represented by the negative portions of the power curve, is being supplied to the circuit during that period when the current is decreasing toward zero from its positive maximum or negative maximum points.

6. The resultant power required for a circuit composed of pure inductance is *zero*. This is because of the equal and opposite nature of the power-curve loops. Power from the source stored during one portion of the cycle is returned during the next. The net source drain is zero.

Under the circumstances noted above in item 6, the question will arise as to the significance of the product of the effective values of *E* and *I*. This product,

$E \times I =$ apparent power or reactive power

The reactive or apparent power represents no actual power drawn from the source. In a circuit composed of an inductance there will be voltage and current readings, but a wattmeter used to measure power will read zero.

28–5 AC CIRCUITS CONTAINING ONLY CAPACITANCE

It was observed in Section 28–1 that a capacitance has properties such that it opposes any change in circuit voltage. In the case of a capacitor, during periods when the voltage is increasing in either a positive or negative direction, electrostatic energy is stored by the capacitor. During periods when the voltage is decreasing from its positive or negative maximums, the stored energy will be released as an emf to oppose the change in voltage. This is shown in Figure 28–12. Note that this is similar to the curve for an inductance shown in Figure 28–6, except that this is a voltage curve.

A capacitance, *C*, of 1 F is present when a change of 1 V in 1 s develops a current of 1 A. This may be expressed in equation form as

$$I_{av} = C \frac{E}{t} \quad \text{A,} \quad \text{where}$$

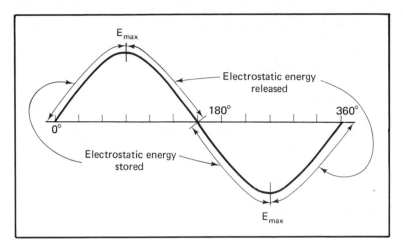

Figure 28–12
Storage and Release of Electrostatic Energy

$$1 \text{ A is produced by 1 F by a } \frac{\text{change of 1 V}}{\text{in 1 s}}$$

A capacitor stores its electrostatic energy in the form of an electrical charge that is retained by plates insulated by a dielectric medium. The charge of a capacitor is expressed by the equation

$$Q = EC, \quad \text{where}$$

Q = charge, coulombs (which is the combined charge of 6.25×10^{18} electrons, or the charge in ampere-seconds)
E = potential, volts placed on the capacitor
C = capacitance, farads

This relationship will provide some understanding of the ability of a capacitor to store energy or charge.

As with the inductor, four separate sequence periods occur during one cycle. As seen above, in the case of a capacitor, a voltage cycle is involved. As a result, for a time period of $\frac{1}{4f}$ s, we may write

$$I_{av} = C \frac{E_{max}}{\frac{1}{4f}} \text{ A}$$

$$= 4fCE_{max} \text{ A}$$

As $I_{av} = \dfrac{2}{\pi} I_{max}$, we may write

$$\frac{2}{\pi} I_{max} = 4fC E_{max}, \quad \text{or}$$

$$I_{max} = 2\pi fC E_{max}$$

Dividing both sides by $\sqrt{2}$ to convert I_{max} and E_{max} to effective values, we may now write

$$I = 2\pi fCE \quad \text{A}$$

Rearranging, we may write

$$\frac{E}{I} = \frac{1}{2\pi fC}$$

As with the inductive circuit, we now have the left member in Ohm's law form. In this instance the $\dfrac{E}{I}$ member designates the capacitive reactance, X_c. We may now write

$$X_C = \frac{1}{2\pi fC} \quad \Omega, \quad \text{or}$$

$$= \frac{1}{\omega C} \quad \Omega, \quad \text{where}$$

$$\omega = 2\pi f$$

$$C = \text{capacitance, farads}$$

As with the purely inductive circuit, Ohm's law for a purely capacitive circuit may be written as

$$X_C = \frac{E}{I} \quad \Omega, \quad \text{or, in the form above}$$

$$= \frac{1}{\omega C} \quad \Omega$$

The opposition, or reactance, to current flow may be expressed in phasor form. The reactance introduced into the circuit by the capacitance is such that the current *leads* the voltage by 90°. This is shown in Figure 28–13. The instantaneous values of voltage and current may be written

$$e = E_{max} \sin \omega t = E_{max} \sin \phi \quad \text{V}$$

$$i = I_{max} \sin (\omega t + \theta) = I_{max} \sin (\phi + \theta) \quad \text{A}$$

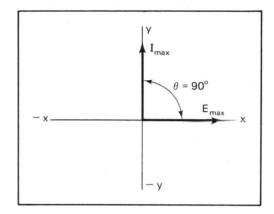

FIGURE 28–13
Circuit Containing Pure Capacitance

In phasor form this is shown in Figure 28–14.

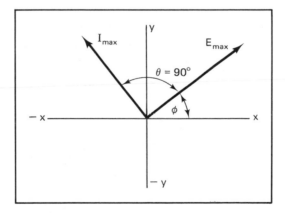

FIGURE 28–14
Phasor Positions for Pure-Capacitance Circuit

example 28–5 Determine the capacitive reactance of the capacitor shown in Figure 28–15. What is the circuit current?

solution:

$$X_C = \frac{1}{\omega C} = \frac{1}{2\pi \times 60 \times 0.5 \times 10^{-6}}$$

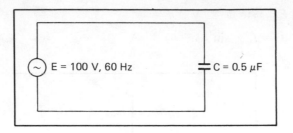

FIGURE 28–15
Circuit for Example 28–5

$$= \frac{1}{377 \times 0.5 \times 10^{-6}} = \frac{1}{188.5 \times 10^{-6}}$$

$$= 0.0053 \times 10^6 \ \Omega$$

$$= 5{,}300 \ \Omega$$

$$X_C = \frac{E}{I} \qquad I = \frac{E}{X_C}$$

$$I = \frac{100}{5{,}300} = 0.019 \ \text{A}$$

$$= 19 \ \text{mA}$$

example 28–6 A 60-Hz 300-V supply is connected to a capacitor. The current measured in the circuit was found to be 356 mA. What is the capacitance of the capacitor?

solution:

$$X_C = \frac{E}{I} = \frac{300}{356 \times 10^{-3}} = 842.7 \ \Omega \ \text{and as}$$

$$X_C = \frac{1}{2\pi f C}$$

$$C = \frac{1}{2\pi f X_C} = \frac{1}{377 \times 842.7}$$

$$= \frac{1}{3.177 \times 10^5}$$

$$= 3.1 \times 10^{-6} \ \text{F}$$

$$= 3.1 \ \mu\text{F}$$

example 28–7 Determine the instantaneous values of voltage and current for the capacitive circuit shown in Figure 28–16.

solution:

$$e = E_{\max} \sin \omega t = E_{\max} \sin \phi$$

$$= 190 \sin 104° = 190 \sin (180° - 104°)$$

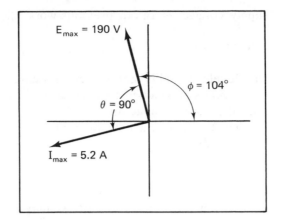

FIGURE 28–16
Circuit for Example 28–7

$$= 190 \sin 76° = 190 \times 0.970$$

$$= 184.3 \text{ V}$$

$$i = I_{max} \sin (\omega t + \theta) = I_{max} \sin (\phi + \theta)$$

$$= 5.2 \sin (104° + 90°) = 5.2 \sin 194°$$

$$= 5.2 \sin (180° - 194°) = 5.2 \sin -14°$$

$$= 5.2 \times -0.242$$

$$= -1.26 \text{ mA}$$

Often capacitors are placed in series in a circuit. The result of this procedure is different from inductors in series in that the capacitances cannot be added to determine the total circuit capacitance. In Figure 28–17, two capacitors have been placed in series across the

FIGURE 28–17
Capacitors in Series

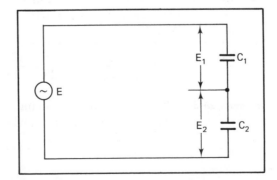

supply voltage, E. In our previous work, the equation

$$Q = EC$$

was developed. This represented the charge, coulombs, on a capacitor of C, farads, developed by a voltage of E, volts. In this circuit, it is seen that as the capacitors are in series, the quantity of electricity, or charge, Q, to each is the same. We may then write, using the equation above,

$$Q = EC_t$$

As Q is common for the circuit, we may write

$$Q = E_1 C_1 = E_2 C_2, \quad \text{or}$$

$$E_1 = \frac{Q}{C_1} \quad \text{and} \quad E_2 = \frac{Q}{C_2}$$

As $E = E_1 + E_2$, it follows that

$$\frac{Q}{C_t} = \frac{Q}{C_1} + \frac{Q}{C_2}, \quad \text{and, dividing both sides by } Q$$

$$\frac{1}{C_t} = \frac{1}{C_1} + \frac{1}{C_2}$$

This we should recognize as an equation in the same form as resistances in parallel. We may then say that *capacitances in series combine as resistances in parallel*. We may now write for two capacitors in series the equation in the form

$$C_t = \frac{C_1 C_2}{C_1 + C_2}$$

example 28-8 Determine the total capacitance of a circuit composed of a capacitor of 5 μF in series with a capacitor of 25 μF.

solution:

$$C_t = \frac{C_1 C_2}{C_1 + C_2} = \frac{(5)(25)}{5 + 25} = \frac{125}{30} = 4.17 \ \mu F$$

example 28-9 What is the total capacitance of a circuit consisting of three capacitors in series, where $C_1 = 15 \ \mu F$, $C_2 = 18 \ \mu F$, and $C_3 = 28 \ \mu F$.

457

Sec. 28–6
POWER
IN A CIRCUIT
CONTAINING ONLY
CAPACITANCE

solution:

$$\frac{1}{C_t} = \frac{1}{C_1} + \frac{1}{C_2} + \frac{1}{C_3}$$

$$= \frac{1}{15} + \frac{1}{18} + \frac{1}{28}$$

$$= 0.067 + 0.055 + 0.036$$

$$= 0.158$$

$$C_t = 6.33 \ \mu F$$

EXERCISE 28–2

1. Determine X_c for a capacitor of 1,500 μF when used in a 15-kHz circuit.

2. What is X_c of a 0.15-μF capacitor when connected in a 1.5-MHz circuit?

3. If the voltage in problem 1 is 100 V, determine the circuit current.

4. What is the circuit current in problem 2 if the voltage is 400 V?

5. The current in a 400-V 400-Hz circuit containing a single capacitor is 3.5 mA. What is the size of the capacitor?

6. What is the total capacitance of a circuit containing a 3.5-μF capacitor and 2,500-$\mu\mu$F capacitor in series?

7. Three capacitors, 1.5 μF, 150 μF, and 3,000 $\mu\mu$F, are connected in series. What is the total capacitance?

8. What current would flow in the circuit of problem 7 if it were connected to a 150-V 1.5-MHz supply?

28–6 POWER IN A CIRCUIT CONTAINING ONLY CAPACITANCE

In Figure 28–18, the waveforms of voltage, current, and power are shown for an ac circuit containing only capacitance. The current is shown leading the voltage by 90°. For purposes of explanation, the current waveform is shown starting at 0°. The similarity with the comparable waveforms for a circuit containing only inductance, as shown in Fig. 28–11, is immediately apparent. As before, the instantaneous power is the product of the instantaneous values of voltage, e, and current, i. For the capacitive circuit it will be noted that during the first and third quarters of the voltage cycle, power is being stored by the capacitor. During the second and fourth quarters of the voltage cycle, power is being returned to the source.

As with the inductive circuit, the net power drain in a capacitive circuit is zero, as the energy taken during one quarter of the voltage

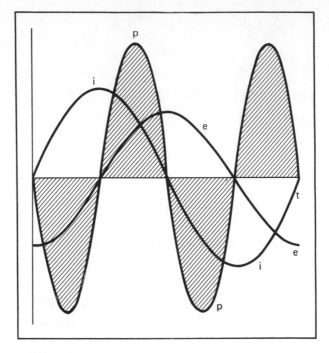

FIGURE 28–18
Waveforms for Circuit Containing Only C

cycle is returned during the next. As a result, the product

$$E \times I = \text{apparent power or reactive power}$$

The result, as with the inductive circuit, permits voltage and current readings with zero power measured with a wattmeter.

28–7 CIRCUITS CONTAINING R AND L IN SERIES

In previous sections, circuits containing resistance or inductance alone were examined. In the former circuit, the voltage and current were in phase, while in the latter circuit, the current lagged the voltage by 90°. As might be expected, circuits containing R and L in series will have a current lagging by less than 90°. Let us examine the reasons for this behavior.

A circuit containing R and L in series is shown in Figure 28–19.

As the current in a series circuit is common to all elements in the circuit, it is used as the reference phasor. This leaves the voltage across the resistance, E_R, and the voltage across the capacitance, E_C, to be properly oriented in relation to the current. The phasors of E_R and E_L

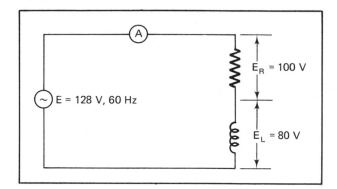

FIGURE 28–19
Circuit Containing *R* and *L* in Series

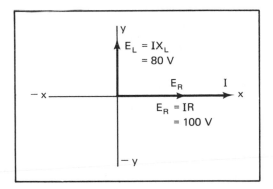

459
Sec. 28–7
CIRCUITS
CONTAINING
R AND *L* IN
SERIES

are drawn in relation to the circuit current as though the other were not in the circuit. This results in the phasor diagram of Figure 28–20.

FIGURE 28–20
Phasor Diagram for *R–L* Series Circuit

Examination of Figure 28–19 shows that the algebraic sum of the voltage across the resistance and the inductance is greater than the supply voltage, *E*. The reason is that these two voltages do not add algebraically but by phasor addition. The graphical construction is shown in Figure 28–21. However, this process as observed earlier in the text is not accurate or convenient. Using rectangular notation, we may write

$$
\begin{aligned}
E_R &= 100 + j0 \quad \text{V} \\
E_L &= \underline{\quad 0 + j80} \quad \text{V} \\
E &= 100 + j80 \quad \text{V}
\end{aligned}
$$

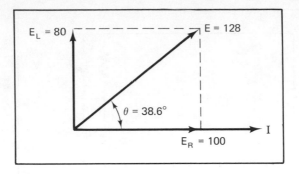

FIGURE 28–21
Graphical Addition of Phasors

Converting to polar form, we have

$$E = \sqrt{(100)^2 = (80)^2}$$

$$128 \text{ V}$$

$$\sin \theta = \frac{80}{128} = 0.625, \qquad \theta = 38.6°$$

This gives the value of E in polar form as

$$E = 128 \underline{|38.6°} \qquad \text{V}$$

It should be noted that the magnitude of phasor, E, is that of the supply voltage. The angle, θ, represents the number of degrees that the current is lagging the voltage.

Observe in Figure 28–21 that

$$E \cos \theta = E_R \qquad \text{V} \quad \text{and} \quad E \sin \theta = E_L \qquad \text{V}$$

These relationships will be used frequently in our later work.

It will be observed that the circuit current was not given in Figure 28–19. Let us examine the procedure for determining this value. Note that the equation above, for the conversion of the phasor E in rectangular form, to polar form is

$$E = \sqrt{(100)^2 + (80)^2} \qquad \text{V}$$

This represents

$$E = \sqrt{(IR)^2 + (IX_L)^2} \qquad \text{V}$$

This may be written

$$E = \sqrt{I^2R^2 + I^2X_L^2} \quad \text{V}$$

from which, we may write

$$E = \sqrt{I^2(R^2 + X_L^2)} \quad \text{V}$$

Then

$$E = I\sqrt{R^2 + X_L^2} \quad \text{V}$$

Transposing, we have

$$\frac{E}{I} = \sqrt{R^2 + X_L^2}$$

The $\frac{E}{I}$ factor represents the Ohm's law relationship for ac circuit opposition to current flow, or the circuit impedance, Z. Then the circuit impedance is

$$Z = \frac{E}{I} = \sqrt{R^2 + X_L^2} \quad \Omega$$

The impedance may also be represented in phasor form as shown in Figure 28–22. In rectangular form we may write

$$Z = 20 + j16 \ \Omega$$

FIGURE 28–22
Phasor Representation of Impedance

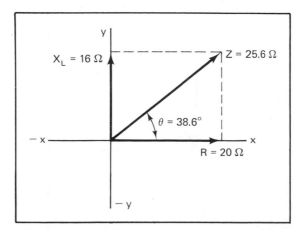

461
Sec. 28–7
CIRCUITS
CONTAINING
R AND L IN
SERIES

Converting to polar form we have

$$Z = \sqrt{(20)^2 + (16)^2} = 25.6 \ \Omega$$

$$\sin \theta = \frac{16}{25.6} = 0.625$$

$$\theta = 38.6°$$

Then we may write

$$Z = 25.6\underline{|38.6°} \ \Omega$$

Then

$$I = \frac{E}{Z} = \frac{128}{25.6} = 5 \ A$$

Note that the angle, θ, between the Z and the R phasors is the same as the angle, θ, between phasors, E and I, in Figure 28–21. Also observe that

$$R = Z \cos \theta \ \Omega \quad \text{and} \quad X_L = Z \sin \theta \ \Omega$$

These relationships also will be used frequently in our later work.

example 28-10   The phasor diagram shown in Figure 28–23 is for a circuit composed of a resistance and inductance in series. Determine the voltage drop across each, and the size of each, if $f = 60$ Hz.

FIGURE   28–23
Phasor Diagrams for Example 28–10

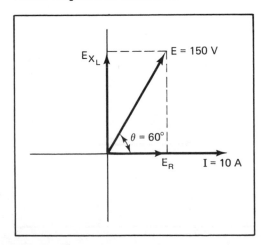

463

Sec. 28–7
CIRCUITS
CONTAINING
R AND L IN
SERIES

solution: The voltage drops across R and L, as shown in Figure 28–23, may be determined as

$$E_R = E \cos 60° = 150 \times 0.5 = 75 \text{ V}$$

$$E_{X_L} = E \sin 60° = 150 \times 0.866 = 130 \text{ V}$$

The circuit, Z, may be determined as

$$Z = \frac{E}{I} = \frac{150}{10} = 15 \text{ Ω}$$

As the circuit, θ, is the same as the $Z\theta$, we may draw the phasor diagram of the impedance as shown in Figure 28–24. From the figure it is seen that

$$R = Z \cos \theta = 15 \cos 60° = 15 \times 0.5 = 7.5 \text{ Ω}$$

$$X_L = Z \sin \theta = 15 \sin 60° = 15 \times 0.866 = 13 \text{ Ω}$$

For the 60-Hz frequency,

$$X_L = 2\pi f L \text{ Ω}$$

$$L = \frac{X_L}{2\pi f} = \frac{13}{377} = 0.034 \text{ H} = 34 \text{ mH}$$

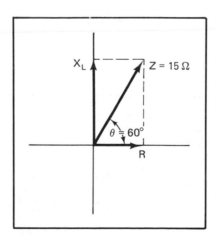

FIGURE 28–24
Impedance Phasors for
Example 28–10

example 28–11 For the circuit shown in Figure 28–25, determine the following: Z, I, θ, E_R, and E_{X_L}.

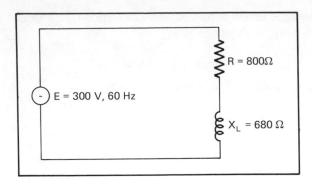

FIGURE 28–25
Circuit for Example 28–11

solution: The impedance phasors are drawn first. This is shown in Figure 28–26. In rectangular form,

$$
\begin{aligned}
R &= 800 + j0 \ \Omega \\
X_L &= 0 + j680 \ \Omega \\
\hline
Z &= 800 + j680 \ \Omega
\end{aligned}
$$

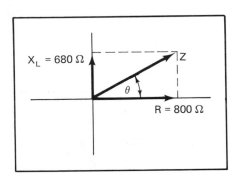

FIGURE 28–26
Impedance Phasors for
Example 28–11

In polar form,

$$Z = \sqrt{(800)^2 + (680)^2}$$

$$= 1{,}050 \ \Omega$$

$$\sin \theta = \frac{680}{1{,}050} = 0.648$$

$$\theta = 40.36°$$

The circuit current may be found as

465

Sec. 28–8
CIRCUITS
CONTAINING
R AND *C* IN
SERIES

$$I = \frac{E}{Z} \times \frac{300}{1,050} = 0.286 \text{ A} = 286 \text{ mA}$$

The voltage across R and X_L is found as

$$E_R = IR = 0.286 \times 800 = 228.8 \text{ V}$$

$$E_{XL} = IX_L = 0.286 \times 680 = 194.5 \text{ V}$$

The circuit phasors are shown in Figure 28–27.

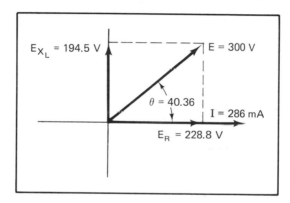

FIGURE 28–27
Circuit Phasors for Example 28–11

28–8 CIRCUITS CONTAINING *R* AND *C* IN SERIES

Circuits and R and C in series are handled in a similar manner as circuits with R and L in series, the only difference being the treatment of the phasors for the voltage, E_{Xc}, and the phasor for the capacitive reactance, X_c. These are shown in Figure 28–28a and b.

Several features of the diagrams in Figure 28–28 should be noted. Observe that the voltage phasor, E_{Xc}, is drawn so that it lags the current vector by 90°. This, when added to the E_R phasor, results in the circuit voltage phasor, E, lagging the circuit current phasor, I. Expressed in a more conventional form, the current leads the voltage by θ^0. This is as expected, for a circuit with only R has $\theta = 0°$, while a circuit with only C has the current leading the voltage by $\theta = 90°$.

The impedance phasors reflect the characteristics of the circuit phasors, the X_c phasor being drawn, lagging the R phasor by 90°. In all

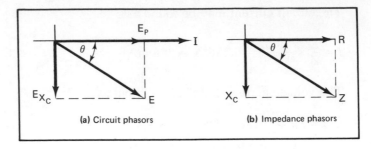

FIGURE 28–28
Phasors for an *R–C* Series Circuit

other respects, the treatment of a series *R–C* circuit is the same as an *R–L* series circuit.

example 28-12 For the circuit shown in Figure 28–29, determine Z, I, θ, E_R, E_C, and C.

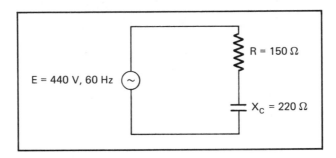

FIGURE 28–29
Circuit for Example 28–12

solution: The impedance phasors are drawn first, as shown in Figure 28–30. In rectangular form,

$$
\begin{aligned}
R &= 150 + j0 \ \Omega \\
X_C &= 0 - j220 \ \Omega \\
\hline
Z &= 150 - j220 \ \Omega
\end{aligned}
$$

In polar form,

$$Z = \sqrt{(150)^2 + (-220)^2} = 266.3 \ \Omega$$

$$\sin \theta = \frac{220}{266.3} = 0.826$$

$$= -55.7°$$

The circuit current and the voltage drops across R and C are now determined:

467
Sec. 28–8
CIRCUITS
CONTAINING
R AND C IN
SERIES

$$I = \frac{E}{Z} = \frac{440}{266.3} = 1.65 \text{ A}$$

$$E_R = IR = 1.65 \times 150 = 247.5 \text{ V}$$

$$E_{XC} = IX_c = 1.65 \times 220 = 363 \text{ V}$$

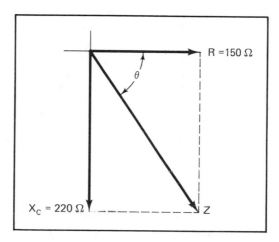

FIGURE 28–30
Impedance Phasors for Example 28–12

The circuit phasors are shown in Figure 28–31. The capacitance, C, may be determined as

$$X_C = \frac{1}{2\pi fC} \quad \Omega, \qquad C = \frac{1}{2\pi fX_c} \quad \text{F}$$

$$C = \frac{1}{377 \times 220}$$

$$= \frac{1}{82,940}$$

$$= 0.000012 \text{ F}$$

$$= 12 \ \mu\text{F}$$

EXERCISE 28–3

1. In a series circuit composed of R and L in series across 400 Hz, determine the voltage drop across each if the circuit $E = 300$ V, $I = 18.2$ A, and $\theta = 38.9°$.

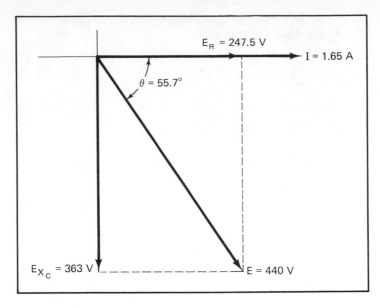

FIGURE   28–31
Circuit Phasors for Example 28–12

2.   What is the size of R and L in problem 1?

3.   Determine the impedance of $R = 15\ \Omega$ and $L = 2500\ \mu$H connected in a series across a 250-V 1,500-Hz supply.

4.   What current would flow in the circuit of problem 3? What is the value of θ?

5.   If a circuit consisting of $R = 1,200\ \Omega$ and an inductor with $X_L = 2,200\ \Omega$ were connected to a 500-V 150-MHz supply, what would be the value of Z, I, and θ?

6.   In the circuit of problem 5, what is the voltage across R and L?

7.   If a circuit consists of $R = 25$ kΩ and a capacitor $X_C = 1,500\ \Omega$ in series, determine Z, I, and θ if $E = 2,500$ V and $f = 2,500$ Hz.

8.   Determine E_R, E_C, and C in problem 7.

28–9   CIRCUITS CONTAINING R, L, AND C IN SERIES

Series circuits containing R, L, and C are handled as an extension of an R–L or R–C circuit. Such a procedure is shown in the following example.

example 28–13   For the circuit shown in Figure 28–32, determine Z, I, θ, E_R, E_{XC}, C, and L.

469
Sec. 28–9
CIRCUITS
CONTAINING
R, *L*, AND *C* IN
SERIES

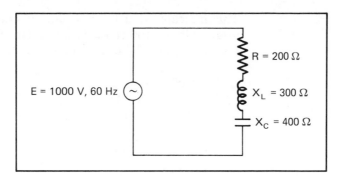

FIGURE 28–32
Circuit for Example 28–13

solution: The impedance diagram is first drawn. This is shown in Figure 28–33. Note that the capacitive reactance, X_c, is opposite to the inductive reactance, X_L, so the effective circuit reactance, X_{eq}, is the algebraic sum of X_c and X_L.

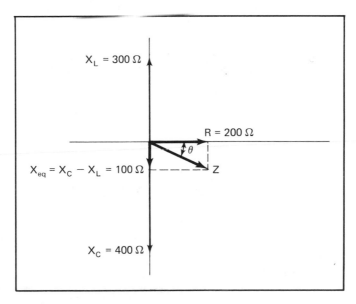

FIGURE 28–33
Impedance Diagram for Example 28–13

In rectangular form, we may write

$$X_C = 0 - j400 \ \Omega$$
$$X_L = 0 + j300 \ \Omega$$
$$\overline{X_{eq} = 0 - j100 \ \Omega}$$

This indicates that the resultant reactance, X_{eq}, has a magnitude of 100 Ω and is capacitive. This is shown in Figure 28–33. The circuit impedance is found as

$$\begin{array}{r} R = 200 + \quad j0 \ \Omega \\ X_{eq} = \quad 0 - j100 \ \Omega \\ \hline Z = 200 - j100 \ \Omega \end{array}$$

$$Z = \sqrt{(200)^2 + (100)^2}$$

$$= 223.6 \ \Omega$$

$$\sin \theta = \frac{X}{Z} = \frac{100}{223.6} = 0.447$$

$$\theta = -26.56°$$

The circuit current may be determined as

$$I = \frac{E}{Z} = \frac{1,000}{223.6} = 4.47 \ \text{A}$$

The circuit phasor diagram may now be drawn. This is shown in Figure 28–34. The voltages E_R and E_X are found as

$$E_R = E \cos \theta = 1,000 \cos -26.56°$$

$$= 1,000 \times 0.894 = 894 \ \text{V}$$

$$E_X = E \sin \theta = 1,000 \sin -26.56°$$

$$= 1,000 \times -0.447 = -447 \ \text{V}$$

FIGURE 28–34
Phasor Diagram for Example 28–13

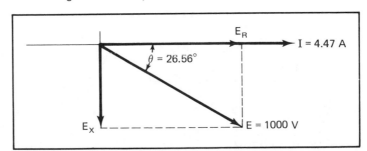

The values of C and L are found as

$$X_C = \frac{1}{2\pi fC} \ \Omega$$

$$C = \frac{1}{2\pi fX_c} = \frac{1}{377 \times 400} = \frac{1}{150,800} \ F = 6.6 \ \mu F$$

$$L = \frac{X_L}{2\pi f} = \frac{300}{377} = 0.796 \ H = 796 \ mH$$

It should be noted that the relationship for the impedance of a circuit containing R, L, and C may also be expressed as

$$Z = \sqrt{R^2 + (X_L - X_C)^2} \ \Omega$$

In this example, we used rectangular notation to establish the effective circuit reactance. Using this relationship, we have

$$Z = \sqrt{(200)^2 + (300 - 400)^2}$$

$$= \sqrt{(200)^2 + (-100)^2}$$

$$= 223.6 \ \Omega$$

$$\sin \theta = \frac{X_{eq}}{Z} = \frac{100}{223.6} = 0.447$$

$$\theta = -26.56°$$

Note that the difference between $(X_L - X_C)$ is capacitive and results in the phasor relationship shown above.

28–10 POWER IN AC SERIES CIRCUITS

In Sections 28–4 and 28–6, the power consumed in circuits containing only inductance or capacitance were examined. It was found that a pure inductance would store electromagnetic energy during one portion of the current cycle and return it to the power source during the next. The pure capacitance would store electrostatic energy during one portion of the voltage cycle and return it to the power source during the next. As a result, over the entire cycle, the energy taken from the source would equal the energy returned to the source. Such circuits require both voltage and current but, as seen, would consume no power.

In the case of a purely resistive circuit, we know that the power consumed is equal to

$$P = EI \quad \text{W}$$

This is referred to as the *real power* of the circuit.

The circuit containing only L or C requires voltage and current but no power. The product of voltage and current is referred to as the *apparent power*, with units of volt-amperes:

$$P_A = EI \quad \text{VA}$$

In a purely resistive circuit, then, the product of EI is equal to the real power. In a circuit composed of pure L or C, the product of EI is equal to apparent power.

In actual ac circuits with L or C present, some R is always present. This means that a situation exists, as far as power is concerned, somewhere between the case of the purely resistive circuit and the purely reactive, L–C circuit. Let us examine this condition, using the circuit of Example 28–12. The circuit diagram and circuit phasors for this example are repeated in Figure 28–35.

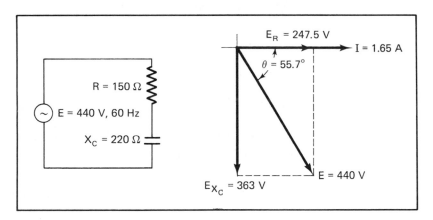

FIGURE 28–35
Circuit Diagrams and Phasors for Examples
28–12

Examination of the circuit phasors show that the common current is in phase with E_R and θ^0 ahead of E. The apparent power in the circuit is

$$P_A = EI \quad \text{VA}$$

The real or true power in the circuit is that dissipated by the resistance of the circuit and is

$$P = E_R I \quad \text{W} \quad \text{or}$$
$$= I^2 R \quad \text{W}$$

It is obvious that the true power, P, and the apparent power, P_A, are not the same. The ratio of the real power consumed by the circuit to the apparent power is called the *power factor*. This is expressed as

$$\text{pf} = \frac{P}{P_A}$$

As $P = I^2 R$ and $P_A = EI$, we may write

$$\text{pf} = \frac{I^2 R}{EI} = \frac{IR}{E}$$

As the circuit voltage is $E = IZ$ we may substitute:

$$\text{pf} = \frac{IR}{E} = \frac{IR}{IZ}$$
$$= \frac{R}{Z}$$

The impedance diagram for Example 28–12 is shown in Figure 28–36.

FIGURE 28–36
Impedance Diagram for Example 28–12

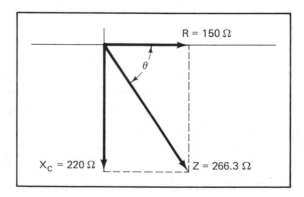

Examination of this figure shows that

$$\cos \theta = \frac{R}{Z} \quad \text{and as}$$

$$\text{pf} = \frac{R}{Z} \quad \text{then}$$

$$\text{pf} = \cos \theta = \frac{R}{Z}$$

The relationship between the impedance diagram and the circuit diagram permits us to develop a power diagram. This is shown in Figure 28–37. Note that a reactive component of power, P_x, has been added. The phasor, P_A, in polar form, may be expressed in rectangular form, where P represents the x-axis component and P_x the y-axis component. The unit of P_x most commonly used is volt-ampere reactive (var).

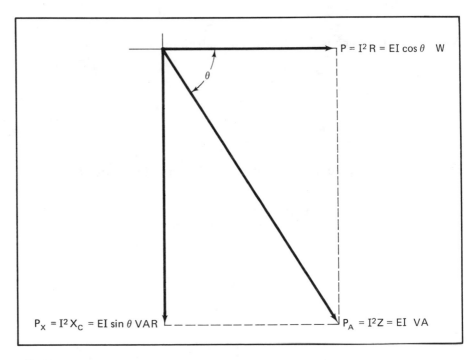

FIGURE 28–37
Power Diagram for Example 28–12

Examination of Figure 28–37 establishes

$$P_A = EI \qquad \text{VA}$$

$$P = EI \cos \theta \quad \text{W}$$

$$P_X = EI \sin \theta \quad \text{var}$$

The power relationships represented by these phasors may be expressed in rectangular form as

$$P_A = P - jP_X$$

or for any circuit as

$$P_A = P \pm jP_X$$

In a practical sense, this means the following:

1. In a circuit in which R and some reactive component is present, the apparent power, P_A, is greater than the real power, P.

2. In a circuit composed of R only, the apparent power P_A is equal to the real power, P. That is,

$$P_A = P \quad \text{as } \theta^0 = 0 \quad \text{and} \quad \cos 0° = 1$$

3. In a circuit composed of only X_C or X_L components, the apparent power, P_A, is equal to the reactive power, P_X. That is

$$P_A = P_X \quad \text{as } \theta = 90° \quad \text{and} \quad \sin 90° = 1$$

Under such circumstances,

$$P = 0 \quad \text{as } \theta = 90° \quad \text{and} \quad \cos 90° = 0$$

For the circuit of Example 28–12, the following values may be calculated:

$$\cos \theta = \frac{R}{Z} = \frac{150}{266.3} = 0.563 \quad \text{or} \quad 56.3\%$$

$$\theta = 55.7°$$

$$P_A = EI = 440 \times 1.65 = 726 \text{ VA}$$

$$P = EI \cos \theta = 762 \cos - 55.7° = 429 \text{ W}$$

$$P_X = EI \sin \theta = 762 \sin - 55.7° = -629.4 \text{ var}$$

Note that the negative sign for P_X denotes that the circuit is capacitive as shown by the phasors in Figure 28–37.

The instantaneous power of a circuit may be obtained as the product of e and i at that instant. Power curves such as those shown in Figures 28–3, 28–11, and 28–18 may be developed for any ac circuit. To plot these curves is, however, time consuming and unnecessary. The curves in these figures were used to show the storage and return of energy that occurred during a cycle. On a practical basis, the power equations above provide us with the information we normally require relative to the power relationships in a circuit.

Note that the pf may be expressed as a percentage as well as the cos θ. For example, a 35 percent power factor is the same as

$$\text{pf} = 0.35, \quad \text{where}$$

$$\theta = \arccos 0.35 = 69.5°$$

example 28–14 For the circuit shown in Figure 28–38, determine the circuit Z, I, θ, pf, P_A, P, and P_X.

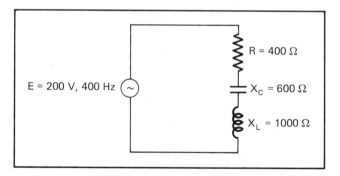

FIGURE 28–38
Circuit for Example 28–14

solution: The impedance diagram is first drawn, as shown in Figure 28–39. In rectangular form,

$$Z = R + jX_{eq} = 400 + j(1{,}000 - 600)$$

$$= 400 + j400$$

$$= \sqrt{400^2 + 400^2} = 565.7 \ \Omega$$

$$\text{pf} = \cos \theta = \frac{R}{Z} = \frac{400}{565.7} = 0.707$$

$$\theta = 45°$$

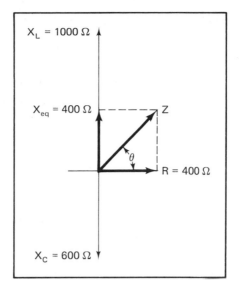

FIGURE 28–39
Impedance Diagram for
Example 28–14

Note: Often another method is used to determine the value of Z and θ. Examination of Figure 28–39 shows that

$$\tan \theta = \frac{X_{eq}}{R} = \frac{400}{400} = 1$$

$$\theta = 45°$$

The value of Z may be found as

$$Z \cos \theta = 400$$

$$Z = \frac{400}{\cos \theta} = \frac{400}{0.707} = 565.7 \ \Omega$$

The answers are, of course, the same. This method may be preferred rather than the method used in the example. In addition, the sine function could also be used to determine Z, if preferred.

example 28–15 A series ac circuit has a lagging pf = 0.792. The impedance of the circuit is 688 Ω. Determine the resistance and reactance of the circuit. What is the nature of the reactance?

solution: The pf $= \cos \theta$, so we may determine θ:

$$\theta = \arccos 0.792 = 37.6°$$

We may now draw the impedance diagram, knowing Z, θ, and that I will lag E by $\theta°$. Examination of Figure 28–40 shows that R and X_L may be determined as follows:

$$R = Z \cos \theta = 688 \cos 37.6° = 688 \times 0.792 = 544.8 \ \Omega$$

$$X_L = Z \sin \theta = 688 \sin 37.6° = 688 \times 0.610 = 419.7 \ \Omega$$

A lagging pf indicates that the reactance of the circuit is inductive in nature.

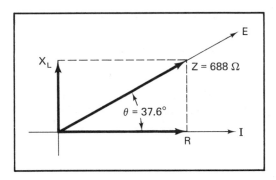

FIGURE 28–40
Impedance Diagram for Example 28–15

example 28–16 Determine the impedance of the circuit shown in Figure 28–41.

solution: The circuit may be simplified by combining units as

$$R_T = R_1 + R_2 = 200 + 600 = 800 \ \Omega$$

$$X_{C_T} = X_{c_1} + X_{c_2} = 350 + 150 = 500 \ \Omega$$

$$L_T = L_1 + L_2 = 100 + 200 = 300 \ \text{mH}$$

X_{L_T} may be determined as

$$X_{L_T} = 2\pi f L_T = 377 \times 300 \times 10^{-3} = 113.1 \ \Omega$$

If desired, X_{L_T} could have been calculated as

$$X_{L_T} = X_{L_1} + X_{L_2} = 2\pi f L_1 + 2\pi f L_2$$

$$= 377 \times 100 \times 10^{-3} + 377 \times 200 \times 10^{-3}$$

$$= 37.7 + 75.4 = 113.1 \ \Omega$$

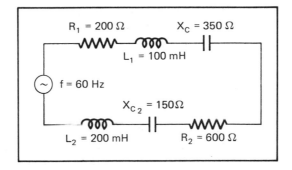

FIGURE 28–41
Circuit for Example 28–16

The equivalent circuit and the impedance diagram is shown in Figure 28–42.

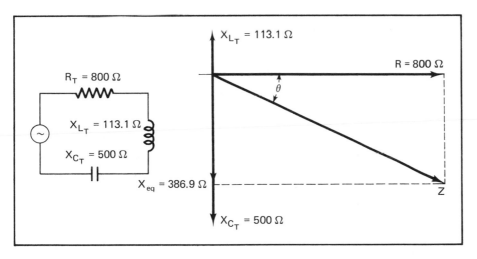

FIGURE 28–42
Equivalent Circuit and Z Diagram for Example 28–16

$$\tan \theta = \frac{X_{eq}}{R_T} = \frac{386.9}{800} = 0.484$$

$$\theta = \arctan 0.484 = -25.8°$$

$$R_T = Z \cos \theta$$

$$Z = \frac{R_T}{\cos \theta} = \frac{800}{\cos 25.6°} = \frac{800}{0.902} = 886.9 \ \Omega$$

In previous examples, it has been shown that the total circuit reactance is the algebraic sum of X_L and X_c. As shown, if X_L is larger, the circuit is inductive. If X_c is larger, the circuit is capacitive. As indicated, we may write for a series circuit

$$Z = R + j(X_L - X_C) \; \Omega, \quad \text{or}$$

$$= R + j\left(2\pi fL - \frac{1}{2\pi fC}\right) \Omega$$

The equation for X_L shows that X_L varies directly with the frequency. As the frequency is increased, the value of X_L is increased.

The equation for X_C shows that X_C varies inversely with the frequency. As the frequency is increased, the value of X_C is decreased.

For a circuit with given values of L and C, there is *one frequency* at which $X_L = X_C$. At this frequency the circuit impedance, the result of X_C and X_L being opposite and equal, is equal to the circuit resistance, so the impedance of the circuit is at its minimum value.

The frequency at which

$$X_L = X_C \quad \text{and} \quad Z = R$$

is called the *series resonant frequency*. As the net reactance of the circuit is zero, the circuit exhibits purely resistive properties. Therefore, the circuit current is in phase with the circuit voltage and

$$\theta = 0°, \quad \text{pf} = 1$$

The frequency at which series resonance occurs, for a given value of L and C, may be determined by equating X_L to X_C as

$$2\pi fL = \frac{1}{2\pi fC}$$

Solving for f, the resonant frequency f_r is

$$f_r = \frac{1}{2\pi\sqrt{LC}} \; \text{Hz}$$

where

$L =$ inductance, henrys

$C =$ capacitance, farads

$f_r =$ frequency, hertz

In many resonant circuits, as will be seen in other of your courses, it will be desirable to keep the resistance of the circuit as low as possible. The resistance present in the inductor is usually the limiting factor. As such, a figure of merit, or quality, Q, is established for the inductor as

$$Q = \frac{\omega L}{R}$$

This means that as the value of R decreases, the quality factor, Q, of the inductor will increase. Of course as R increases, Q will decrease.

At resonance, as I is common to all circuit elements and $X_L = X_c$, we may write

$$IX_C = IX_L \quad \text{or} \quad E_C = E_L$$

As $E_L = IX_L$ we may write

$$E_L = I\omega L$$

At resonance the circuit current is

$$I = \frac{E}{R} \quad \text{as} \quad X_L = X_C$$

Substituting for I in $E_L = I\omega L$, we have

$$E_L = \frac{E\omega L}{R}$$

As $Q = \dfrac{\omega L}{R}$,

$$E_L = EQ$$

and as $E_L = E_C$ at resonance, we have

$$E_L = E_C = EQ$$

This relationship tells us that the voltage developed across the capacitor and inductor of a circuit at resonance is Q times the circuit voltage. The higher the value of Q, the greater will be this voltage. This characteristic of a series resonant circuit is often found to be useful in electronics work.

example 28-17 A series circuit is composed of an inductor that has a resistance of $R = 10$ Ω and $L = 2.5$ mH and a capacitance of $C = 3.5 \ \mu\text{F}$. Determine (a) the resonant frequency, (b) the Q of the inductor, (c) the voltage that would appear across the capacitor and inductor at the resonance if the supply voltage were 300 V, and (d) the voltages across E_C and E_L at resonance if the resistance of the inductor were 1.2 Ω.

solution:

(a) $f_r = \dfrac{1}{2\pi\sqrt{LC}} = \dfrac{1}{6.28\sqrt{2.5 \times 10^{-3} \times 3.5 \times 10^{-6}}}$

$= \dfrac{1}{6.28\sqrt{87.5 \times 10^{-10}}} = \dfrac{1}{6.28 \times 9.35 \times 10^{-5}}$

$= \dfrac{1}{58.7 \times 10^{-5}}$

$= 0.0170 \times 10^5$

$= 1,700 \text{ Hz}$

(b) $Q = \dfrac{\omega L}{R} = \dfrac{2\pi f_r L}{R} = \dfrac{6.28 \times 1,700 \times 0.0025}{10}$

$= \dfrac{26.69}{10} = 2.669$

(c) $E_L = E_C = EQ = 300 \times 2.669 = 800.7 \text{ V}$

(d) If $R = 1.2$ Ω,

$$Q = \dfrac{\omega L}{R} = \dfrac{26.69}{1.2} = 22.24$$

$$E_L = E_C = EQ = 300 \times 22.24 = 6,672 \text{ V}$$

example 28–18   If the resonant frequency of the circuit of Figure 28–43 is 3.5 kHz, determine the value of L and C.

FIGURE   28–43
Circuit Diagram for
Example 28–18

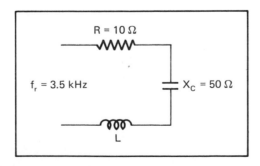

R = 10 Ω

f_r = 3.5 kHz

X_C = 50 Ω

L

solution: At resonance, $X_L = X_C$; therefore,

$$X_L = X_C = 50 \ \Omega$$

$$2\pi fL = \frac{1}{2\pi fC} = 50$$

$$2\pi fL = 50,$$

$$6.28 \times 3,500 \times L = 50,$$

$$21,980L = 50,$$

$$L = 0.0023 \ \text{H},$$

$$L = 2.3 \ \text{mH},$$

$$\frac{1}{2\pi fC} = 50$$

$$\frac{1}{6.28 \times 3,500 \times C} = 50$$

$$C = \frac{1}{1.099 \times 10^6}$$

$$= 0.91 \ \mu\text{F}$$

28–12 SUMMARY

The impedance and power relationships for an ac series circuit are shown in summary form in Figure 28–44. This should be helpful in reviewing the characteristics of a series ac circuit. Note that the phasor diagrams are not drawn to scale because of space limitations. Keep in mind that the circuit impedance of any ac circuit is

$$Z = \frac{E}{I_T} \ \Omega, \quad \text{where}$$

E = circuit voltage

I_T = circuit current

EXERCISE 28-4 In problems 1–8, determine the missing values marked by a question mark.

Prob-lem	E	I	Z	f	R	L	C	P	X_L	X_C
1.	100	15 mA	?	60 Hz	750	?	—	—	—	?	—
2.	200	?	252 Ω	60 Hz	?	—	—	?	?	—	30 Ω
3.	300	2.5 A	?	60 Hz	?	—	—	?	—	15 Ω	—
4.	150	?	?	400 Hz	150 Ω	15 mH	—	—	—	?	—

5.	250	?	?	600 Hz	200 Ω	—	15 μF	—	—	—	?
6.	350	?	?	1,500 Hz	1.5 kΩ	20 mH	40 μF	—	—	?	?
7.	400	?	?	1.5 MHz	5 kΩ	?	?	?	—	15 Ω	15 Ω
8.	500	?	?	6 MHz	30 Ω	0.15 H	1.5 μμF	?	?	?	?

9. What is the resonant frequency of a circuit composed of $R = 20\ \Omega$, $C = 16\ \mu\mu\text{F}$, and $L = 3.7$ mH?

10. If a circuit is composed of $R = 1,500\ \Omega$ and X_C and $X_L = 18.25\ \Omega$, what is the resonant frequency and the value of C if $L = 2.5$ mH?

FIGURE 28–44
Series-Circuit Relationships

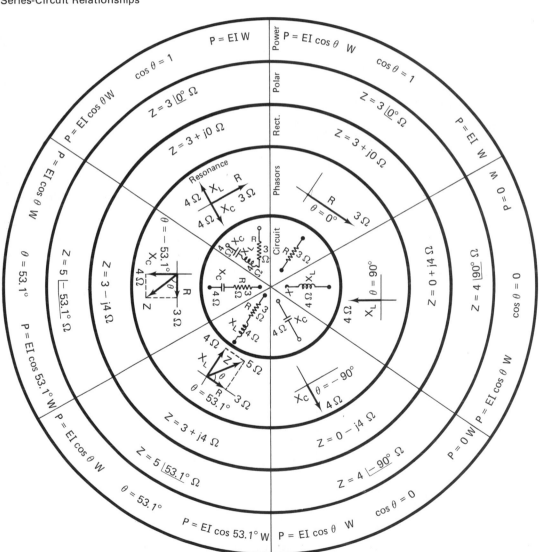

29

ALTERNATING-CURRENT PARALLEL AND COMPLEX CIRCUITS

$\mathbf{O}$ur work with ac series circuits has established a sound foundation for the parallel and complex circuits of this chapter. Parallel circuit theory and circuit behavior develops both logically and systematically from this basic background.

There is one basic difference between series and parallel circuits. In the series circuit, the current is common to all circuit elements. The current is used as a reference in circuit calculations and phasor diagrams. In the parallel circuit, the voltage is common to all circuit elements. In these circuits, the voltage will be used as a reference in phasor diagrams and circuit calculations.

29–1 PARALLEL CIRCUITS CONTAINING SIMILAR BRANCH ELEMENTS

In this section, we shall examine the ac parallel circuit, in which each parallel branch consists of only one similar element. The first circuit will involve only resistance elements, which will be followed by circuits containing similar reactive elements. In our ac series circuits consisting of only resistances, it was found that the circuit characteristics were identical to those of dc series circuits. This is also true of parallel circuits. The circuit impedance will be found to equal the equivalent circuit resistance. As there are no reactive elements present, the circuit voltage and current are in phase and the circuit power is equal to the product of the circuit voltage and current. This is shown in the following example.

example 29–1 Determine the circuit I, θ, P, and Z for the circuit of Figure 29–1.

FIGURE 29–1
Circuit for Example 29–1

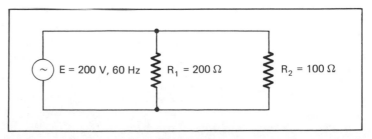

solution: The voltage is seen to be common to both resistors. The current through each may be calculated as

487
Sec. 29–1
PARALLEL
CIRCUITS
CONTAINING
SIMILAR BRANCH
ELEMENTS

$$I_1 = \frac{E}{R_1} = \frac{200}{200} = 1 \text{ A}$$

$$I_2 = \frac{E}{R_2} = \frac{200}{100} = 2 \text{ A}$$

As branches 1 and 2 contain only resistance, the current through each is in phase with the voltage. The current may be expressed in rectangular form as $I_T = I_1 + I_2$ A, we have

$I_1 = 1 + j0$ A
$I_2 = 2 + j0$ A
$I_T = 3 + j0$ A

In polar form, $I_T = 3 \underline{|0°}$ A. The voltage, as noted, is used as a reference. Drawing the phasor diagram for the circuit we have Figure 29–2. As $Z = \dfrac{E}{I_T} \, \Omega$,

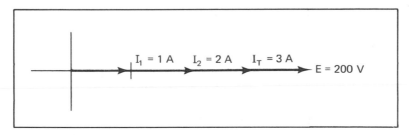

FIGURE 29–2
Phasor Diagram for Example 29–1

$$Z = \frac{200}{3} = 66.6 \ \Omega$$

As $Z = R_T$, we may also calculate Z as

$$Z = R_T = \frac{R_1 R_2}{R_1 + R_2} = \frac{(200)(100)}{200 + 100} = \frac{20{,}000}{300} = 66.6 \ \Omega$$

As the voltage and current are in phase,

$$\theta = 0°, \quad \cos \theta = 1$$

$$P = EI \cos \theta = 200 \times 3 \times 1 = 600 \text{ W}$$

488

Ch. 29

ALTERNATING-
CURRENT
PARALLEL AND
COMPLEX CIRCUITS

In the following circuit, two inductors are connected in parallel. The solution is similar to that of the resistive circuit of Example 29–1, except for the 90° phase angle of the branch and circuit currents.

example 29–2   Determine the circuit I, θ, P, and Z for the circuit of Figure 29–3.

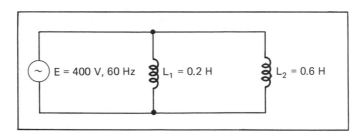

FIGURE 29–3
Circuit for Example 29–2

solution:

$$X_{L_1} = 2\pi f L_1 = 377 \times 0.2 = 75.2 \ \Omega$$

$$X_{L_2} = 2\pi f L_2 = 377 \times 0.6 = 226.2 \ \Omega$$

The impedances of branches 1 and 2 may be written in rectangular form as

$$Z_1 = 0 + 75.2 \ \Omega$$

$$Z_2 = 0 + 226.2 \ \Omega$$

In polar form this becomes

$$Z_1 = 75.2 \underline{|90°} \ \Omega$$

$$Z_2 = 226.2 \underline{|90°} \ \Omega$$

The current in branches 1 and 2 may now be calculated:

$$I_1 = \frac{E}{Z_1} = \frac{400}{75.2 \underline{|90°}} = 5.32 \underline{|-90°} \ A$$

$$I_2 = \frac{E}{Z_2} = \frac{400}{226.2 \underline{|90°}} = 1.77 \underline{|-90°} \ A$$

Note that in the above calculation of I and I_2, the impedances have an angle of +90°. On division the current has an angle of −90°. This procedure is seen to be correct because the resultant current lags the voltage by 90°, as it must in an inductive circuit. In normal practice the angle will not be shown affixed to the impedance. You should, however, check your work to be certain that the phasors reflect the fact that the current must lead the voltage in a capacitive branch and lag the voltage in an inductive branch. As both branch circuits are inductive, we may write the branch currents in rectangular form as

489
Sec. 29–1
PARALLEL
CIRCUITS
CONTAINING
SIMILAR BRANCH
ELEMENTS

$I_1 = 0 - j5.32$ A
$I_2 = 0 - j1.77$ A
$I_T = \overline{0 - j7.09}$ A   or $I_T = 7.09 \underline{|-90°}$ A

The circuit phasors are shown in Figure 29–4. As Figure 29–4 and I_T in rectangular or polar form show,

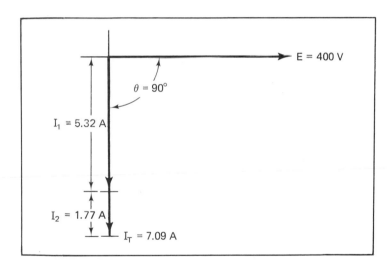

FIGURE 29–4
Phasors for Example 29–2

$\theta = 90°$

$P = EI_T \cos \theta$

$\quad = 400 \times 7.09 \times \cos 90°$

$\quad = 400 \times 7.09 \times 0$

$\quad = 0$ W

$Z = \dfrac{E}{I_T} = \dfrac{400}{7.09} = 56.4 \ \Omega$

490

Ch. 29
ALTERNATING-
CURRENT
PARALLEL AND
COMPLEX CIRCUITS

It should be noted that the impedances of L_1 and L_2 could have been combined to form a single equivalent impedance in the same manner as resistances in parallel. For example,

$$Z_1 = X_{L_1} = 75.2 \ \Omega$$

$$Z_2 = X_{L_2} = 226.2 \ \Omega$$

$$Z = \frac{Z_1 Z_2}{Z_1 + Z_2} = \frac{75.2 \times 226.2}{75.2 + 226.2} = \frac{17,010}{301.2} = 56.4 \ \Omega$$

This is the same as the value of the impedance determined above. In this process we neglected the impedance phase angles because they were both the same. In other situations where the impedance phase angles are different, they could not be neglected in the calculations.

example 29–3 Determine the circuit I, θ, P, and Z for the circuit of Figure 29–5.

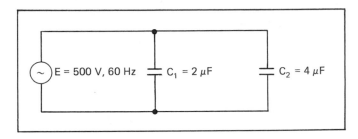

FIGURE 29–5
Circuits for Example 29–3

solution:

$$X_1 = \frac{1}{2\pi f C_1} = \frac{1}{377 \times 2 \times 10^{-6}} = 1,326.2 \ \Omega$$

$$X_2 = \frac{1}{2\pi f C_2} = \frac{1}{377 \times 4 \times 10^{-6}} = 663.1 \ \Omega$$

$$Z_1 = R - jX_1 = 0 - j1,326.2 \ \Omega$$

$$Z_2 = R - jX_2 = 0 - j663.1 \ \Omega$$

In polar form we have

$$Z_1 = 1,326.2 \underline{|-90°} \ \Omega$$

$$Z_2 = 663.1 \underline{|-90°} \ \Omega$$

491
Sec. 29–1
PARALLEL
CIRCUITS
CONTAINING
SIMILAR BRANCH
ELEMENTS

$$I_1 = \frac{E}{Z_1} = \frac{500}{1,326.2} = 0.377 \underline{/90°} \text{ A}$$

$$I_2 = \frac{E}{Z_2} = \frac{500}{663.1} = 0.754 \underline{/90°} \text{ A}$$

In rectangular form we may write

$I_1 = 0 + j0.377$ A
$I_2 = 0 + j0.754$ A
$I_T = 0 + j1.131$ A   or $I_T = 1.131 \underline{/90°}$ A

The circuit phasors are shown in Figure 29–6.

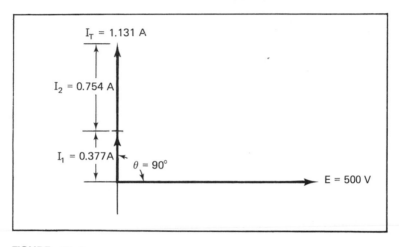

FIGURE 29–6
Phasors for Example 29–4

$$P = EI_T \cos \theta$$
$$= 500 \times 1.131 \times \cos 90°$$
$$= 500 \times 1.131 \times 0$$
$$= 0 \text{ W}$$

$$Z = \frac{E}{I_T} = \frac{500}{1.131} = 442.1 \ \Omega$$

In the previous example, the procedure for combining two inductors, to form an equivalent inductance, was demonstrated. A somewhat different procedure may be used for capacitors in parallel. For this purpose, it would be helpful to review Section 28–5, where capacitances in series were discussed.

492

Ch. 29

ALTERNATING-
CURRENT
PARALLEL AND
COMPLEX CIRCUITS

For the parallel capacitors in Example 29–3, with a common voltage E, we may express the charge on each capacitor as

$$Q_1 = C_1 E \tag{1}$$

$$Q_2 = C_2 E \tag{2}$$

The total charge may be represented as

$$C_{par} E = Q_1 + Q_2 \tag{3}$$

where C_{par} is the total capacitance. This may be rewritten as

$$C_1 E + C_2 E = Q_1 + Q_2$$

Factoring E from the left side, we have

$$E(C_1 + C_2) = Q_1 + Q_2 \tag{4}$$

Substituting value for $Q_1 + Q_2$ from equation (3) into (4),

$$E(C_1 + C_2) = C_{par} E \tag{5}$$

Dividing both sides by E and rearranging,

$$C_{par} = C_1 + C_2$$

It is seen, then, that the total capacitance of capacitors in parallel is the total of the individual capacitances. In Example 29–3,

$$C_T = C_1 + C_2 = 2\ \mu F + 4\ \mu F = 6\ \mu F$$

$$X_{C_T} = \frac{1}{2\pi f C_T} = \frac{1}{377 \times 6 \times 10^{-6}} = 442.1\ \Omega$$

$$Z = X_{C_T} = 442.1\ \Omega \quad \text{as previously calculated}$$

29-2 PARALLEL CIRCUITS CONTAINING DISSIMILAR BRANCH ELEMENTS

In the following example, a parallel circuit with a resistance branch and an inductive branch is used. In the solution that follows, note the similarity of the relationships of the current phasor in the parallel circuit and the voltage phasor in the series circuits of Chapter 28.

example 29–4 For the circuit shown in Figure 29–7, determine I, θ, pf, P, and Z.

493
Sec. 29–2
PARALLEL CIRCUITS
CONTAINING
DISSIMILAR
BRANCH ELEMENTS

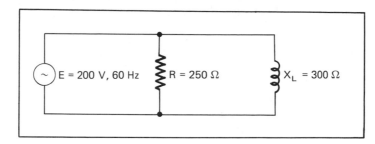

FIGURE 29–7
Circuit for Example 29–4

solution: The circuit current is first determined. As each branch has a common voltage, the branch current is found as

$$I_R = \frac{E}{R} = \frac{200}{250} = 0.800 \text{ A}$$

$$I_L = \frac{E}{X_L} = \frac{200}{300} = 0.667 \text{ A}$$

In rectangular form,

$$\begin{aligned}
I_R &= 0.800 + j0 &&\text{A} \\
I_{XL} &= 0 \quad\quad - j0.667 &&\text{A} \\
\hline
I_T &= 0.800 - j0.667 &&\text{A}
\end{aligned}$$

The voltage and current phasors are shown in Figure 29–8. From the figure it is seen that θ may be calculated as

$$\tan \theta = \frac{I_{XL}}{I_R} = \frac{0.667}{0.800} = 0.834$$

$$\theta = -39.8°$$

FIGURE 29–8
Phasor Diagram for Example 29–4

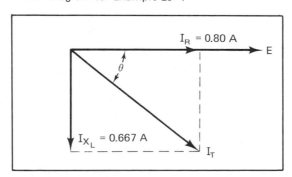

494

Ch. 29
ALTERNATING-
CURRENT
PARALLEL AND
COMPLEX CIRCUITS

$$I_T \cos\theta = I_R$$

$$I_T = \frac{I_R}{\cos\theta} = \frac{0.80}{\cos - 39.8°} = \frac{0.80}{0.768} = 1.04 \text{ A}$$

In polar form,

$$I_T = 1.04\underline{|-39.8°} \text{ A}$$

The circuit pf is the $\cos\theta$,

$$\text{pf} = \cos 39.8° = 0.768 \quad \text{lagging}$$

The circuit power is found as

$$P = EI_T \cos\theta$$
$$= 200 \times 1.04 \times 0.768$$
$$= 159.7 \text{ W}$$

The circuit impedance is calculated as

$$Z = \frac{E}{I_T} = \frac{200}{1.04} = 192.3 \ \Omega$$

The next example will involve three branches. In this case the voltage will not be provided. This will be for the purpose of illustrating the fact that the voltage does not affect the circuit impedance and power factor. As a result, the selection of any suitable voltage will permit the circuit impedance and power factor to be determined. These values may then be applied for any circuit voltage.

example 29–5   Determine the circuit impedance and power factor for the circuit shown in Figure 29–9. Determine the equivalent series circuit.

solution: The reactances of L and C are first calculated.

$$X_L = 2\pi fL = 6.28 \times 400 \times 0.0025 = 6.28 \ \Omega$$

$$X_C = \frac{1}{2\pi fC} = \frac{1}{6.28 \times 400 \times 50 \times 10^{-6}} = 7.9 \ \Omega$$

A suitable voltage is selected to obtain reasonable values of current with which to work. In this case, 10 V is chosen.

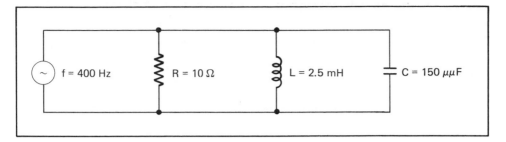

FIGURE 29–9
Circuit for Example 29–5

The current through each branch is now calculated:

$$I_R = \frac{E}{R} = \frac{10}{10} = 1 \text{ A}$$

$$I_{XL} = \frac{E}{X_L} = \frac{10}{6.28} = 1.59 \text{ A}$$

$$I_{XC} = \frac{E}{X_C} = \frac{10}{7.9} = 1.26 \text{ A}$$

The current through the resistive branch is in phase with the applied voltage. The current through the capacitive branch leads the voltage by 90°, while the inductive branch current lags the voltage by 90°. This is shown in the phasor diagram of Figure 29–10. The result of the graphical addition of I_{XC} and I_{XL} to form I_{XT} is shown in the figure. The addition of phasors I_R and I_{XT} to form I_T is also shown. Algebraically the circuit current is determined as

$$
\begin{aligned}
I_R &= 1 + j0 \quad \text{A} \\
I_{XC} &= 0 + j1.26 \text{ A} \\
I_{XL} &= 0 - j1.59 \text{ A} \\
\hline
I_T &= 1 - j0.33 \text{ A}
\end{aligned}
$$

In polar form,

$$\tan \theta = \frac{0.33}{1} = 0.33$$

$$\theta = -18.26°$$

496

Ch. 29
ALTERNATING-
CURRENT
PARALLEL AND
COMPLEX CIRCUITS

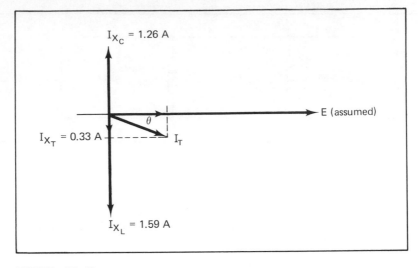

FIGURE 29–10
Phasor Diagram for Example 29–5

$$I_T \cos \theta = I_R$$

$$I_T = \frac{I_R}{\cos \theta} = \frac{1}{\cos - 18.26} = \frac{1}{0.949} = 1.05 \text{ A}$$

$$= 1.05 \underline{|-18.26°} \quad \text{A}$$

The circuit impedance is

$$Z_T = \frac{E}{I_T} = \frac{10}{1.05} = 9.52 \ \Omega$$

The power factor is

pf $= \cos \theta = \cos 18.26° = 0.949$ lagging

The parallel circuit of this example could be replaced by a series circuit composed of a resistor and an inductor whose impedance is equal to the parallel impedance. The inductor would be required because of the lagging pf. The impedance diagram for an equivalent series circuit is shown in Figure 29–11. The values of R and X_L are found as

$$R = Z \cos \theta = 9.52 \cos 18.26° = 9.52 \times 0.949 = 9.03 \ \Omega$$

$$X_L = Z \sin \theta = 9.52 \sin 18.26° = 9.52 \times 0.313 = 2.98 \ \Omega$$

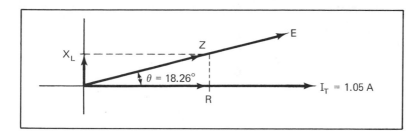

497
Sec. 29–3
PARALLEL CIRCUITS
CONTAINING
MULTIPLE
BRANCH ELEMENTS

FIGURE 29–11
Equivalent Series Circuit Phasors for Example
29–5

EXERCISE 29–1

1. A circuit consists of $L_1 = 20$ mH, $L_2 = 30$ mH, and $L_3 = 40$ mH, in parallel. Determine I, θ, P, and Z. The frequency is $f = 1.25$ MHz and $E = 300$ V.

2. A parallel circuit has a supply voltage of $E = 1{,}000$ V and $f = 4$ kHz. Determine I, θ, P, and Z if the circuit consists of three parallel branches of $C_1 = 0.5$ μF, $C_2 - 1.0$ μF, and $C_3 = 2.0$ μF.

3. Determine the values of I, θ, P, and Z for a circuit consisting of $R = 100$ Ω in a parallel with $L = 15$ mH, where $E = 250$ V and $f = 25$ MHz.

4. Determine the values of R and L in series to replace the parallel circuit of problem 3.

5. A circuit consists of a resistance of $R = 300$ Ω in parallel with a capacitance of $C = 200$ $\mu\mu$F. What is the circuit I, pf, P, and Z if $f = 3{,}000$ Hz and $E = 2{,}000$ V?

6. Draw the phasor diagram for the circuit of problem 5. Determine the equivalent series circuit that could be used to replace this parallel circuit.

7. A parallel circuit consists of three branches of $R = 5$ kΩ, $L = 25$ mH, and $C = 25$ μF. Determine the values of I, pf, P, and Z if $f = 2{,}500$ Hz and $E = 550$ V.

8. Determine the series equivalent circuit of the parallel circuit shown in Figure 29–12.

**29–3 PARALLEL CIRCUITS CONTAINING
MULTIPLE BRANCH ELEMENTS**

The circuits studied in previous sections involved branches containing only a single element. The current phasors had 90°, 0°, and−90° phase positions.

498

Ch. 29
ALTERNATING-
CURRENT
PARALLEL AND
COMPLEX CIRCUITS

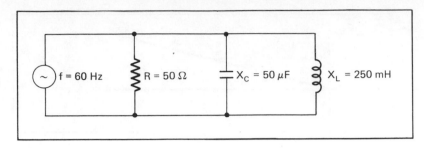

FIGURE 29-12
Circuit for Problem 8

A logical extension of this knowledge will involve branches that contain several elements. When the elements of a branch are different, the current flow through that branch will not fall on the in-phase or 90° phase positions that existed for a single branch element. Aside from that, the phasor addition, whether graphical or algebraic, will be handled in exactly the same manner as in our previous work. This will be illustrated in the examples that follow.

example 29-6 For the circuit of Figure 29–13, determine I_1, I_2, I_T, Z_T, and P.

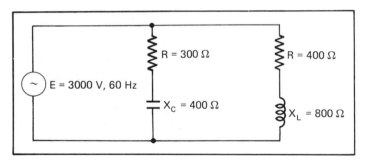

FIGURE 29-13
Circuit for Example 29-6

solution: The impedance of branches 1 and 2 is first determined. This is found as

$$Z = R \mp jX$$

$$Z_1 = R - jX_C = 300 - j400 = 500\underline{|-53.1°}\ \Omega$$

$$Z_2 = R + jX_L = 400 + j800 = 894.4\underline{|63.4°}\ \Omega$$

The current may now be found, using the common branch voltage, as

499

Sec. 29–3
PARALLEL CIRCUITS
CONTAINING
MULTIPLE
BRANCH ELEMENTS

$$I_1 = \frac{E}{Z_1} = \frac{3,000}{500} = 6\underline{|53.1°}\ \ A$$

$$I_2 = \frac{E}{Z_2} = \frac{3,000}{894.4} = 3.35\underline{|-63.4°}\ \ A$$

These currents are shown in the phasor diagram of Figure 29–14. The total current may be determined graphically using the figure. This also may be deter-

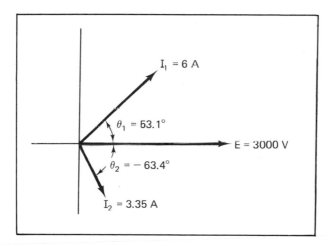

FIGURE 29–14
Phasor Diagram for Example 29–6

mined by converting the branch currents to rectangular form and adding algebraically. This is shown as

$$I_1 = 6\underline{|53.1°} = 6\cos 53.1° + j6 \sin 53.1° = 3.60 + j4.80\ A$$

$$I_2 = 3.35\underline{|-63.4°} = 3.35 \cos -63.4° - j3.35 \sin -63.4°$$

$$= 1.50 - j2.99\ A$$

$$I_T = I_1 + I_2$$

$$I_1 = 3.60 + j4.80\ A$$
$$I_2 = \underline{1.50 - j2.99\ A}$$
$$I_T = 5.10 + j1.81\ A$$

500
Ch. 29
ALTERNATING-
CURRENT
PARALLEL AND
COMPLEX CIRCUITS

In polar form,

$$I_T = 5.41 \underline{|19.5°} \text{ A}$$

The circuit phasors are shown in Figure 29–15. The circuit impedance is found as

$$Z_T = \frac{E}{I_T} = \frac{3,000}{5.41} = 554.5 \ \Omega$$

The power factor is

$$\text{pf} = \cos \theta = \cos 19.5° = 0.943 \text{ leading}$$

The power is determined as

$$P = EI_T \cos \theta = 3,000 \times 5.41 \times 0.943$$
$$= 15,304.9 \text{ W}$$
$$= 15,305 \text{ kW}$$

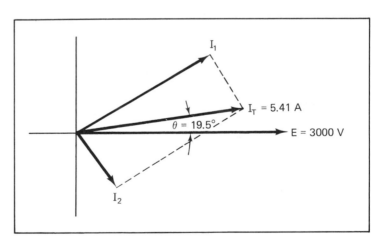

FIGURE 29–15
Circuit Phasors for Example 29–6

example 29-7 For the circuit of Figure 29–16, determine I, I_2, I_3, I_T, Z_T, and P.

solution:

$$Z_1 = R + j(X_L - X_C) = 0 + j(30 - 90)$$
$$= 0 - j60 = 60 \underline{|-90°} \ \Omega$$
$$Z_2 = R + jX_L = 50 + j40 = 64 \underline{|+38.6°} \ \Omega$$

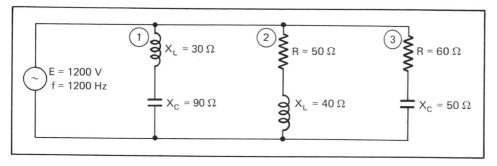

FIGURE 29-16
Circuit for Example 29-7

$$Z_3 = R - JX_C = 60 - j50 = 78.1 \underline{|-39.8°} \; \Omega$$

$$I_1 = \frac{E}{Z_1} = \frac{1,200 \underline{|0°}}{60 \underline{|-90°}} = 20 \underline{|90°} \; A$$

$$I_2 = \frac{E}{Z_2} = \frac{1,200 \underline{|0°}}{64 \underline{|38.6°}} = 18.75 \underline{|-38.6°} \; A$$

$$I_3 = \frac{E}{Z_3} = \frac{1,200 \underline{|0°}}{78.1 \underline{|-39.8°}} = 15.36 \underline{|39.8°} \; A$$

These are shown in phasor form in Figure 29–17. The total circuit current, I_T is determined as

$$I_1 = 20 \underline{|90°} = 20 \cos 90°$$

$$+ j20 \sin 90°$$

FIGURE 29-17
Current Phasors for Example 29-7

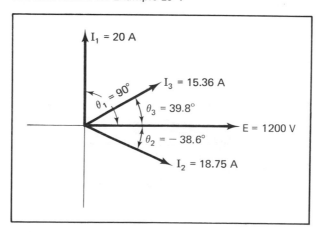

502

Ch. 29
ALTERNATING-
CURRENT
PARALLEL AND
COMPLEX CIRCUITS

$$I_2 = 18.75\underline{|-38.6°} = 18.75 \cos -38.6°$$
$$+ j18.75 \sin -38.6°$$
$$I_3 = 15.36\underline{|39.8°} = 15.36 \cos 39.8°$$
$$+ j15.36 \sin 39.8°$$

Adding:

$$
\begin{aligned}
I_1 &= 0 + j20 \quad && \text{A} \\
I_2 &= 14.65 - j11.70 \quad && \text{A} \\
I_3 &= \underline{11.8 + j9.83} \quad && \text{A} \\
I_T &= 26.45 + j18.13 \quad && \text{A} \\
&= 32.06\underline{|34.4°} \quad && \text{A}
\end{aligned}
$$

In phasor form we have Figure 29–18.

$$Z_T = \frac{E}{I_T} = \frac{1,200}{32.06} = 37.43 \ \Omega$$

$$P = EI_T \cos \theta = 1,200 \times 32.06 \times \cos 34.4°$$

$$= 1,200 \times 32.06 \times 0.825 = 31,739.4 \ \text{W}$$

$$= 31.739 \ \text{kW}$$

FIGURE 29–18
Circuit Phasors for Example 29–7

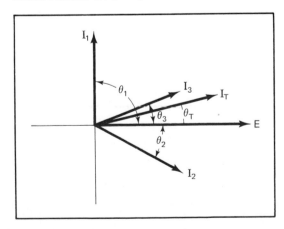

In previous sections we have examined the series circuit and the parallel circuit separately. In this section the series and parallel circuits will be combined to form a complex circuit. The series–parallel circuit of Figure 29–19 is a complex circuit.

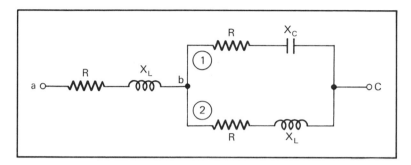

FIGURES 29–19
Series–Parallel Circuit

Solutions involving circuits of the series–parallel type require little more than the application of techniques developed in our previous work. Essentially this procedure requires treating the series and the parallel portions of the circuit separately. These results are then combined to form a simplified equivalent circuit. This procedure is illustrated for the circuit of Figure 29–19. The solution procedure is outlined as follows:

1. The parallel branch is first simplified. This procedure requires the determination of the current flow in branches 1 and 2. The total current between *b* and *c* may then be determined. Using this current and the parallel branch voltage, the impedance may be determined. As with our previous work with parallel circuits, if the voltage across the parallel branch is unknown, a suitable voltage is assumed.
2. The impedance of the parallel branch is next converted to its equivalent series impedance.
3. The equivalent series impedance is then combined with the series portion of the circuit. The result is a series circuit with a common current. The total impedance of the circuit may then be obtained.

The procedures outlined above are illustrated in the following example.

504
Ch. 29
ALTERNATING-
CURRENT
PARALLEL AND
COMPLEX CIRCUITS

example 29-8 Determine the equivalent impedance of the complex circuit of Figure 29–20. Find the circuit current I_T, θ, and P.

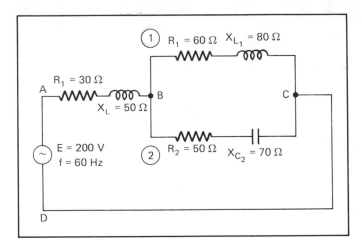

FIGURE 29-20
Circuit for Example 29-8

solution: Following the solution procedure outlined above, the first step involves the simplification of the parallel branch. As the voltage of this branch is not known, a suitable voltage will be assumed. Initially the impedances of branches 1 and 2 will be determined, in order that the assumed voltage will be a reasonable one for calculation purposes.

Writing the impedance of branches 1 and 2 in rectangular form and converting to polar, we have

$$Z_1 = R + jX_L = 60 + j80 \ \Omega$$

$$\tan \theta = \frac{X_L}{R} = \frac{80}{60} = 1.33$$

$$\theta = \arctan 1.33 = 53.1°$$

$$R = Z_1 \cos \theta$$

$$Z_1 = \frac{R}{\cos \theta} = \frac{60}{\cos 53.1°} = \frac{60}{0.6} = 100 \ \Omega$$

$$= 100 \underline{|53.1°} \ \Omega$$

$$Z_2 = R - jX_C = 50 - j70 \ \Omega$$

$$\tan \theta = \frac{X_C}{R} = \frac{70}{50} = 1.4$$

$$\theta = \arctan 1.4 = -54.5°$$

$$Z_2 = \frac{R}{\cos \theta} = \frac{50}{\cos 54.5°} = \frac{50}{0.580} = 86.2 \ \Omega$$

$$= 86.2 \underline{|-54.5°} \ \Omega$$

A parallel branch voltage of 100 V is assumed

$$I_1 = \frac{E}{Z_1} = \frac{100}{100 \underline{|53.1°}} = 1 \underline{|-53.1°} \ \text{A}$$

$$I_2 = \frac{E}{Z_2} = \frac{100}{86.2 \underline{|-54.5°}} = 1.16 \underline{|54.5°} \ \text{A}$$

In rectangular form, we have

$$I_1 = 1 \cos -53.1° - j1 \sin -53.1°$$

$$= 0.60 - j0.80 \ \text{A}$$

$$I_2 = 1.16 \cos 54.5° + j1.16 \sin 54.5°$$

$$= 0.674 + j0.944 \ \text{A}$$

As $I_T = I_1 + I_2$, we have

$$I_1 = 0.60 \quad - j0.80 \quad \text{A}$$
$$I_2 = 0.674 + j0.944 \ \text{A}$$
$$I_T = 1.274 + j0.144 \ \text{A}$$

The current phasors for the parallel branch are shown in Figure 29–21. Converting to polar form,

$$\tan \theta = \frac{0.114}{1.27} = 0.089$$

$$\theta = 5.13°$$

$$I_R = I_T \cos \theta \ \text{A}$$

$$I_T = \frac{I_R}{\cos \theta} = \frac{1.27}{\cos 5.13°} = \frac{1.27}{0.996} = 1.275 \underline{|5.13°} \ \text{A}$$

The impedance of the parallel branch is found as

$$Z_{B-C} = \frac{E}{I_T} = \frac{100}{1.275 \underline{|5.13°}} = 78.4 \underline{|-5.13°} \ \Omega$$

506

Ch. 29
ALTERNATING-
CURRENT
PARALLEL AND
COMPLEX CIRCUITS

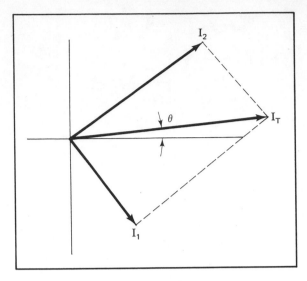

FIGURE 29–21
Parallel Branch Phasors for Example 29–8

The resistive and reactive components of this impedance, which will be the equivalent series impedance, are found by converting from polar to rectangular form:

$$R = Z_{B-C} \cos 5.13° = 78.4 \times 0.996 = 78.1 \ \Omega$$

$$X_C = Z_{B-C} \sin 5.13° = 78.4 \times 0.089 = 7.01 \ \Omega$$

$$Z_{B-C} = R - jX_C = 78.1 - j7.01 \ \Omega$$

This equivalent series impedance of the parallel branches $B - C$ is now combined with the impedance of the series circuit $A - B$. The equivalent circuit is shown in Figure 29–22.

FIGURE 29–22
Equivalent Circuit for Example 29–8

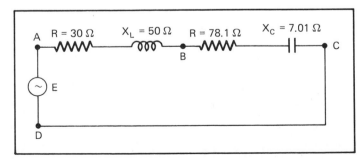

$$Z_{A-B} = \quad 30 \quad + j50 \quad \Omega$$
$$Z_{B-C} = \quad 78.1 - \quad j7.01 \; \Omega$$
$$Z_T = Z_{A-D} = \overline{108.1 + j42.99 \; \Omega}$$

The circuit phasors for the circuit of Example 29–8 are shown in Figure 29–23. Converting $Z_T = 108.1 + j42.99 \; \Omega$ to polar form, we have

$$\tan \theta = \frac{X_T}{R_T} = \frac{42.99}{108.1} = 0.398$$

$$\theta = \arctan 0.398 = 21.7°$$

$$Z_T \cos \theta = R_T$$

$$Z_T = \frac{R_T}{\cos \theta} = \frac{108.1}{\cos 21.7°} = \frac{108.1}{0.929} = 116.4 \underline{|21.7°} \; \Omega$$

$$I_T = \frac{E}{Z_T} = \frac{200}{116.4 \underline{|21.7°}} = 1.72 \underline{|-21.7°} \; A$$

$$\text{pf} = \cos \theta = 0.929 \quad \text{lagging}$$

$$P = EI_T \cos \theta$$

$$= 200 \times 1.72 \times 0.929$$

$$= 319.6 \; W$$

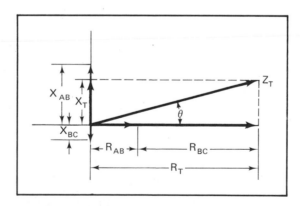

FIGURE   29–23
Impedance Phasors for Example 29–8

The circuit phasors for Example 29–8 are shown in Figure 29–24.

The preceding example is representative of the procedures that will be required in working with complex circuits. It was seen that this problem solution involved

508

Ch. 29
ALTERNATING-
CURRENT
PARALLEL AND
COMPLEX CIRCUITS

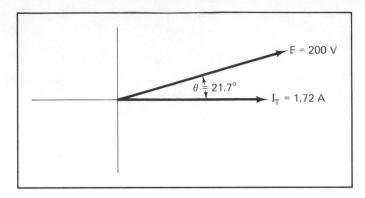

FIGURE 29–24
Circuit Phasors for Example 29–8

no new principles. The solution required only the application of techniques previously developed.

EXERCISE 29–2

1. For the circuit of Figure 29–25, determine I_1 and I_2.

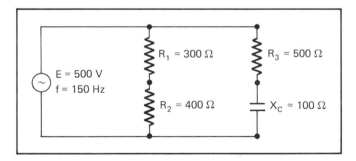

FIGURE 29–25
Circuit for Problems 1 and 2

2. For the circuit of problem 1, determine the circuit I_T, Z, pf, and P.

3. For the circuit of Figure 29–26, determine I_1, I_2, and I_T.

4. For the circuit of problem 3, determine the circuit Z, pf, and P.

5. For the circuit of Figure 29–27, write the branch currents in rectangular and polar form.

6. Determine the total current for the circuit of problem 5.

7. What is the size of the inductor and capacitor in problem 5?

8. Determine the circuit Z, pf, and P for the circuit of problem 5.

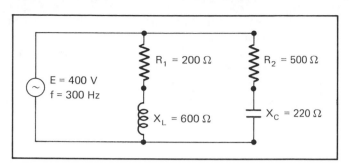

FIGURE 29–26
Circuit for Problems 3 and 4

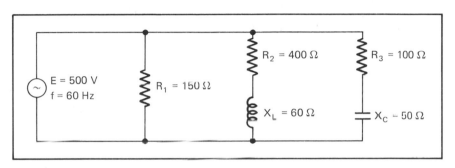

FIGURE 29–27
Circuit for Problems 5–8

29–5 PARALLEL RESONANT CIRCUITS

In Section 28–11, we discussed resonance in a circuit composed of R, L, and C in series. In this section, we shall examine the phenomena of parallel resonance. The circuit that we shall consider is shown in Figure 29–28.

FIGURE 29–28
Parallel L–C Circuit

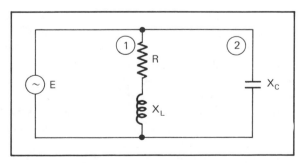

510

Ch. 29
ALTERNATING-
CURRENT
PARALLEL AND
COMPLEX CIRCUITS

It will be noted that the circuit of Figure 29–28 has two branches. One branch is inductive and the other is capacitive. The resistance in the inductive branch is that resulting from the structure and materials of the inductor and is quite small. The capacitor is considered to have negligible resistance.

Let us examine what occurs in this circuit as the frequency is varied. Remember that

$$X_L = 2\pi fL \quad \text{and} \quad X_C = \frac{1}{2\pi fC} \tag{1}$$

This means that as the frequency increases, X_L will increase and X_C will decrease. As the frequency decreases, X_L will decrease and X_C will increase. This is shown as

$$f \uparrow \quad X_L \uparrow \quad X_c \downarrow$$
$$f \downarrow \quad X_L \downarrow \quad X_c \uparrow$$

Examination of this relationship will show that at one frequency

$$X_L = X_C$$

The frequency at which this occurs is called *parallel resonant frequency*. This is found to have the same relationship as for a series circuit,

$$2\pi fL = \frac{1}{2\pi fC} \tag{2}$$

As shown in our work with series resonance, this converts to

$$f_r = \frac{1}{2\pi\sqrt{LC}} \text{ Hz} \tag{3}$$

where L = inductance in henrys and C = capacitance in farads.

Let us examine what occurs in the parallel circuit as resonance is approached. A parallel circuit such as this has two branch currents, one inductive and one capacitive. The inductive branch has, as noted, a small amount of resistance. Our work with parallel circuits has shown that the total circuit current is the result of the addition of the branch current phasors. The problems that were provided showed that as a circuit moved toward unity power factor, the current decreased. When unity power factor occurred, the circuit current was represented by the resistance current phasor and was at the minimum value.

As noted above, when parallel resonance occurs, $X_L = X_L$. As the voltage is common to both branches, at resonance we have

$$I_{X_L} = I_{X_C}$$

As these currents are 180° out of phase and equal, the circuit current is represented by the resistance current phasor. The circuit current at resonance, then, is at a minimum. The circuit voltage and current are in phase, hence we have unity power factor at resonance.

Another important feature of resonance relates to the circuit impedance. As the circuit current is minimum at resonance, it follows that as

$$Z = \frac{E}{I}$$

the circuit impedance is maximum. This characteristic of parallel resonance is a useful feature which is widely applied to various filter circuits.

Summarizing, the conditions that occur at parallel resonance are

1. $X_L = X_C$.
2. $I_{X_L} = I_{X_C}$.
3. The circuit current is in phase with the resistance of the circuit, hence unity pf exists.
4. The circuit current is minimum.
5. The impedance of the circuit is maximum.

example 29-9 Determine the circuit I, pf, and Z for the circuit of Figure 29–29 at 60 Hz. Determine the resonant frequency and the circuit I, pf, and Z at resonance.

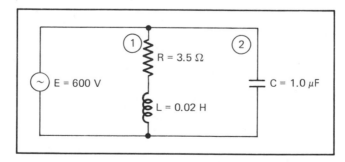

FIGURE 29–29
Circuit for Example 29-9

512

Ch. 29
ALTERNATING-
CURRENT
PARALLEL AND
COMPLEX CIRCUITS

solution:

At 60 Hz,

$$X_L = 2\pi f L = 377 \times 0.02 = 7.54 \; \Omega$$

$$X_C = \frac{1}{2\pi f C} = \frac{1}{377 \times 1 \times 10^{-6}} = 2652.5 \; \Omega$$

$$Z_1 = 3.5 + j7.54 = 8.31 \underline{|65.1°} \; \Omega$$

$$I_1 = E = \frac{600}{8.31 \underline{|65.1°}} = 72.2 \underline{|-65.1°} = 30.4 - j65.5 \; A$$

$$Z_2 = 0 - j2652.2 = 2652.2 \underline{|-90°} \; \Omega$$

$$I_2 = \frac{E}{Z_2} = \frac{600}{2652.2 \underline{|-90°}} = 0.226 \underline{|90°} = 0 + j0.226 \; A$$

$$I_T = I_1 + I_2$$

$$
\begin{aligned}
I_1 &= 30.4 - j65.5 \quad A \\
I_2 &= \underline{\;\;0 \;\;+ \; j \; .226 \; A} \\
I_T &= 30.4 - j65.3 \quad A \\
&= 72 \underline{|-65°} \; A
\end{aligned}
$$

$$Z_T = \frac{E}{I_T} + \frac{600}{72 \underline{|-65°}} = 8.33 \underline{|65°} \; \Omega$$

$$pf = \cos 65° = 0.423 \quad \text{lagging}$$

at f_r

$$f_r = \frac{1}{2\pi \sqrt{LC}} = \frac{1}{6.28 \sqrt{0.02 \times 1 \times 10^{-6}}}$$

$$= \frac{1}{6.28 \sqrt{0.02 \times 10^{-6}}} = \frac{1}{6.28 \times 0.1414 \times 10^{-3}}$$

$$= \frac{1}{0.888 \times 10^{-3}} = 1.126 \times 10^3$$

$$= 1{,}126 \; Hz$$

At 1126 Hz

$$X_L = 2\pi f L = 6.28 \times 1{,}126 \times 0.02 = 141.4 \; \Omega$$

$$X_C = \frac{1}{2\pi f C} = \frac{1}{6.28 \times 1126 \times 1 \times 10^{-6}} = \frac{1}{7{,}071.3 \times 10^{-6}}$$

$$= 141.4 \; \Omega$$

513
Sec. 29–6
FURTHER ANALYSIS
OF THE PARALLEL
RESONANCE
CIRCUIT

$$Z_1 = 3.5 + j141.4 = 141.5\underline{|88.6°}\ \Omega$$

$$I_1 = \frac{E}{Z_1} = \frac{600}{141.5\underline{|88.6°}} = 4.24\underline{|-88.6°} = 0.103 - j4.24\ A$$

$$Z_2 = 0 - j141.4 = 141.4\underline{|-90°}\ \Omega$$

$$I_2 = \frac{E}{Z_2} = \frac{600}{141.4\underline{|-90°}} = 4.243\underline{|90°} = 0 + j4.24\ A$$

$$
\begin{aligned}
I_1 &= 0.103 - j4.24\ A\\
I_2 &= 0\qquad + j4.24\ A\\
\hline
I_T &= 0.103 + j0\qquad A\\
&= 0.103\underline{|0°}\ A
\end{aligned}
$$

$$Z_T = \frac{E}{I_T} = \frac{600}{0.103\underline{|0°}} = 5{,}825.2\ \Omega$$

$$\text{pf} = \cos 0° = 1.0 = 100\%$$

Note the drastic change in circuit properties that occurs at resonance. These are summarized as

$f = 60$ Hz	$f = f_r = 1{,}126$ Hz
$I_T = 72\underline{|-65°}$ A	$I_T = 0.103\underline{|0°}$ A
pf = 0.423 (lagging)	pf = 1.0 (unity)
$Z = 8.33\ \Omega$	$Z = 5{,}825.2\ \Omega$

29–6 FURTHER ANALYSIS OF THE PARALLEL RESONANCE CIRCUIT

The relationships developed in Section 29–5, although accurate for many circuits, are not completely correct for all circuits. Let us examine the reason for this situation.

In Figure 29–30, the circuit phasors are shown for a typical parallel resonant circuit such as that of Figure 29–28. At resonance,

$$I_T = I_1 + I_2 \quad \text{or, in rectangular form}$$

$$= I_1 \cos \theta - jI_1 \sin \theta \quad + \quad 0 + jI_2 \qquad (4)$$

where the reactive components of I_1 and I_2 are equal and 180° apart at resonance. That is,

$$-jI_1 \sin \theta = +jI_2 \qquad (5)$$

514
Ch. 29
ALTERNATING-
CURRENT
PARALLEL AND
COMPLEX CIRCUITS

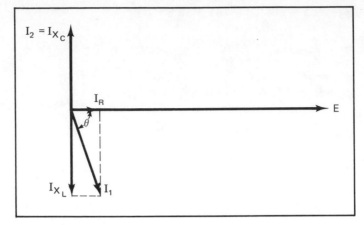

FIGURE 29-30
Circuit Phasors for Example 29–26 at
Resonance

Examination of the current through the inductive branch shows that

$$I_1 = \frac{E}{Z_1} = \frac{E}{R + jX_L} \tag{6}$$

Rationalizing the denominator produces

$$I_1 = \frac{E}{R + jX_L} \cdot \frac{R - jX_L}{R - jX_L} \tag{7}$$

$$I_1 = \frac{E(R - jX_L)}{R^2 + X_L^2} = \frac{ER}{R^2 + X_L^2} - \frac{jEX_L}{R^2 + X_L^2} \tag{8}$$

At resonance, the circuit current must be in phase with the circuit
voltage, pf $= 1$. At resonance it was also observed that the reactive
currents are equal. That is, the reactive component of I_1 above must
be equal to $I_2 = I_{XC}$. The value of I_2 is

$$I_2 = \frac{E}{Z_2} = \frac{E}{\dfrac{1}{\omega C}} = E\omega C \tag{9}$$

We may now write, for resonance,

$$\frac{EX_L}{R^2 + X_L^2} = E\omega C \tag{10}$$

As $X_L = \omega L$ we may write

515

Sec. 29–6
FURTHER ANALYSIS
OF THE PARALLEL
RESONANCE
CIRCUIT

$$\frac{E\omega L}{R^2 + (\omega L)^2} = E\omega C \qquad (11)$$

As $E\omega$ occurs on both sides of the equation, we may simplify as

$$\frac{L}{R^2 + (\omega L)^2} = C \qquad (12)$$

Rearranging

$$L = C[R^2 + (\omega L)^2]$$

Then

$$\frac{L}{C} = R^2 + (\omega L)^2$$

or

$$(\omega L)^2 = \frac{L}{C} - R^2 \qquad (13)$$

Solving for ω produces

$$\omega L = \sqrt{\frac{L}{C} - R^2}$$

$$\omega = \frac{\sqrt{\frac{L}{C} - R^2}}{L} = \sqrt{\frac{1}{LC} - \frac{R^2}{L^2}} \qquad (14)$$

As $\omega = 2\pi f$ and at resonance $f = f_r$, we have

$$2\pi f_r = \sqrt{\frac{1}{LC} - \frac{R^2}{L^2}}$$

Solving for f_r produces

$$f_r = \frac{1}{2\pi} \sqrt{\frac{1}{LC} - \frac{R^2}{L^2}} \qquad (15)$$

We now see that, to be completely accurate, Equation (15) should be used at parallel resonance instead of Equation (3). However, if the Q

516

Ch. 29
ALTERNATING-
CURRENT
PARALLEL AND
COMPLEX CIRCUITS

value of the inductor is large, then the value of R is small and the second term may be considered negligible and (15) reduces to (3) or

$$f_r = \frac{1}{2\pi\sqrt{LC}} \text{ Hz} \tag{3}$$

Normally $\frac{R^2}{L^2}$ is considered negligible when

$$Q = \frac{\omega L}{R} > 10$$

This is usually the case in most practical applications.

29-7 PHASOR ALGEBRA AND THE PARALLEL CIRCUITS

In previous sections, the addition and subtraction of phasors have been explored. It was seen that phasors in polar form were converted to rectangular form, and then the addition or subtraction procedures were performed algebraically. If desired, the results were converted back to polar form.

In this section, we shall examine the processes of phasor multiplication and division and how this is applied to parallel electronic circuits.

Multiplication of Phasors

The multiplication of phasors may be performed with the phasors in either polar or rectangular form. This process will be shown in the examples that follow.

Phasors in rectangular form are binomials. The multiplication of phasors in this form is performed in the same manner as the multiplication of binominals. The resultant product does, however, have a j^2 term that must be converted. As $j^2 = -1$, this will be used in this conversion process, as shown in the examples.

The multiplication of phasors in polar form consists of multiplying the phasor magnitudes and then adding the angles algebraically.

example 29-10 Multiply the phasors

$$8 + j6 = 10 \underline{|36.8°} \text{ by } 12 + j18 = 21.6 \underline{|56.3°}$$

solution:

Multiplication in

Rectangular Form	Polar Form

$$8 + j6$$
$$\times\ \underline{12 + j18}$$
$$96 + j72$$
$$\underline{ + j144 + j^2108}$$
$$96 + j216 + j^2108$$

$$10\underline{|36.8°}$$
$$\times\ \underline{21.63\underline{|56.3°}}$$
$$216.3\underline{|93.1°}$$

As $j^2 = -1$, we have

$$96 + j216 - 108$$

or

$$-12 + j216$$

or

$$216.3\underline{|180° - 86.9°} = 216.3\underline{|93.1°}$$

example 29–11 Multiply the phasors

$$16 + j24 = 28.84\underline{|56.3°} \text{ by } 3 - j6 = 6.71\underline{|-63.4°}$$

solution:

Multiplication in

Rectangular Form	Polar Form

$$16 + j24$$
$$\times\ \underline{3 - j6}$$
$$48 + j72$$
$$\underline{ - j96 - j^2144}$$
$$48 - j24 - j^2144$$

$$28.83\underline{|56.3°}$$
$$\times\ \underline{6.71\underline{|-63.4°}}$$
$$193.4\underline{|-7.1°}$$

As $j^2 = -1$, we have

$$48 - j24 + 144$$

or

$$192 - j24$$

or

$$193.4\underline{|-7.1°}$$

518

Ch. 29
ALTERNATING-
CURRENT
PARALLEL AND
COMPLEX CIRCUITS

Division of Phasors

The division of phasors in rectangular form requires the rationalization of the denominator and the multiplication of both the numerator and denominator by the conjugate of the denominator.

The division of phasors in polar form requires dividing the phasor magnitudes and then algebraically subtracting the angles.

example 29–12 Divide the phasors

$$15 + j20 = 25\underline{|53.1°} \text{ by } 5 + j10 = 11.2\underline{|63.4°}$$

solution: Division in

Rectangular Form | Polar Form

$$\frac{15 + j20}{5 + j10}$$
$$\frac{25\underline{|53.1°}}{11.2\underline{|63.4°}} = 2.23\underline{|-10.3°}$$

$$= \frac{15 + j20}{5 + j10} \cdot \frac{5 - j10}{5 - j10}$$

$$= \frac{275 - j50}{125} = \frac{275}{125} - \frac{j50}{125}$$

$$= 2.2 - j0.4 = 2.23\underline{|-10.3°}$$

Applications—Phasor Multiplication and Division

In parallel circuits consisting of two resistive branches, it was seen that

$$\frac{1}{R_T} = \frac{1}{R_1} + \frac{1}{R_2} \quad \text{or} \quad R_T = \frac{R_1 R_2}{R_1 + R_2}$$

When impedances are involved, we may write

$$\frac{1}{Z_T} = \frac{1}{Z_1} + \frac{1}{Z_2} \quad \text{or} \quad Z_T = \frac{Z_1 Z_2}{Z_1 + Z_2}$$

In a resistive circuit the phase relationships were not a problem. When impedances are involved, the phase angles must be used. Using the above impedance relationship involves multiplication and division of phasors. This is shown in the following examples.

example 29–13 Determine the impedance of the circuit shown in Figure 29–31.

solution: Writing the phasors in rectangular and polar form, we have

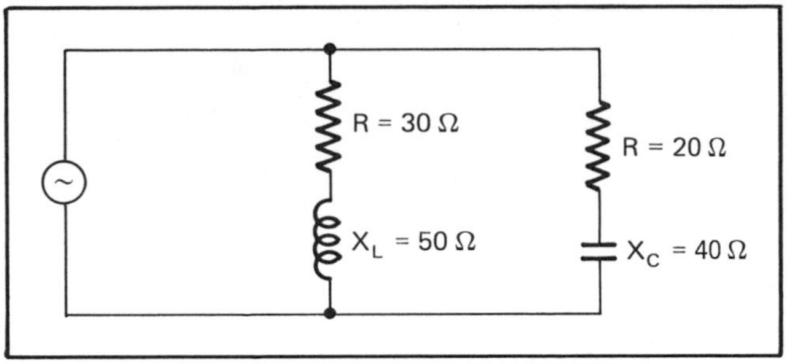

FIGURE 29–31
Circuit for Example 29–13

Inductive branch: $Z_1 = 30 + j50 = 58.3\underline{|59°}\ \Omega$

Capacitive branch: $Z_2 = 20 - j40 = 44.7\underline{|-63.4°}\ \Omega$

$$Z_T - \frac{Z_1 Z_2}{Z_1 + Z_2}$$

$$= \frac{58.3\underline{|59°} \times 44.7\underline{|-63.4°}}{30 + j50 + 20 - j40}$$

$$= \frac{2,606\underline{|-4.4°}}{50 + j10}$$

Converting the denominator to polar form to perform the indicated division results in

$$Z_T = \frac{2,606\underline{|-4.4°}}{51\underline{|11.3°}} = \frac{2,606}{51}\underline{|-4.4° - \underline{|11.3°}}$$

$$= 51.1\underline{|-15.7°}\ \Omega$$

example 29-14 Determine the impedance of circuit shown in Figure 29–32.

solution: $Z_1 = 0 - j50\ \Omega$

$Z_2 = 25 + j30\ \Omega$

$$Z_T = \frac{(0 - j50) \times (25 + j30)}{0 - j50 + 25 + j30} \quad \text{or we may write}$$

$$= \frac{50\underline{|-90°} \times 39\underline{|50.2°}}{25 - j20}$$

$$= \frac{1,950\underline{|-39.8°}}{32\underline{|-38.6°}}$$

$$= 60.9\underline{|-1.2°}\ \Omega$$

520
Ch. 29
ALTERNATING-
CURRENT
PARALLEL AND
COMPLEX CIRCUITS

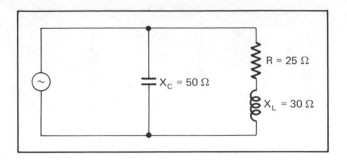

FIGURE   29–32
Circuit for Example 29–14

29–8   SUMMARY

Parallel-circuit relationships are shown in summary form in Figure 29–33. This figure shows typical basic parallel circuits, current phasors, power factor, power, and impedance equations. This figure should be helpful in reviewing the mathematical relationships for parallel circuits.

EXERCISE   29–3

1. For the circuit of Figure 29–34, determine the I, I_2, I_T, and Z.

2. For the circuit of Figure 29–34, determine the circuit pf and P. What is the value of C and L?

3. For the circuit of Figure 29–35, determine I_1, I_2, I_T, θ, pf, and P.

4. For the circuit of Figure 29–36, determine I_1, I_2, I_3, I_T, θ, pf, and P.

5. An ac motor has a lagging pf of 28 percent. The line voltage is 120 V and the line current is 9.68 A. Determine the impedance of the motor and the components of the impedance.

6. An impedance of $Z = 15 + j25$ is connected across a 120-V source. Determine the current, power factor, and power consumed by the circuit. What effect would placing a capacitor of $Z = 0 - j30$ in parallel with this circuit have on I, pf, and P?

7. Determine the effect on the circuit power factor of placing a capacitor in parallel with a load of $Z = 25 + j60$. The capacitor has a reactance of 52 Ω and $E = 200$ V, $f = 60$ Hz.

8. In problem 7, what would be the results if $f = 400$ Hz?

9. A load of $Z = 15 + j36$ is connected to an $E = 300$-V 60-Hz source. A capacitor of what size is required to produce a unity power factor (pf $= 1$)?

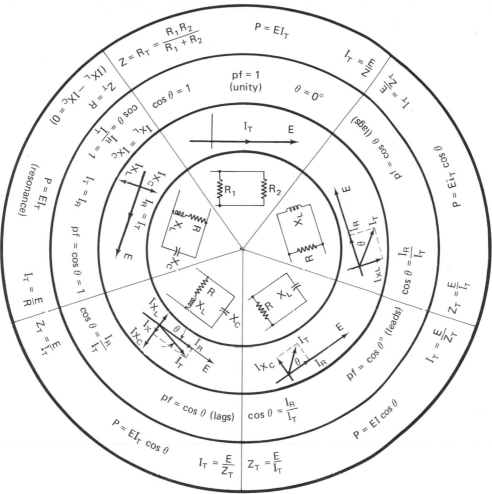

FIGURE 29–33
Parallel–Circuit Relationships

FIGURE 29–34
Circuit for Problems 1 and 2

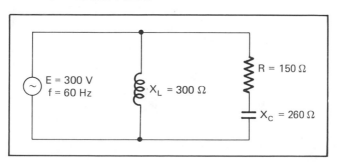

522
Ch. 29
ALTERNATING-
CURRENT
PARALLEL AND
COMPLEX CIRCUITS

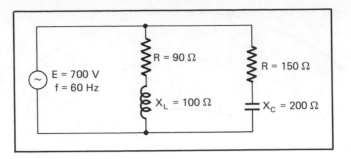

FIGURE 29-35
Circuit for Problem 3

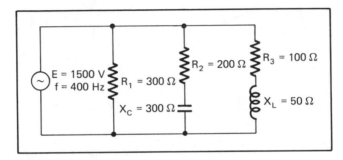

FIGURE 29-36
Circuit for Problem 4

10. What effect would adding a capacitor with $Z = 0 - j30$, in parallel with a load of $Z = 50 - j20$, have on the circuit power factor? The circuit has $E = 500$ V, $f = 400$ Hz.

11. A capacitor of what size would have to be added to bring the circuit power factor to unity if the circuit $Z = 500 + j250$? The circuit $E = 450$ V and $f = 2,000$ Hz.

12. Determine Z, I, pf, and P of the circuit shown in Figure 29-37.

FIGURE 29-37
Circuit for Problem 12

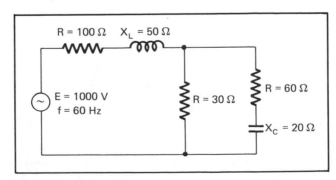

13. Determine f_r for the circuit of Figure 29–38.

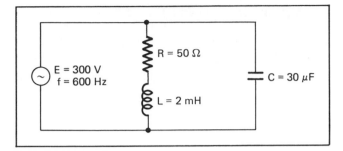

FIGURE 29–38
Circuit for Problems 13 and 14

14. In the circuit of Figure 29–38, what is the value of X_L and X_C?

15. What capacitance would have to be placed in parallel with an impedance at resonance of $Z = 3 + j60$ to produce a $f_r = 3,000$ Hz?

16. In the circuit of Figure 29–39, it is desired to have a resonant frequency occur at 59 kHz. How much capacitance would have to be added in series or parallel with C for this to occur?

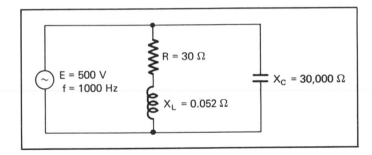

FIGURE 29–39
Circuit for Problems 16 and 17

17. In the circuit of Figure 29–39, how much inductance would have to be added in series or parallel with L to have $f_r = 3.26$ MHz?

18. A circuit has an inductive branch of $Z = 5 + j16$ at $f = 600$ Hz. What size capacitor would have to be added in parallel to produce a $f_r = 16$ MHz?

19. A parallel circuit has a capacitive branch with $Z = 0 - j90$ at $f = 400$ Hz and the inductive branch has a $Z = 15 + j25$. What amount of inductance with negligible resistance would have to be added to make $f_r = 1.5$ kHz?

20. In the circuit of problem 19, what amount of C would have to be added to produce unity pf at 250 Hz? What is f_r when pf = 1?

524

Ch. 29
ALTERNATING-
CURRENT
PARALLEL AND
COMPLEX CIRCUITS

21. Multiply $3 + j8$ by $16 - j45$.

22. What is the product of $-15 - j20$ and $17\underline{|-35°}$?

23. Divide $22 - j44$ by $3 + j5$.

24. A parallel circuit has two branches, with $Z_1 = 5 - j6$ and $Z_2 = 3 + j4$. Determine the total impedance using the relationship

$$Z_T = \frac{Z_1 Z_2}{Z_1 + Z_2}$$

30

LOGARITHMS

Prior to the modern hand-held scientific calculator, the engineer and technician relied heavily on the slide rule for many of their calculations. The slide rule was made possible by the development of logarithms by John Napier in the early 1600s.

This use of logarithms in mathematics, beginning in the seventeenth century, provided great accuracy with a substantial savings in time. The use of logarithms reduced

1. Multiplication to addition.
2. Division to subtraction.
3. Raising a number to a power to multiplication.
4. Root extraction to division.

The above simplifications provide ample evidence of the value of logarithms. The impact of this discovery nearly 400 years ago on our technological advances cannot be underestimated.

30–1 LOGARITHMS

In our previous work with exponents, we found that

$$a^5$$

meant that a was to be taken as a factor five times:

$$a \times a \times a \times a \times a$$

Written in exponential form this provided a "shorthand" method of saying what was meant. In this form,

----

a was called the base
5 was called the power

In addition to being called a power, 5 in this example is also called both an *exponent* and a *superscript*. In this chapter, we shall provide yet another name, *logarithm*.

In our work with exponents it was seen that

$$10^2 = 100$$

$10^3 = 1,000$

$10^4 = 10,000$ etc.

In general terms, then,

$a^x = N$

The logarithm of the number, N, is defined as the exponent, x, to which the base, a, must be raised to produce the number, N. For example,

$10^2 = 100$ 2 is the logarithm of N, 100, to the base, 10

$10^4 = 10,000$ 4 is the logarithm of 10,000 to the base 10

Other bases may be used, and similarly,

$2^4 = 16$ 4 is the logarithm of 16 to the base 2

$12^3 - 1,728$ 3 is the logarithm of 1,728 to the base 12

From the above, it is evident that

[base]$^{\log}$ = number,   where

$[a]^x = N$

A shorthand form of logarithm notation is

$$\boxed{\log_a N = x}$$

Here we have expressed an exponential relationship in logarithmic form. Examples of this notation are shown as

Exponential Form	Logarithmic Form
$3^2 = 9$	$\log_3 9 = 2$
$4^3 = 48$	$\log_4 48 = 3$
$16^{0.5} = 4$	$\log_{16} 4 = 0.5$
$x^y = Z$	$\log_x Z = y$

In the preceding examples there are two observations that should be noted. First, the example

$16^{0.5} = 4$ may be written $16^{\frac{1}{2}} = 4$

which in exponential form means

$$\sqrt{16} = 4$$

Similarly, we may write

$$10,000^{\frac{1}{4}} = 10 \quad \text{or} \quad 10,000^{0.25} = 10$$

In logarithmic form this becomes

$$\log_{10,000} 10 = 0.25$$

Another feature of these examples is that the base is a positive number, either numerical or general. Any such number, with the exception of 1, may be used as a base. A 1 raised to any power is equal to 1, and so it may not be used as a base.

EXERCISE 30-1

1. $3^4 = 81$
2. $4^5 = 1,024$
3. $16^3 = 4,096$
4. $3,136^{0.5} = 56$
5. $x^b = a$
6. $y^0 = 1$
7. $z^{0.25} = P$
8. $t^1 = t$

Express the following logarithmic-form equations in exponential form.

9. $\log_5 25 = 2$
10. $\log_6 216 = 3$
11. $\log_{15} 50,625 = 4$
12. $\log_{77} 5,929 = 2$
13. $\log_{361} 19 = 0.5$
14. $\log_x 1 = 0$
15. $\log_{4,096} 64 = 0.25$
16. $\log_z W = 6$

30-2 THE LAWS OF LOGARITHMS

The most important thing to remember about operations with logarithms is that

----

The logarithm is an exponent. As such, the laws of exponents apply to logarithms.

We have spent considerable time in our previous work with exponents. This background will make our work with logarithms considerably easier. If the student has any questions regarding exponents, it is suggested that he review Chapter 20.

From our work with exponents it was found that

$$a^m \cdot a^n = a^{m+n} \qquad \qquad (1)$$

If we let

$$a^m = M \qquad \qquad (2)$$

$$a^n = N \qquad \qquad (3)$$

$$a^{m+n} = P \qquad \qquad (4)$$

then the product, P, is formed by the multiplication of factors M and N as

$$P = MN$$

This may be expressed in logarithmic form as

$$\log_a P = \log_a MN$$

This is possible, as this will not change the equality. Using equations (2) and (3), we may write

$$\log_a M = m \qquad \qquad (5)$$

$$\log_a N = n \qquad \qquad (6)$$

It follows that

$$\log_a P = m + n \qquad \qquad (7)$$

The laws of logarithms for multiplication may then be expressed as

$$\boxed{\log_a P = \log_a MN = m + n = \log_a M + \log_a N}$$

example 30–1

$$3^2 = 9, \qquad 3^4 = 81$$

or, in logarithmic form,

$$\log_3 9 = 2 \quad \text{and} \quad \log_3 81 = 4$$

Then

$$\log_3 (9 \times 81) = 2 + 4$$

$$\log_3 729 = 6 \qquad [3 \cdot 3 \cdot 3 \cdot 3 \cdot 3 \cdot 3 = 729]$$

It follows that

$$\log_3 (9 \times 81) = \log_3 9 + \log_3 81$$

example 30-2

$$2^3 = 8 \quad \text{and} \quad 2^5 = 32$$

$$\log_2 8 = 3 \quad \text{and} \quad \log_2 32 = 5$$

Then

$$\log_2 (8 \times 32) = 3 + 5$$

$$\log_2 256 = 8 \qquad [2 \cdot 2 \cdot 2 \cdot 2 \cdot 2 \cdot 2 \cdot 2 \cdot 2 = 256]$$

Then

$$\log_2 (8 \times 32) = \log_2 8 + \log_2 32$$

DIVISION

From our work with exponents we found that

$$\frac{a^m}{a^n} = a^{m-n} \tag{8}$$

If we let

$$a^m = M \tag{9}$$

$$a^n = N \tag{10}$$

$$a^{m-n} = Q \tag{11}$$

then the quotient, Q, is formed by the division of the factors, M by N, as

$$Q = \frac{M}{N} \tag{12}$$

This may be expressed in logarithmic form as

$$\log_a Q = \log_a \frac{M}{N} \tag{13}$$

However, since $\log_a Q = m - n$ and $\log_a M = m$ and $\log_a N = n$ we may formulate the law of logarithms in division as

$$\log_a Q = \log_a \frac{M}{N} = m - n = \log_a M - \log_a N$$

example 30–3

$$4^4 = 256, \quad 4^2 = 16$$

which in logarithmic form is

$$\log_4 256 = 4 \quad \text{and} \quad \log_4 16 = 2$$

In the form of the problem, we may write

$$\log_4 \left(\frac{256}{16}\right) = \log_4 256 - \log_4 16$$

Then

$$\log_4 \left(\frac{256}{16}\right) = \log_4 16 - 2$$

as

$$\log_4 256 = 4$$
$$\log_4 16 = 2$$
$$4 - 2 = 2$$

Then

$$\log_4 \left(\frac{256}{16}\right) = \log_4 256 - \log_4 16$$

example 30–4 If $2^6 = 64$ and $2^3 = 8$, establish that $\log_2 8 = 3$.

solution: In logarithmic form,

$$\log_2 \left(\frac{64}{8}\right) = \log_2 64 - \log_2 8$$

$$\log_2 \left(\frac{64}{8}\right) = \log_2 8 = 3$$

Since

$$\log_2 64 = 6$$

$$\log_2 8 = 3$$

$$6 - 3 = 3$$

Then

$$\log_2 \left(\frac{64}{8}\right) = \log_2 64 - \log_2 8$$

RAISING A NUMBER TO A POWER

From our work with exponents,

$$[a^m]^n = a^{mn} \tag{14}$$

If we let

$$a^m = M \tag{15}$$

then

$$\log_a M = m \tag{16}$$

Both sides of (15) may be raised to the n power as

$$a^{mn} = M^n \tag{17}$$

Equation (17) in logarithmic form is written as

$$\log_a M^n = mn \tag{18}$$

The value of m from (16) substituted in (18) produces

$$\boxed{\log_a M^n = n \log_a M}$$

example 30-5 Prove that

$$\log_{10} (100)^3 = 3 \log_{10} 100$$

solution: $\log_{10} (100)^3 = \log_{10} 1{,}000{,}000 = 6$

$$\log_{10} 100 = 2$$

$$3 \log_{10} 100 = 2 \times 3 = 6$$

Then

$$3 \log_{10} 100 = \log_{10} (100)^3$$

Our work with exponents established that

$$\sqrt[n]{a} = a^{\frac{1}{n}} \qquad\qquad (19)$$

If we let $M = a^m$ and $\qquad\qquad (20)$

$$\sqrt[n]{a^m} = a^{\frac{m}{n}} \qquad\qquad (21)$$

we may write

$$M^{\frac{1}{n}} = a^{\frac{m}{n}} \qquad\qquad (22)$$

which in logarithmic form is written

$$\log_a M^{\frac{1}{n}} = \frac{m}{n} \qquad\qquad (23)$$

and, from (20), we may write

$$m = \log_a M \qquad\qquad (24)$$

Substituting in (23) we have

$$\boxed{\log_a M^{\frac{1}{n}} = \frac{\log_a M}{n} = \frac{1}{n} \log_a M}$$

example 30-6 Prove that $\log_{10} \sqrt[4]{10{,}000} = \frac{1}{4} \log_{10} 10{,}000$

solution: $\qquad \log_{10} \sqrt[4]{10{,}000} = \log_{10} 10 = 1$

Also,

$\frac{1}{4} \log_{10} 10{,}000 = \frac{1}{4} \times 4 = 1$

Then as both are equal to the same quantity, 1, we have

$\log_{10} \sqrt[4]{10{,}000} = \frac{1}{4} \log_{10} 10{,}000$

30-3 LOGARITHMIC TABLES

In Section 30–2, various bases such as, 2, 3, 4, and 10 were used. Using these, or other numbers as a base, a logarithmic system could be developed. The most widely used system has 10 as a base. The data for this system are arranged in tables referred to as "tables of common logarithms." Such a table is found in Table A in the Appendix. The base 10 will be normally used in this text. As such, when no base designation is given, it is understood that it is to the base$_{10}$. If another base is used, it will be so designated—as log$_4$, log$_2$, etc.

Another logarithmic system is often used in scientific calculations. This is called the *system of natural logarithms*. Tables for this base, which is 2.71828, have also been developed. These are called "tables of natural logarithms." This system is found useful because of the way it relates to certain electrical and electromagnetic phenomena. Such behavior and the application of this logarithmic system to it will be presented in other courses of instruction. The system of natural logarithms is designated as log$_e$.

A table of logarithms in the base 10 system for integers may be easily developed. Such a table is shown as Table 30–1. This table has a range from 10^5 to 10^{-5}.

TABLE 30–1 Basic logarithmic table

FORM $a^n = N$	FORM $\log_{10} N = n$
$10^5 = 100{,}000$	$\log 100{,}000 = 5$
$10^4 = 10{,}000$	$\log 10{,}000 = 4$
$10^3 = 1{,}000$	$\log 1{,}000 = 3$
$10^2 = 100$	$\log 100 = 2$
$10^1 = 10$	$\log 10 = 1$
$10^0 = 1$	$\log 1 = 0$
$10^{-1} = 0.1$	$\log 0.1 = -1$
$10^{-2} = 0.01$	$\log 0.01 = -2$
$10^{-3} = 0.001$	$\log 0.001 = -3$
$10^{-4} = 0.0001$	$\log 0.0001 = -4$
$10^{-5} = 0.00001$	$\log 0.00001 = -5$

Examination of this table reveals several interesting features. These include:

1. This table provides only integers. If the log for which we were looking was for a particular power of 10, all well and good, this table would be adequate. Normally, however, our work is not so simple, and a method of developing suitable tables adaptable for all numbers is required.

2. Note that Table 30–1 does provide us with some knowledge of the magnitude of the log for the various ranges. For example, a number between 1 and 10 would have a log between 0 and 1, a number between 1,000 and 10,00 would have a log between 3 and 4, and so on.

We now have a starting point for a table of logarithms. We also know the range of the logarithms between various limits. Let us see how our table of logarithms could be expanded. In this process we will work between the limits of 10^0 and 10^1.

We know that

$$10^{\frac{1}{n}} = \sqrt[n]{10}$$

We may use this relationship to develop the logarithms for various fractional points between 1 and 10. Let us start with

$$10^{0.50} = 10^{\frac{1}{2}} = \sqrt{10} = 3.16228$$

We may now write $\log 3.16228 = 0.5$.

In a similar manner, other logarithms may be calculated. Several of these are shown.

$$10^{0.25} = 10^{\frac{1}{4}} = \sqrt[4]{10}$$

This may be written

$$\sqrt{\sqrt{10}}$$

As the $\sqrt{10}$ has already been determined, we may write

$$10^{0.25} = \sqrt{3.16228} = 1.77764$$

$$10^{0.125} = 10^{\frac{1}{8}} = \sqrt{\sqrt{10^{\frac{1}{4}}}} = \sqrt{1.77764} = 1.33328$$

$$10^{\frac{1}{16}} = 10^{0.0625} = \sqrt{\sqrt{10^{\frac{1}{8}}}} = \sqrt{1.33328} = 1.15468$$

Various combinations of these values may also be determined: for example,

$$10^{0.25} \times 10^{0.5} = 10^{0.75} = 1.77764 \times 3.16228 = 5.62139$$

$$10^{0.25} \times 10^{0.125} = 10^{0.40} = 1.77764 \times 1.33328 = 2.37009$$

$$10^{0.125} = 10^{0.0625} = 10^{0.1875} = 1.33328 \times 1.15468 = 1.53951$$

The above procedure may be expanded to obtain as detailed a logarithmic table as desired. Another method would be to plot the values calculated above, and using the curve thus obtained, read intermediate values from the curve. The calculated values are shown in tabular form in Table 30-2, and these are shown plotted in Figure 30-1.

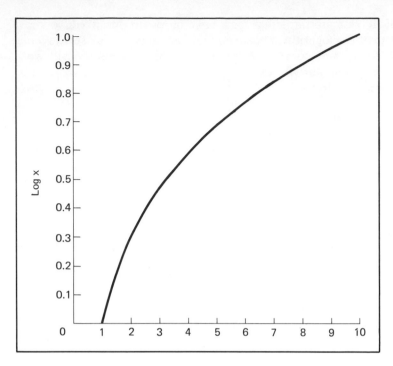

FIGURE 30–1
Logarithms for Numbers 1–10

TABLE 30–2 Logarithms table for numbers between 1 and 10

$10^0 = 1$	log $1.000 = 0.000$
$10^{0.0625} = 1.1547$	log $1.1547 = 0.0625$
$10^{0.125} = 1.3333$	log $1.3333 = 0.125$
$10^{0.1875} = 1.5395$	log $1.5395 = 0.1875$
$10^{0.250} = 1.7776$	log $1.7776 = 0.250$
$10^{0.40} = 2.3701$	log $2.3701 = 0.400$
$10^{0.50} = 3.1623$	log $3.1623 = 0.500$
$10^{0.75} = 5.6214$	log $5.6214 = 0.750$
$10^1 = 10.0$	log $10.0 = 1.000$

The curve shown in Figure 30–1 provides us with logarithms for numbers only between 1 and 10. Other such curves would have to be developed to cover the range of values required. Even after these curves were developed, the results in reading intermediate values would not be as accurate as necessary. The above calculations and the curves do, however, provide an indication as to the procedures used to develop logarithmic tables. Accurate tables of logarithms are fortunately available, and calculations as above are not necessary. A table of common logarithms is, as noted, presented in Table A in the Appendix.

Using scientific notation and converting large and small numbers to a number between 1 and 10 times the appropriate power of 10, the logarithms we will use will be in the form of decimal fractions. There is then the question of how to handle the appropriate power of 10 involved with the number. This procedure is shown in the following examples.

example 30–7   What is the logarithm of 56,214?

solution: Writing the number in scientific notation, we have

$$5.6214 \times 10^4$$

Examination of our calculated values show that the

$$\log 5.6214 = 0.750$$

For the number 56,214, we could write

$$56,214 = 5.6214 \times 10^4 = 10^{0.750} \times 10^4 \quad \text{or} \quad 10^{4.750}$$

In this form, the decimal part provides the logarithm of the number involved while the integer provides the information on the appropriate power of 10. The combination of the two designates the complete number.

example 30–8   What is the logarithm of

3,162.3,   316.23,   31.623,   and   3.1623?

solution: Writing these numbers in scientific notation, we have

$$3.1623 \times 10^3, \quad 3.1623 \times 10^2, \quad 3.1623 \times 10^1,$$
and   3.1623

The logarithm of 3.1623, from the Table 30–2, is

$$\log 3.1623 = 0.500$$

We may then write

$$3.1623 \times 10^3 = 10^{0.500} \times 10^3 = 10^{3.500}$$
$$3.1623 \times 10^2 = 10^{0.500} \times 10^2 = 10^{2.500}$$
$$3.1623 \times 10^1 = 10^{0.500} \times 10^1 = 10^{1.500}$$
$$3.1623 \qquad = 10^{0.500}$$

Or, expressed in logarithmic form,

$$\log 3{,}162.3 = 3.500$$

$$\log 316.23 = 2.500$$

$$\log 31.623 = 1.500$$

$$\log 3.1623 = 0.500$$

In the above examples, it is seen that the decimal part of the number remains unchanged, and only the integer is changed to reflect the size of the number involved.

If we were to carry the above illustration still further, it would be seen to apply as well to numbers smaller than unity. As before, the number would first be expressed as a number between 1 and 10 times the appropriate power of 10. The decimal point may then be obtained from the table and the integer applied to reflect the magnitude of the number.

example 30-9   Determine the logarithm of the following numbers:

$$0.15395, \quad 0.015395, \quad \text{and} \quad 0.00015395$$

solution: Writing these numbers in scientific notation, we have

$$1.5395 \times 10^{-1}, \quad 1.5395 \times 10^{-2}, \quad \text{and} \quad 1.5395 \times 10^{-4}$$

Examination of our calculated Table 30-2 shows that

$$\log 1.5395 = 0.1875$$

From the basic log table of Table 30-1 it is seen that the integers for the three numbers of our example will be -1 for 0.15395, -2 for 0.015395, and -4 for 0.0001539. We may now write

$$\log 0.15395 \quad\;\; = \bar{1}.1875$$

$$\log 0.015395 \quad = \bar{2}.1875$$

$$\log 0.00015395 = \bar{4}.1875$$

Note the manner in which the integer is designated as negative.

Examining the solutions to Examples 30-8 and 30-9 enables us to provide some guides to follow in our work with logarithms. First we should establish the names and relationships which exist for the various parts of the logarithm.

THE CHARACTERISTIC——*This is the integer part of the logarithm, which we establish based on the size of the number involved and our knowledge of scientific notation. Our work with examples established these facts regarding the characteristic.*
  a. *The characteristic of numbers greater than 1 is positive. Its value is always 1 less than the number of places to the left of the decimal point in the original number.*
  b. *The characteristic of numbers less than 1 is negative. Its value is always 1 more than the number of zeros to the right of the decimal point. In addition to the method of designating a negative characteristic, such as $\overline{4}.1875$, one other system is often used. This is written with a positive characteristic, with a −10 placed to the right of the decimal fraction. The logarithm $\overline{4}.1875$ would thus be written $6.1875 − 10$. The +6 and the −10 would designate the −4 characteristic as before. This method of designating a negative characteristic will be used in this text.*
  c. *The characteristic of a number between 1 and 10 is zero and is considered in the positive category of fact a above.*

THE MANTISSA——*This is the fraction that we obtain from the table of logarithms. It is* always *positive and it is* always *a fraction. It would be well to point out that the tables of common logarithms, including that of Table A in the Appendix, normally omit the decimal point. This is a matter of convention. It is understood, then, that* the mantissa is a decimal fraction.
  The above examples point out one other important feature of the mantissa. That is, the mantissa does not change as long as the figures of the numbers do not change. For example, the mantissa is the same for 31.564, 3.1564, 0.0031564, and so on. The characteristic does, however, change to reflect the magnitude of the number.

Table A in the appendix is a four-place table of common logarithms. Four-place tables will be adequate for our purposes. More accurate tables of up to 15 places are available but are not often used.

There are two basic steps involving the use of a table of logarithms. These are the procedures for finding the logarithm of a given number and the procedures for finding the number that corresponds to a given logarithm. Each of these procedures will be discussed at length in the following sections.

To assist the reader in the understanding of this procedure, a portion of Table A of the Appendix is reproduced as Table 30–3. The use of this portion will be representative of procedures to be used throughout the table. Table 30–3 is observed to have the first of its columns

TABLE 30–3 Portion of Table A of the Appendix

N	0	1	2	3	4	5	6	7	8	9
70	8451	8457	8463	8470	8476	8482	8488	8494	8500	8506
71	8513	8519	8525	8531	8537	8543	8549	8555	8561	8567
72	8573	8579	8585	8591	8597	8603	8609	8615	8621	8627
73	8633	8639	8645	8651	8657	8663	8669	8675	8681	8686
74	8692	8698	8704	8710	8716	8722	8727	8733	8739	8745

labeled N. This is an abbreviation for number. In this table, column N covers numbers from 70 through 74. The numbers in column N represent the first two digits of a number with three significant figures. The third digit is found in the vertical columns numbered from 0 through 9. This use of this table will be shown in the discussion and examples that follow.

Prior to these examples, it is necessary to point out an important step, in obtaining the logarithm of a given number from the table. This is the determination of the characteristic. This is always obtained first, prior to using the table. This procedure is outlined in Section 30–3 and requires expressing the number as a number between 1 and 10 times the appropriate power of 10. This establishes the characteristic. The logarithm may then be obtained from the table. On this basis we may establish the following procedure for numbers with three significant figures.

1. Find the characteristic by writing the number as a number between 1 and 10 times the appropriate power of 10.
2. Locate the line under column N for the first two digits of the number.
3. Move horizontally along this line to the column with the heading of the third significant figure. This locates the mantissa.
4. Combine the characteristic and the mantissa to form the logarithm. Round off where necessary.

example 30-10 Determine log 731.

solution: The characteristic is first obtained. $731 = 7.31 \times 10^2$. This establishes the characteristic as 2. The first two digits of 731 are located under column N. The third digit, 1, is located under the column numbered 1. The mantissa is located on the $N = 73$ line under the 1 column. That is,

$$\log 731 = 2.8639$$

example 30–11 Determine log 7,240.

solution: The characteristic is found as $7,240 = 7.24 \times 10^3$, and is 3. The mantissa is found on line $N = 72$ and under column 4, which for this number represents 40.

$$\log 7,240 = 3.8597$$

example 30–12 What is log 0.00739?

solution: $0.00739 = 7.39 \times 10^{-3}$. The characteristic is $\overline{3}$, or $7 - 10$. The mantissa is found on the line for $N = 73$ and under the column for 9.

$$\log 0.00739 = 7.8686 - 10$$

The determination of the logarithm for a number with more than three significant figures requires a process called *interpolation*. For example, the mantissa for a number of 7,252 would fall between 725, which could be considered 7,250, and 726, which could be considered 7,260.

Number		Mantissa
7,250		0.8603
7,260		0.8609
10	difference	0.0006

This shows that an increase of 10 in the numbers from 7,250 to 7,260 results in an increase of 0.0006 in the mantissa. Therefore, one number change will result in 1/10, or 0.1, of the increase in the mantissa. As the fourth significant digit of the number is 2, the mantissa will increase above the 7,250 number by

$$0.2 \times 0.0006 = 0.00012$$

We may now write

Number		Mantissa
7,250		0.8603
	increase	0.00012
7,252		0.86042

As the log tables are for four places, interpolation resulting in more than four places incorrectly implies a greater accuracy. As a result, always round off the mantissa to four places.

example 30–13 What is the log 7,159?

solution: $7,159 = 7.159 \times 10^3$. The characteristic is 3.

Number		Mantissa
7,150		0.8543
7,160		0.8549
10	difference	0.0006

A change of 10 numbers results in a change of 0.0006. An increase of nine numbers will cause a 0.9 of the increase in the mantissa or $0.9 \times 0.0006 = 0.00054$.

Number		Mantissa
7,150		0.8543
	increase	0.00054
7,159		0.85484

$$\log 7,159 = 3.8548$$

example 30–14 What is log 0.0073674?

solution: $0.0073674 = 7.3674 \times 10^{-3}$. The characteristic is $7 - 10$.

Number		Mantissa
73,600		0.8669
73,700		0.8675
100	difference	0.0006

An increase of 74 results in an increase in the mantissa of

$$0.74 \times 0.0006 = 0.00044$$

Number		Mantissa
7,360		0.8669
	increase	0.00044
		0.86734

$$\log 0.007367 = 7.8673 - 10$$

543

Sec. 30–5
FINDING THE
NUMBER
REPRESENTED BY A
GIVEN LOGARITHM

As shown in the above examples, we may establish the following procedures to follow *for a number with more than three significant figures.*

1. Find the characteristic by writing the number as a number between 1 and 10 times the appropriate power of 10.

2. Locate the line under column *N* for the first two digits of the number.

3. Move horizontally along this line to the column with the heading of the third significant figure, to determine this mantissa.

4. Determine the mantissa for the next highest three significant figures. The mantissa for the number with more than three significant figures will be between these two.

5. Determine the change in mantissa resulting from the change in the three-significant-figure numbers.

6. Use the actual increase in number, above the lower number, as a decimal multiplied by the change that occurs in the mantissa.

7. Add this product to the mantissa of the lower number.

8. Combine the characteristic and the mantissa to form the logarithm. Round off where necessary.

EXERCISE 30–2 Use Table A to determine the logarithms of the following numbers.

1. 35	**2.** 9.2	**3.** 653
4. 928.0	**5.** 2.60×10^6	**6.** 0.025×10^{-3}
7. 163×10^4	**8.** 21,300	**9.** 0.0298
10. 0.000364	**11.** 61.64×10^{-4}	**12.** 39.27×10^6
13. 21×10^{-5}	**14.** 10×10^{-3}	**15.** 856
16. 921,000	**17.** $42,600 \times 10^6$	**18.** 156,700
19. 0.341	**20.** 12,700	**21.** 360.0
22. 21.7×10^3	**23.** 600×10^{-5}	**24.** 322×10^8

30–5 FINDING THE NUMBER REPRESENTED BY A GIVEN LOGARITHM

The process of finding the number represented by a given logarithm is the reverse of that of Section 30–4. The number that is represented by a given logarithm is called the *antilogarithm*. This is normally written in shortened form, *antilog*. An example of this procedure is

$$\log 7,240 = 3.8597$$

$$\text{antilog } 3.8597 = 7,240$$

The following examples will demonstrate the method used in determining the antilogarithm of a given logarithm.

example 30-15 Determine the numbers represented by the logarithms 3.6542, 2.6542, 1.6542, and 8.6542 − 10.

solution: In Section 30–4, it was shown that the characteristic represented the position of the decimal point. The mantissa represented the logarithm to the number of significant figures of the number. To obtain the antilog, we must determine the number from the mantissa found in Table A and then establish the decimal point. From Table A, the mantissa, 0.6542, is found on line 45 under *N*. This establishes the first two figures of the number, 45. The third figure is found to be 1, for the mantissa is located under column 1. As the characteristic is 3, there are four figures to the left of the decimal point. We may now write

$$\text{antilog } 3.6542 = 4,510$$

Changing the characteristic changes only the location of the decimal point, as

$$\text{antilog } 2.6542 = 451.0$$

$$\text{antilog } 1.6542 = 45.1$$

$$\text{antilog } 8.6542 - 10 = 0.0451$$

example 30-16 What is the number whose logarithm is 5.3488?

solution: The first two digits of the number from Table A are found to be 22. The mantissa is found to be between two third-figure columns. That is,

$$0.3483 = \text{mantissa of log } 223$$
$$\underline{0.3502} = \text{mantissa of log } \underline{224}$$
$$0.0019 \quad \text{difference} \quad 1$$

Our number is seen to lie between 223 and 224. The mantissa of the given logarithm is

0.3488 − 0.3483 = 0.0005 unit above 223,   or

$\dfrac{0.0005}{0.0019}$ of the 1-unit difference between 223 and 224, or

$0.263 \times 1 = 0.263$

545
Sec. 30–5
FINDING THE
NUMBER
REPRESENTED BY A
GIVEN LOGARITHM

Added to 223 results in

223.263   or   rounded off to 223.3

Then antilog 5.3488 = 233,300.

example 30–17   Determine the number whose logarithm is 6.5882 − 10.

solution: 0.5877 = mantissa of log 387
0.5888 = mantissa of log 388
—————   ———
0.0011   difference   1

The mantissa of the given log is

0.5882 − 0.5877 = 0.0005 unit above 387,   or

$\dfrac{0.0005}{0.0011} \times 1 = 0.454$

Added to 387 results in

387.454,   rounded off to 387.5

Then

antilog 6.5882 − 10 = 0.0003875

$$= 3.875 \times 10^{-4}$$

example 30–18   What is the number whose logarithm is 3.6554?

solution: 0.6551 = mantissa of log 452
0.6561 = mantissa of log 453
—————   ———
0.0010   difference   1

The mantissa of the given logarithm is

0.6554 − 0.6551 = 0.0003 unit above 452,   or

$\dfrac{0.0003}{0.0010} \times 1 = 0.3$

Added to 452 produces 452.3.
Then antilog 3.6554 = 4,523.

EXERCISE 30-3

1.	3.5560	**2.**	1.3592
3.	0.7865	**4.**	4.2867
5.	8.2210 − 10	**6.**	0.7980
7.	3.7388	**8.**	6.1121
9.	3.9015	**10.**	2.2221
11.	0.8035	**12.**	7.3652 − 10
13.	0.0367	**14.**	9.4327 − 10
15.	5.6674	**16.**	2.9010

30-6 ADDITION OF LOGARITHMS

The addition of logarithms is a relatively simple procedure. There are several basic rules to follow.

1. The mantissas are always positive and are added as such, regardless of the sign of the characteristic.
2. The characteristics are added algebraically, in the same manner as signed numbers.
3. When the sum of the mantissas results in a value greater than 1, the whole number is carried over to be added with the characteristic. As the mantissas are always positive, the whole number resulting from their addition is always positive.

example 30-19   Add the logarithms 3.6560 and 4.2156.

solution:
$$\begin{array}{r} 3.6560 \\ 4.2156 \\ \hline 7.8716 \end{array}$$

example 30-20   Add the logarithms 7.6523 − 10 and 8.4157 − 10.

solution:
$$\begin{array}{r} 7.6523 - 10 \\ 8.4157 - 10 \\ \hline 16.0680 - 20 \end{array}$$

When an answer appears in this form, the procedure is to subtract the characteristic and number that follows the mantissa from 10 or the largest 10 multiple that will result in a characteristic below 10. In this example, subtracting 10 from both will produce this result:

answer: 6.0680 − 10

example 30–21 Add the logarithms 3.1794, 7.3426, 5.8750 − 10, and 6.6532.

solution:

$$3.1794$$
$$7.3426$$
$$5.8750 - 10$$
$$\underline{6.6532}$$
$$23.0502 - 10 \quad \text{or} \quad 13.0502$$

Note that the sum of the mantissas is is 2.0502. The 2 is carried over, to be added to the characteristic total, as shown.

30–7 SUBTRACTION OF LOGARITHMS

The following rules apply for the subtraction of logarithms:

1. The subtrahend mantissa is subtracted from the minuend mantissa.
2. If the minuend mantissa is smaller than the subtrahend mantissa, 1 is borrowed from the minuend characteristic.
3. If the minuend characteristic is smaller than the subtrahend characteristic, a suitable multiple of 10 is added to the minuend characteristic to make it larger. The same 10 multiple is added as a negative multiple following the minuend mantissa.
4. In subtracting the characteristics, the sign of the subtrahend characteristic is changed and then the characteristics are added algebraically.

example 30–22 Subtract log 3.5314 from log 6.7526.

solution:

$$6.7526$$
$$\underline{3.5314}$$
$$\text{answer} \quad 3.2212$$

example 30–23 Subtract log 6.8642 − 10 from log 9.3214 − 10.

solution:

$$9.3214 - 10$$
$$\underline{6.8642 - 10}$$
$$2.4572$$

Note that the sign of the 10 multiple that follows the subtrahend mantissa is changed, as is the subtrahend characteristic, before adding algebraically.

example 30–24 Subtract log 5.8760 from log 2.1508.

solution: 2.1508

5.8760

Note that as the characteristic of the minuend is smaller than the subtrahend characteristic, 10 is added to the minuend characteristic while a −10 is placed following the minuend mantissa:

$$2.1508 = 12.1508 - 10$$

then subtracting, we have

$$12.1508 - 10$$
$$\underline{5.8760}$$
$$6.2748 - 10$$

example 30–25 Subtract log 8.3672 − 10 from log 3.1567.

solution: 3.1567

8.3672 − 10

Adding 10 to the characteristic and −10 following the mantissa of the minuend.

$$3.1567 = 13.1567 - 10$$

then subtracting, we have

$$13.1567 - 10$$
$$\underline{8.3672 - 10}$$
$$4.7895$$

EXERCISE 30–4   Complete the indicated logarithm additions.

1. $3.2156 + 5.6172$ 2. $4.1231 + 3.1258$

3. $1.2987 + 7.2941$ 4. $6.1791 + 1.4385$

5. $5.2941 - 10 + 3.2748$ 6. $8.3674 - 10 + 7.5654 - 10$

7. $3.1780 + 6.3567 - 10$ 8. $2.5874 - 10 + 6.5217 - 10$

Complete the indicated subtractions of logarithms.

9. $8.5764 - 2.3567$ 10. $5.6431 - 3.1428$

11. $3.1472 - 1.2145$ 12. $5.2981 - 7.4215$

13. $6.3589 - 10 - 3.6572 - 10$

14. $5.2974 - 10 \quad - \quad 3.1560$

15. $6.9541 - 10 \quad - \quad 4.7648 - 10$

16. $8.1543 - 10 \quad - \quad 3.2960 - 10$

The logarithm of a product is found to be equal to the sum of the logarithms of its factors. This is shown in the following examples.

example 30–26 Multiply 12×11.

solution: It is helpful to arrange the logarithms in a systematic format for addition, first establishing the characteristics.

$$
\begin{aligned}
\text{Format:} \qquad \log 12 &= 1.\\
\log 11 &= \underline{1.\qquad}\\
\log \text{ of sum} &=
\end{aligned}
$$

answer = antilog sum =

With this sort of systematic arrangement, simple and multiple multiplications may be easily completed.

$$
\begin{aligned}
\log 12 &= 1.0792\\
\log 11 &= \underline{1.0414}\\
\log \text{ of sum} &= 2.1206
\end{aligned}
$$

answer = antilog sum = 132

example 30–27 Multiply $162 \times 356 \times 281$.

solution:
$$
\begin{aligned}
\text{Format:} \qquad \log 162 &= 2.\\
\log 356 &= 2.\\
\log 281 &= \underline{2.\qquad}\\
\log \text{ of sum} &=
\end{aligned}
$$

answer = antilog sum =

$$
\begin{aligned}
\log 162 &= 2.2095\\
\log 356 &= 2.5514\\
\log 281 &= \underline{2.4487}\\
\log \text{ of sum} &= 7.2096
\end{aligned}
$$

$$
\begin{aligned}
0.2095 &= \text{mantissa of log } 162\\
\underline{0.2122} &= \text{mantissa of log } \underline{163}\\
0.0027 &\quad \text{difference} \qquad 1
\end{aligned}
$$

mantissa of answer 0.0001 above the mantissa of 162, or

$$\frac{0.0001}{0.0027} \times 1 = 0.037, \quad \text{or}$$

$$162 + 0.037 = 162.037, \quad \text{rounded off to } 162.0$$

Then

$$\text{antilog } 7.2096 = 16,200,000 = 1.62 \times 10^7$$

example 30–28 Multiply 0.00128 by 167.

solution: Format: $\log 0.00128 = 7.$ -10
              $\log 167 = \underline{2}$
              $\log \text{ of sum} =$

answer = antilog =

$$\log 0.00128 = 7.1072 - 10$$
$$\log 167 = \underline{2.2227}$$
$$\log \text{ sum} = 9.3299 - 10$$

answer = antilog sum =

0.3284 = mantissa log 213
$\underline{0.3304}$ = mantissa log $\underline{214}$
0.0020 difference   1

mantissa of answer, $0.3299 - 0.3284 = 0.0015$ above the mantissa of 213,   or

$$\frac{0.0015}{0.0020} \times 1 = 0.75, \quad \text{or}$$

213.75,   rounded off to 213.8

Then

$$\text{antilog } 9.3299 - 10 = 0.2138$$

30–9 NEGATIVE NUMBERS IN LOGARITHMIC COMPUTATIONS

Negatives numbers cannot be used in logarithmic computations because negative numbers have imaginary logarithms. This is because there is no power of 10, or any other positive base for that matter, which will result in a negative number. As a result, the procedure to follow is to initially determine the sign of the product of the multiplication by visual examination. Then, considering all factors positive, proceed with the multiplication as in Section 30–8. When the answer has been determined, affix the required sign.

example 30-29 Multiply 30 × −22.

solution: Visual examination shows that the result of the multiplication will be −.

$$\begin{aligned} \log 30 &= 1.4771 \\ \log 22 &= \underline{1.3424} \\ \log \text{ of sum} &= 2.8195 \end{aligned}$$

antilog sum = antilog 2.8195 = 660

answer with appropriate sign = −660

30–10 DIVISION USING LOGARITHMS

The logarithm of the quotient of two numbers is found to be the logarithm of the dividend minus the logarithm of the division. This is shown in the following examples.

example 30-30 Determine, using logarithms, the value of $\dfrac{300}{60}$.

solution: As with multiplication, it is helpful to use a systematic format in working with logarithmic problems. Placing the characteristic first is also of assistance. Such an arrangement follows:

$$\begin{aligned} \text{Format: } \log 300 &= 2. \\ \log \ \ 60 &= \underline{1.\qquad} \\ \log \text{ difference} &= \end{aligned}$$

answer = antilog difference =

With this format, the solution is obtained as

$$\begin{aligned} \log 300 &= 2.4771 \\ \log \ \ 60 &= \underline{1.7782} \\ \log \text{ difference} &= 0.6989 \end{aligned}$$

answer = antilog 0.6989 = 5

example 30-31 Using logarithms, determine the value of $\dfrac{45{,}000}{1{,}500}$.

solution:
$$\log 45{,}000 = 4.$$

$$\begin{aligned} \log \ \ 1{,}500 &= \underline{3.\qquad} \\ \log \text{ difference} &= \end{aligned}$$

answer = antilog difference =

$$\log 45{,}000 = 4.6532$$
$$\log \quad 1{,}500 = \underline{3.1761}$$
$$\log \text{ difference} = \overline{1.4771}$$

answer = antilog 1.4771 = 30.0

example 30–32 Determine using logarithms, the value of

$$R = \frac{(4)(28.6)(153)}{(32)(0.054)(17.6)}$$

The products of the numerator and denominator will first be obtained.

numerator:
$$\log 4 = 0.6021$$
$$\log 28.6 = 1.4564$$
$$\log 153 = \underline{2.1847}$$
$$\log \text{ of sum} = \overline{4.2432}$$

denominator:
$$\log 32 = \quad 1.5051$$
$$\log 0.054 = \quad 8.7324 - 10$$
$$\log 17.6 = \quad \underline{1.2455}$$
$$\log \text{ of sum} = \overline{11.4830 - 10} \quad \text{or} \quad 1.4830$$

Then

$$\log \text{ numerator} = 4.2432$$
$$\log \text{ denominator} = \underline{1.4830}$$
$$\log \text{ difference} = \overline{2.7602}$$

$$0.7597 = \text{mantissa of log } 575$$
$$\underline{0.7604} = \text{mantissa of log } \underline{576}$$
$$\overline{0.0007} \quad \text{difference} \qquad \overline{1}$$

Mantissa of answer 0.0005 above mantissa log 575 or

$$\frac{0.0005}{0.0007} \times 1 = 0.714 \text{ or } 575.714 \text{ rounded off to } 575.7.$$

Then antilog 2.7602 = 575.7, and R = 575.7

Falling under division is the reciprocal relationship of the *cologarithm*. The cologarithm is the logarithm of the reciprocal of a number. This cologarithm is normally shortened to *colog*.

From our definition, we may write, for a number *N*,

$$\text{colog } N = \log \frac{1}{N} \tag{25}$$

From our division relationships, we may write

$$\text{colog } N = \log 1 - \log N \qquad (26)$$

As the log $1 = 0$, we then have

$$\boxed{\text{colog } N = \log \frac{1}{N} = 0 - \log N}$$

The negative sign for the log N, and the resultant effect on the characteristic and the mantissa, is avoided by considering

$$0 = 10.0000 - 10$$

We then have a subtraction from zero which may be logically performed, as shown in the following examples.

example 30-33 Determine the colog 67.3.

solution: colog $67.3 = \log 1 - \log 67.3$

As log $1 = 0$ and $0 = 10.000 - 10$, we have

$$\begin{array}{ll} \log 1 = 0 = & 10.0000 - 10 \\ \log 67.3 = & \underline{1.8280} \\ \text{colog } 67.3 = & 8.1720 - 10 \end{array}$$

It is seen that the colog may be used when combined multiplications and divisions are required, as in Example 30-31.

example 30-34 Complete Example 30-32 using cologs where possible.

solution: This problem could be set up as:

$$R = (4)(28.6)(153) \times \frac{1}{32} \times \frac{1}{0.054} \times \frac{1}{17.6}$$

$$= \log 4 + \log 28.6 + \log 153 + \text{colog } 32$$

$$+ \text{colog } 0.054 + \text{colog } 17.6$$

$$\begin{array}{ll} & 10.0000 - 10 \\ & \underline{1.5051} \\ \text{colog } 32 = & 8.4949 - 10 \end{array}$$

$$\begin{array}{ll} & 10.0000 - 10 \\ & \underline{8.7324 - 10} \\ \text{colog } 0.054 = & 1.2676 \end{array}$$

$$\text{colog } 17.6 = \dfrac{\begin{array}{r} 10.0000 - 10 \\ 1.2455 \\ \hline 8.7545 - 10 \end{array}}{}$$

We may then solve as

$$R = 0.6021 + 1.4564 + 2.1847 + 8.4949 - 10 + 1.2676$$
$$+ 8.7545 - 10 = 22.7602 - 20 \quad \text{or} \quad 2.7602$$

Then antilog $2.7602 = 575.7$, which is the same as Example 30–32.

EXERCISE 30–5   Solve the following, using logarithms.

1. 3×23
2. 16×37
3. 121×52
4. 362×428
5. 0.567×325
6. 0.056×0.527
7. $3.56 \times -3.2 \times 10^6$
8. $6.25 \times 10^8 \times 4.25 \times 10^6$
9. 1.528×-3.67
10. $132.6 \times 15.7 \times 321.2$
11. $\dfrac{36.2}{57.8}$
12. $\dfrac{3}{0.278}$
13. $\dfrac{16.56}{32.4}$
14. $\dfrac{156.7}{0.328}$
15. $\dfrac{1.62 \times 10^5}{3.56 \times 10^8}$
16. $\dfrac{-16.75}{527.2}$
17. $\dfrac{35 \times 10^{-2}}{4.72 \times 10^4}$
18. $\dfrac{16 \times 27.2 \times 21.3}{12.7 \times 36.1}$

Determine the cologarithms of the following.

19. 56.2
20. 78.15
21. 15.28
22. 35.45
23. 24.21
24. 156.17

30–11 EXPONENTIAL OPERATIONS USING LOGARITHMS

In our work in this chapter with exponents, it was seen that

$$\boxed{\log a^m = m \log a}$$

The solution of this type of procedure is shown in the following examples.

555

Sec. 30–11
EXPONENTIAL
OPERATIONS
USING
LOGARITHMS

example 30–35 Using logarithms, solve 15^3.

solution: As $\log 15^3 = 3 \log 15$, we may write

$3 \times 1.1761 = 3.5283$

$\dfrac{\begin{array}{l} 0.5276 = \text{mantissa log } 3{,}370 \\ 0.5289 = \text{mantissa log } 3{,}380 \end{array}}{0.0013 \quad \text{difference} \qquad 10}$

mantissa of answers, $0.5283 - 0.5276 = 0.0007$ above mantissa log 3,370

$\dfrac{0.0007}{0.0013} \times 10 = 5.38$ or

$3{,}370 + 5.38 = 3{,}375.38$ or $3{,}375$

Then

$15^3 = 3{,}375$

example 30–36 Using logarithms, solve 6^4.

solution: As $\log 6^4 = 4 \log 6$, we have $4 \times 0.7782 = 3.1128$.

$\dfrac{\begin{array}{l} 0.1106 = \text{mantissa log } 1{,}290 \\ 0.1139 = \text{mantissa log } 1{,}300 \end{array}}{0.0033 \quad \text{difference} \qquad 10}$

mantissa of answer, $0.1128 - 0.1106 = 0.0022$ above log 1,290

$\dfrac{0.0022}{0.0033} \times 10 = 6.6$ or

$1{,}290 + 6.66 = 1{,}296.66 = 1{,}297$

Then

$6^4 = 1{,}297$

example 30–37 Using logarithms, solve $(16)^3$.

$\log (16)^3 = 3 \log 16 = 3 \times 1.2041 = 3.6123$

$\dfrac{\begin{array}{l} 0.6117 = \text{mantissa log } 4{,}090 \\ 0.6128 = \text{mantissa log } 4{,}100 \end{array}}{0.0009 \quad \text{difference} \qquad 10}$

mantissa of answer $= 0.6123 - 0.6117 = 0.0006$ above
mantissa log 4,090   or

$$\frac{0.0006}{0.0009} \times 10 = 6.66 \quad \text{or}$$

$4,090 + 6.66 = 4,096.66$ or, rounded off,

$(16)^3 = 4,097$

example 30–38 Using logarithms, solve $(0.352)^2$.

solution: $\log (0.352)^2 = 2 \log (0.352) = 2 \times 9.5465 - 10$

$$= 19.0930 - 20$$

$$= 9.0930 - 10$$

$0.0899 =$ mantissa log 0.123
$0.0934 =$ mantissa log $\rbrace$ 0.124
$\overline{0.0035}$ difference $\int$ $\overline{0.001}$

mantissa of answer $= 0.0930 - 0.0899 = 0.0031$ above
mantissa log 0.123 or

$$\frac{0.0031}{0.0035} \times 0.001 = 0.0088 \quad \text{or}$$

$0.123 + 0.00088 = 0.12388$ or, rounded off,

$(0.352)^2 = 0.1239$

In our work with exponents it was also shown that

$$\sqrt[n]{a} = a \tag{27}$$

Using logarithms we may write

$$\boxed{\log a^{\frac{1}{n}} = \frac{1}{n} \log a} \tag{28}$$

This procedure is shown in the following examples.

example 30–39 Using logarithms, solve $\sqrt[4]{81}$

solution: $\log 81^{\frac{1}{4}} = \frac{1}{4} \log 81$

$$= \frac{1}{4} \times 1.9085$$

$$= 0.4771$$

antilog $0.4771 = 3$

557

Sec. 30–11
EXPONENTIAL
OPERATIONS
USING
LOGARITHMS

example 30–40   Using logarithms, solve $\sqrt[3]{15.6}$.

solution: $\log 15.6^{\frac{1}{3}} = \frac{1}{3} \log 15.6 = \frac{1}{3} \times 1.1931 = 0.3977$

$0.3962 = $ mantissa $\log 2.49$
$\underline{0.3979} = $ mantissa $\log \underline{2.50}$
$\overline{0.0017}$ difference $\overline{0.01}$

mantissa of answer, $0.3977 - 0.3962 = 0.0015$ above
mantissa $\log 2.49$

$\dfrac{0.0015}{0.0017} \times 0.01 = 0.0088$ or

$2.49 + 0.0088 = 2.4988$ or, rounded off

$\sqrt[3]{15.6} = 2.499$

Fractional exponents are handled in the same manner as with root extraction. Remember that

$$\sqrt[n]{a} = a^{\frac{1}{n}} \tag{29}$$

and that

$$\sqrt[n]{a^m} = a^{\frac{m}{n}} \tag{30}$$

Then we have

$$\log a^{\frac{1}{n}} = \frac{1}{n} \log a \quad \text{and} \quad \log a^{\frac{m}{n}} = \frac{m}{n} \log a$$

The solution of this type of problem using logarithms may be handled in two different ways. For example, if $m = 6$ and $n = 2$, we may write

$$a^{\frac{m}{n}} = a^{\frac{6}{2}}$$

This may be solved as

$$\frac{6 \log a}{2} \quad \text{or} \quad 3 \log a$$

The answer will, of course, be the same. In certain instances one method of solution may be preferable to the other.

EXERCISE 30-6 Solve the following using logarithms.

1. 12^5

2. 3.25^6

3. 1.78^3

4. 4.62^4

5. 0.378^5

6. 1.212^3

7. 3.6^2

8. 1.718^3

9. $\sqrt[3]{156.2}$

10. $\sqrt[4]{36.98}$

11. $\sqrt[5]{3.656}$

12. $17.87^{\frac{1}{4}}$

13. $67.28^{\frac{3}{4}}$

14. $\sqrt[4]{17.28^2}$

30-12 LOGARITHMIC COMPUTATIONS

In the work we have performed with logarithms, we have used logarithms to obtain an arithmetic solution to a problem. Often we will be faced with the use of logarithms in mathematical operations that are not part of a numerical solution to a problem. Such situations are demonstrated in the following examples.

In Section 30-8 and Example 30-26, we were asked to use logarithms to obtain the product of 12×11. This was found as

$$\begin{array}{r} \log 12 = 1.0792 \\ \log 11 = 1.0414 \\ \hline \log \text{ of sum} = 2.1206 \end{array}$$

answer = antilog of sum = 132

An entirely different operation is required in the following example.

example 30-41 Compute $\log 12 + \log 11$.

solution: $\log 12 + \log 11 = 1.0792 + 1.0414 = 2.1206$

This is the solution to the problem. There is no requirement for obtaining the antilog and a numerical evaluation.

example 30-42 Compute $(\log 12)(\log 11)$.

solution: This may be solved as

$(\log 12)(\log 11) = (1.0792)(1.0414) = 1.1239$

In this solution we have taken the logarithm of 12 and the logarithm of 11 and found the product.

Another solution, which would result in the same answer, would be to perform the multiplication by the conventional means of adding logarithms, interpolation if required, and evaluation using the antilogarithm. This is shown as

(log 12)(log 11) = (1.0792)(1.0414)

Then

log 1.0792 = 0.0330
log 1.0414 = 0.0174
log sum   = 0.0504

antilog 0.0504 = 1.1239

The important thing to remember is that the solution to a problem be correctly interpreted and completed as required. One problem may require the use of logarithms to obtain an arithmetic solution. Other problems only require operations with logarithms, with no numerical evaluation required.

30–13 CHANGE OF BASE

In our basic work with logarithms in this chapter, we used logarithms with several bases. Often in our electronics work we will find it necessary to use logarithms with a base other than 10.

We shall frequently use logarithms to the base$_e$, the natural system of logarithms, in our work. While logarithm tables to the base$_e$ are available, we may convert logarithms to the base$_{10}$ to logarithms to the base$_e$ directly. Logarithms to the base$_{10}$ may also be directly converted to any other base in a similar manner. This is shown as follows. From Section 30–1, we have $a^x = N$, and

$$\log_a N = x \tag{31}$$

We may take the logarithm of any base, for example base b, of both sides of this equation as

$$\log_b N = \log_b a^x \tag{32}$$
$$\log_b N = x \log_b a \tag{33}$$

The substitution of Equation (31) into (33) produces

$$\boxed{\log_b N = \log_a N \log_b a}$$

However, since

$$\log_b a = \frac{1}{\log_a b} \tag{34}$$

we have

$$\log_a N = \frac{\log_b N}{\log_b A} \tag{35}$$

Converting from the base 10 to any other base x, (35) becomes

$$\boxed{\log_x N = \frac{\log_{10} N}{\log_{10} X}}$$

The most common conversion is to the base e, which has as its base, 2.71828. Substitution in the equation above produces

$$\log_e N = \frac{1}{\log_{10} e} \log_{10} N$$

$$= \frac{1}{\log_{10} 2.71828} \log_{10} N$$

$$= \frac{1}{0.4343} \log_{10} N$$

or

$$\boxed{\log_e N = 2.3026 \log_{10} N} \tag{36}$$

The following examples show changes of base.

example 30–43 Determine $\log_{12} 86$.

solution: $\log_{12} 86 = \dfrac{\log_{10} 86}{\log_{10} 12} = \dfrac{1.9345}{1.0792} = 1.7925$

example 30–44 Determine $\log_e 512$.

solution: $\log_e 512 = 2.3026 \log_{10} 512 = 2.3026 \times 2.7093$

$$= 6.2383$$

The *exponential equation* is one in which the unknown is the exponent:

$$6^x = 475$$

Taking logarithms of both sides of the equation will not change the equality of the equation. The equation then becomes a *logarithmic equation* whose solution is shown in the following examples.

example 30–45   Determine the value of the exponent x in the equation $6^x = 475$.

solution: Taking the log of both sides results in

$$\log 6^x = \log 475,$$

which may be written

$$x \log 6 = \log 475$$

Then

$$x = \frac{\log 475}{\log 6} = \frac{2.6767}{0.7781} = 3.44$$

example 30–46   Determine the value of the exponent t in the equation $1.5^t = 3.67$.

solution: $t \log 1.5 = \log 3.67$

$$t = \frac{\log 3.67}{\log 1.5} = \frac{0.5647}{0.1761} = 3.21$$

Logarithmic equations may take other forms, as shown in the following examples. In this form the logarithm of the unknown must be determined.

example 30–47   Solve $4.23 + \log x = 6.75$.

solution: Transposing, the equation may be written

$$\log x = 6.75 - 4.23$$
$$= 2.52$$
$$x = 311$$

example 30–48 Solve $3 \log x - 3.567 = 4.651$.

solution: Transposing, $3 \log x = 4.651 + 3.567$,

$$3 \log x = 8.218$$

$$\log x = 2.7393$$

$$x = 548.6$$

EXERCISE 30–7 Compute the following.

1. $(\log 56.2)(\log 22.1)$

2. $(\log 156)(\log 28.7)$

3. $(\log 1.56)(\log 3.87)$

4. $(\log 232)(\log 356)$

5. Determine $\log_e 35.2$.

6. Determine $\log_6 36.2$.

7. Determine $\log_8 157.2$.

8. Determine the value of x in $15^x = 376.2$.

9. What is the value of y in $3^y = 15.78$?

10. Determine the value of z in $12^z = 136.52$.

11. Solve the equation

$$5 \log x + 3.74 = 2 \log x + 5.62$$

12. Solve the equation

$$3 \log z - 1.52 = \log z$$

13. Solve the equation

$$3 \log y + 127.2 = \log y + 129.1$$

31

APPLICATIONS OF LOGARITHMS

Logarithms have many applications in electronics as well as in the physical world around us. In this chapter, we shall explore a few of these applications. We shall examine the use of logarithmic ratios as a means of measuring such quantities as sound levels, power gain, and power loss. We shall touch briefly on the use of the slide rule, with its logarithmic scales, which has been of such great value to technicians and engineers in the past.

31–1 THE DECIBEL

It has been established experimentally that the responses of our eyes and ears to changes in light and sound can be expressed as logarithmic ratios. Our physical evaluation of such quantities is related to the relative levels of the quantities involved. Our eyes and ears are continually evaluating light and sound levels. The level of light intensity that exists at the present instant is compared to the level that existed in the previous instant. Similarly, sound levels are continually being compared and evaluated by our ears.

A single candle brought into a darkened room would represent a substantial change of light levels to the eye. However, bringing a second candle into the room would not represent as substantial a change in light levels as did the first.

In a similar way our ears evaluate sound levels. A pencil dropped to the floor in a quiet library represents a substantial change in sound levels to our ears. The same pencil dropped to the floor of a busy cafeteria might not even be noticed.

In effect, then, our eyes and our ears respond to a relationship between sound or light levels—more accurately, the ratio of levels. The eye evaluates as equal, changes in light intensity that are of the same ratio. Similarly, the ear evaluates as equal, changes in sound intensity of the same ratio.

It has been established experimentally that in order to be detected by the ear, a change of about 25 percent in sound levels is required. This would mean that a 100-W sound amplifier would have to have its output increased to 125 W or decreased from 100 W to 75 W in order for the change to be detected by the ear. An amplifier with a 10 W output would require only an increase in power to 12.5 W or a decrease from 10 W to 7.5 W to have this change detected by the ear. The ratios of the changes from 100 to 125 W and from 10 to 12.5 W are seen to be the same:

$$\frac{125}{100} = \frac{12.5}{10} = 1.25$$

The changes in sound level reflected by these ratios are equal on a logarithmic scale. That is, logarithms of equal ratios are equal. As seen above, this does not depend on the levels of the quantities, only on the ratios:

$$\log \frac{125}{100} = \log \frac{12.5}{10} = \log \frac{1.25}{1} = \log \frac{12,500}{10,000} = \ldots$$

Thus our ears, and our eyes as well, consider as equal, changes of equal logarithmic quantities, regardless of the relative levels involved.

The comparison of sound amplifiers used above to demonstrate the response of the human ear to sound levels had their output measured in watts. It follows, then, that if the ear considers as equal, changes of equal logarithmic values that are dependent on the amplifier output power, then a similar logarithmic ratio exists in the amplifier output power ratio. This unit of measurement was named the "bel" after the telephone pioneer, Alexander Graham Bell. The *bel* is defined as

$$\text{bel (B)} = \log \frac{P_2}{P_1}$$

where P_1 is the initial or input power level and P_2 is the final or output power level. This is seen to be the logarithm of a ratio, and therefore the units of P_1 and P_2 do not matter as long as they are the same.

In practice, the bel was found to be too large to measure the rather small quantities encountered in most applications. This led to the designation of the decibel, one-tenth of a bel. This is defined as

$$\text{decibel (dB)} = 10 \log \frac{P_2}{P_1}$$

In the relationship above, if the value of the output power level, P_2, is smaller than the input power level, P_1, a power loss is represented.

It is common practice to obtain the ratio of the larger value of power divided by the smaller value. The purpose of this is to obtain a ratio value greater than 1 rather than go through the procedure of working with a negative characteristic. When a loss is indicated by $P_1 > P_2$, the power ratio is obtained by dividing P_1 by P_2 and designating the result in decibels, as negative.

example 31–1 The output of an amplifier is 125 W and the input is 22 W. What is the gain, in dB?

---

solution: $\quad \text{dB} = 10 \log \dfrac{P_2}{P_1} = 10 \log \dfrac{125}{22} = 10 \log 5.68$

$$= 10 \times 0.754 = 7.54 \quad \text{gain}$$

example 31–2 The input to a network connecting two transistor amplifiers has a power level of 1.52 mW and the output has a power level of 1.24 mW. What is the power loss, in dB?

solution: In this problem, $P_1 > P_2$. As a result,

$$dB = 10 \log \frac{P_1}{P_2} = -10 \log \frac{1.52}{1.24} = -10 \log 1.22$$

$$= -10 \times 0.086$$

$$= -0.86 \quad \text{power loss}$$

Inasmuch as the power of a circuit depends on the circuit voltage, current, and resistance, dB relationships may be developed involving these quantities. From our previous work, we know that

$$P = I^2 R \tag{1}$$

$$P = \frac{E^2}{R} \tag{2}$$

Substituting Equation (1) in the dB equation, we may write

$$dB = 10 \log \frac{P_2}{P_1} = 10 \log \frac{I_2^2 R_2}{I_1^2 R_1}$$

$$= 20 \log \frac{I_2}{I_1} + 10 \log \frac{R_2}{R_1} \tag{3}$$

In Equation (3) if $R_1 = R_2$, then $\frac{R_2}{R_1} = 1$, and as $\log 1 = 0$, the second term cancels and we have

$$dB = 20 \log \frac{I_2}{I_1} \quad \text{(when } R_2 = R_1\text{)} \tag{4}$$

Substituting Equation (2) in the dB equation, we have

$$dB = 10 \log \frac{P_2}{P_1} = 10 \log \frac{\dfrac{E_2^2}{R_2}}{\dfrac{E_1^2}{R_1}} = 10 \log \left(\frac{E_2}{E_1}\right)^2 \frac{R_1}{R_2}$$

$$= 20 \log \frac{E_2}{E_1} + 10 \log \frac{R_1}{R_2} \tag{5}$$

If $R_1 = R_2$, then $\frac{R_1}{R_2} = 1$ and $\log 1 = 0$, and

$$dB = 20 \log \frac{E_2}{E_1} \quad \text{(when } R_1 = R_2 \text{)} \tag{6}$$

example 31–3 A transistor amplifier has an input resistance of 30 Ω and an output resistance of 1,800 Ω. The input current is found to be 3.2 mA and the output current is 15.5 mA. Determine the input and output power. Calculate the dB power gain by two methods.

solution:

$$P_1 = I_1{}^2 R_1 = (3.2 \times 10^{-3})^2(30) = (10.24 \times 10^{-6})(30)$$

$$= 0.307 \text{ mW}$$

$$P_2 = I_2{}^2 R_2 = (15.5 \times 10^{-3})^2(1.8 \times 10^3)$$

$$= (240.3 \times 10^{-6})(1.8 \times 10^3) = 432.5 \text{ mW}$$

$$dB = 10 \log \frac{P_2}{P_1} = 10 \log \frac{432.5}{0.307}$$

$$= 10 \log 1408.8 \quad = \quad 10 \times 3.148$$

$$= 31.48 \quad \text{power gain}$$

Using the current and resistances in Equation (3) we have

$$dB = 20 \log \frac{I_2}{I_1} + 10 \log \frac{R_2}{R_1}$$

$$= 20 \log \frac{15.5}{3.2} + 10 \log \frac{1,800}{30}$$

$$= 20 \log 4.84 + 10 \log 60$$

$$= 20 \times 0.685 + 10 \times 1.778$$

$$= 13.7 + 17.78$$

$$= 31.48 \quad \text{power gain}$$

example 31–4 A solid-state amplifier has an input resistance of 320 Ω and an output resistance of 1,850 Ω. The voltage measured at the input was 1.26 V and at the output 187.2 V. Determine the input and output power and the dB gain by two methods.

solution:

$$P_1 = \frac{E_1{}^2}{R_1} = \frac{(1.26)^2}{320} = \frac{1.587}{320} = 4.95 \text{ mW}$$

$$P_2 = \frac{E_2{}^2}{R_2} = \frac{(187.2)^2}{1,850} = \frac{35,043.8}{1,850} = 18,924.6 \text{ mW}$$

$$\text{dB} = 10 \log \frac{P_2}{P_1} = 10 \log \frac{18{,}924.6}{4.95}$$

$$= 10 \log 3{,}823.1 = 10 \times 3.582$$

$$= 35.82 \quad \text{power gain}$$

Using Equation (5),

$$\text{dB} = 20 \log \frac{E_2}{E_1} + 10 \log \frac{R_1}{R_2}$$

$$\text{dB} = 20 \log \frac{187.2}{1.26} + 10 \log \frac{320}{1{,}850}$$

Note that the ratio $\dfrac{R_1}{R_2}$ will result in a quotient less than 1, with the need for a negative characteristic. To avoid this, we will use the ratio $\dfrac{R_2}{R_1}$ and consider this term to represent a dB loss.

$$\text{dB} = 20 \log \frac{187.2}{1.26} - 10 \log \frac{1{,}850}{320}$$

$$= 20 \log 148.6 - 10 \log 5.781$$

$$= 20 \times 2.172 - 10 \times 0.7620$$

$$= 43.44 - 7.62$$

$$= 35.82 \quad \text{power gain}$$

example 31–5 A network is used to connect two transistor amplifiers. It has a loss of 12.6 dB. Determine the power ratio represented by this loss. If the input power to the network is 34.8 mW, what is the output power?

solution: As such a network results in a power loss, the input power $P_1 > P_2$. Considering the 12.6 dB positive for purposes of calculation, we write

$$12.6 \text{ dB} = 10 \log \frac{P_1}{P_2}$$

$$\log \frac{P_1}{P_2} = \frac{12.6}{10} = 1.26$$

Taking the antilog of both sides produces

$$\frac{P_1}{P_2} = 18.2$$

As $P_1 = 34.8$ mW,

$$P_2 = \frac{P_1}{18.2} = \frac{34.8}{18.2} = 1.91 \text{ mW}$$

example 31–6 An electronic network has an input current of 3.7 mA and an output current of 2.9 mA. The input and output resistances are equal. Determine the power ratio in dB. Is this a loss or a gain?

solution: As the input current is greater than the output current, with the input resistance and the output resistances equal, a power loss is represented.

With $R_1 = R_2$,

$$dB = 20 \log \frac{I_2}{I_1}$$

With $I_1 > I_2$,

$$dB = 20 \log \frac{I_1}{I_2} = 20 \log \frac{3.7}{2.9}$$

$$= 20 \log 1.27$$

$$= 20 \times 0.104$$

$$= -2.08 \quad \text{power loss}$$

example 31–7 An amplifier has a power gain of 38.2 dB. What is the output power if the input power is equal to 1.32 mW?

solution: $$dB = 10 \log \frac{P_2}{P_1}$$

$$38.2 = 10 \log \frac{P_2}{P_1}$$

$$3.82 = \log \frac{P_2}{P_1}$$

The antilog of both sides produces

$$6{,}610 = \frac{P_2}{P_1} = \text{power ratio}$$

As $P_1 = 1.32$ mW,

$$P_2 = 6{,}610 P_1 = 6{,}610 \times 1.32$$
$$= 8{,}725 \text{ mW}$$

31-2 REFERENCE LEVELS

The decibel represents a ratio of power levels. In our previous examples, the dB gain or loss of a device was calculated using the input and output power. A zero value of input or output power was not used as a reference, for this would result in a power ratio of zero or infinity. The use of decibels permits the user to choose his own reference level. This flexible relationship does create some problems when large organizations or industries are involved. As a result, several levels have been established and are in general use.

In the telephone and electronics field, reference levels of 1 mW and 6 mW are commonly used. A dB gain or loss is referred to the particular reference level used. This permits the output power to be quickly established. This is shown in the following examples.

example 31-8 An amplifier has a gain of 32 dB. The reference level is 1 mW, often designated dB_m. What is the output power?

solution:

$$dB_m = 10 \log \frac{P_2}{P_1}$$

$$32 = 10 \log \frac{P_2}{1 \text{ mW}}$$

$$3.2 = \log \frac{P_2}{1 \text{ mW}}$$

Taking the antilog of each side,

$$1{,}585 = \frac{P_2}{1 \text{ mW}}$$

$$P_2 = 1{,}585 \times 1 = 1{,}585 \text{ mW}$$

example 31-9 An amplifier has a gain of 19.6 dB. The reference level is 6 mW. What is the output power?

solution:

$$dB = 10 \log \frac{P_2}{P_1}$$

$$19.6 = 10 \log \frac{P_2}{6}$$

Taking the antilog of each side,

$$1.96 = \log \frac{P_2}{6}$$

$$91.2 = \frac{P_2}{6}$$

$$P_2 = 91.2 \times 6 = 547.2 \text{ mW}$$

example 31–10 Determine the power loss that is represented by −16.2 dB. The reference level is 1 mW.

solution:

$$-dB_m = 10 \log \frac{P_2}{P_1}$$

As a power loss is represented, the reference level power, P_1, will be greater than P_2. To avoid a negative characteristic, the ratio is reversed. We then have

$$dB_m = 10 \log \frac{P_1}{P_2}$$

$$16.2 = 10 \log \frac{1}{P_2}$$

$$1.62 = \log \frac{1}{P_2}$$

Taking the antilog of each side,

$$41.7 = \frac{1}{P_2}$$

$$P_2 = \frac{1}{41.7} = 0.024 \text{ mW}$$

31–3 SYSTEM GAIN CALCULATIONS

The overall gain of an electronic system composed of several stages in cascade is the product of the gains of the individual stages. The losses, expressed as a value less than 1, would be introduced as one or more factors of the product.

The use of power gains or losses, expressed in decibels, eliminates the multiplication process. The total gain is found by determining the algebraic sum of the gains and losses expressed in decibels. This is expressed as

$$dB_T = dB_1 + dB_2 + dB_3 + \ldots$$

example 31–11 Stage 1 of a three-stage amplifier has a gain of 12.8 dB; stage 2, a 14.7-dB gain; and stage 3, a 21.8-dB gain. The connecting network between stages 1 and 2 has a −1.4-dB loss; the network between stages 2 and 3 has a −0.96-dB loss. What is the overall gain of the system?

solution: $dB_T = 12.8 - 1.4 + 14.7 - 0.96 + 21.8$

$$= 46.94 \quad \text{gain}$$

EXERCISE 31–1

1. Determine the gain, in dB, of a transistor amplifier whose input is 3.25 W and output is 56.7 W.

2. What is the dB gain of an amplifier whose input is 56.2 mW and output is 15.6 W?

3. A network connecting two amplifiers has an input of 35.2 mW and an output of 31.7 mW. What is the power loss, in dB?

4. A transistor amplifier has an input resistance of 152 Ω and an output resistance of 2,500 Ω. The input current is 1.62 mA and the output current is 12.3 mA. Determine the input and output power and the dB gain.

5. A solid-state amplifier has $R_1 = 186$ Ω and $R_2 = 1,287$ Ω. The input voltage was found to be 3.78 V and the output voltage was measured as 89.6 V. Determine the input and output power. What is the dB gain?

6. A network between two amplifiers has a loss of −2.5 dB. What is the power ratio represented by this loss? If the input power is 5.28 mW, what is the output power?

7. A network between two amplifiers has an input current of 1.54 μA and an output current of 1.36 μA. Determine the dB loss if the input and output resistances are equal.

8. An amplifier has a gain of 12.6 dB. What is the input power if the output power is 3.2 mW?

9. A connecting network between transistors has a dB loss of −1.16 dB. What is the output power if the input power is 1.45 mW?

10. An amplifier has a 18.9-dB gain with a 1-mW reference level. What is the output power?

11. An amplifier has a 22.8-dB gain with a 6-mW reference level. What is the output power?

12. An amplifier system has four amplifier stages, with gains of 15.2 dB, 19.6 dB, 37.4 dB, and 52.8 dB. The coupling network between stages 1 and 2 has a -1.54-dB loss, the network between stages 2 and 3 has a -2.6-dB loss, and the network between stages 3 and 4 has a -3.2-dB loss. What is the overall system gain?

31–4 DECIBEL MEASUREMENTS

Commercial multimeters normally have a decibel scale. This permits the decibel value to be measured directly. The measurements made using these meters are in ac voltage. It is necessary, then, to have the ac voltage readings related to decibels. For this purpose, a measurement reference level, 0 dB, must be established. Most of the commercial meters use 1 mW for this purpose. A resistance of 600 Ω is also specified at this reference level. The 0–2.5-V range is often used for measurement purposes. On this scale, the voltage reading for the 0-dB reference is calculated as

$$P = \frac{E^2}{R}, \qquad PR = E^2, \qquad E = \sqrt{PR}$$

As the value for P is 1 mW and R is 600 Ω, we calculate

$$E = \sqrt{(1 \times 10^{-3})(600)} = \sqrt{0.6} = 0.775 \text{ V}$$

This means that the 0-db level (1 mW) on the decibel scale would represent 0.775 V on the 0–2.5-V scale.

Once the reference level has been established, the voltage reading for any dB level may be calculated. Similarly, the dB reading for any voltage reading may be determined. In this manner, a dB scale could be developed for a multimeter that did not include this scale. For example, the voltage reading could be determined for the $+5$-dB and -5-dB points as follows.

For $+5$ dB,

$$dB = 10 \log \frac{P_2}{P_1}, \qquad 5 = 10 \log \frac{P_2}{1}$$

$$0.5 = \log \frac{P_2}{1}$$

Taking the antilog of both sides produces

$$3.16 = \frac{P_2}{1}, \qquad P_2 = 3.16 \text{ mW}$$

$$P_2 = \frac{E^2}{R}, \qquad 3.16 \times 10^{-3} = \frac{E^2}{600}$$

$$E^2 = (3.16 \times 10^{-3})(600) = 1.896$$

$$E = 1.37 \text{ V}$$

At -5 dB, as we have a $-$dB, representing a power loss with $P_1 > P_2$, the power ratio is reversed in order to avoid a negative characteristic. We then have

$$\text{dB} = 10 \log \frac{P_1}{P_2}, \qquad 5 = 10 \log \frac{1}{P_2}$$

$$0.5 = \log \frac{1}{P_2}$$

Taking the antilogs of each side produces

$$3.16 = \frac{1}{P_2}, \qquad P_2 = \frac{1}{3.16} = 0.316 \text{ mW}$$

$$P = \frac{E^2}{R}, \qquad 0.316 \times 10^{-3} = \frac{E^2}{600}$$

$$E^2 = (0.316 \times 10^{-3})(600) = 0.1896$$

$$E = 0.435 \text{ V}$$

The voltage for any dB reading could be determined in a similar manner. The dB scale could be thus developed for the 0–2.5-V range. Similar calculations would have to be performed to develop a dB scale for any other voltage range. However, most meters provide a conversion procedure in the form of a factor to be used when measuring dB on other than the specified voltage range. If this is not available, the following procedure may be used. If the 250-V scale were chosen for this purpose, the voltage multiplying factor above the 2.5-V scale would be

$$\frac{250}{2.5} = 100$$

On ·the 2.5-V scale the 1-mW (0-dB) reference was found to be at

0.775 V. The 0-dB point on the 0–2.5-V range would be equivalent to

$$0.775 \times 100 = 77.5 \text{ V} \quad \text{on the 250-V range}$$

However, we found in our previous work with decibels that the decibel represented a power ratio that depended upon the reference level involved. Remember that 25 W was required at a 100-W level to bring about the same dB change that 0.25 W brought about at the 1-W level. In a similar manner, the 0-dB point on the 0–2.5-V meter range will not represent 0 dB on the 0–250-V meter range. The actual dB value for this point may be determined as

$$dB = 20 \log \frac{E_2}{E_1}$$

where

$$E_2 = 77.5 \text{ V} \quad \text{and} \quad E_1 = 0.775$$

$$dB = 20 \log \frac{77.5}{0.775} = 20 \log 100 = (20)(2) = 40$$

This establishes that the 0-dB point on the 0–2.5-V range represents a 40-dB reading when the 0–250-V scale is used. In a similar manner, other equivalent readings could be calculated. This is, fortunately, often unnecessary. As noted, most meters include a conversion factor which establishes quickly and quite accurately the actual dB reading for a particular scale.

31–5 TRANSMISSION-LINE APPLICATIONS

A transmission line is a device whose characteristics are found to vary on a logarithmic basis. As such, they are a suitable device for examination in our study of the application of logarithms.

The transmission line is basically a device to transfer electrical energy from one location to another. It is structured in many forms. One of the common types is the two-wire open-air line. This is often called a *ladder line*, as it consists of two conductors whose parallel position is maintained by equally spaced insulators.

The inductance (in henrys) of this type of transmission line is expressed by the following logarithmic equation:

$$L = l \left(1.48 \log \frac{d}{r} + 0.161 \right) \times 10^{-3} \quad \text{H}$$

where

$l = $ line length, miles

$d = $ conductor spacing, same units as r

$r = $ conductor radius, same units as d

The capacitance (in microfarads) for this type of transmission line is expressed by the following equation:

$$C = \frac{0.0194\, l}{\log \dfrac{d}{r}}\ \mu\text{F}$$

where l, d, and r have the same units as those in the inductance equation above.

The use of these equations is shown in the following example.

example 31–12 Determine the inductance and capacitance of a two-wire open-air transmission line, with $l = 1{,}250$ ft, a wire spacing of 1.5 in, and a wire size of 64 mils.

solution: Converting to required units, we have

$$l = \frac{1{,}250}{5{,}280} = 0.237 \text{ mi}$$

$$64 \text{ mils} = 0.064 \text{ in}, \quad \text{then } r = \frac{0.064}{2} = 0.032 \text{ in}$$

$$L = 0.237\left(1.48 \log \frac{1.5}{0.032} + 0.161\right) \times 10^{-3}$$

$$= 0.237(1.48 \log 46.87 + 0.161) \times 10^{-3}$$

$$= 0.237(1.48 \times 1.671 + 0.161) \times 10^{-3}$$

$$= 0.237(2.47 + 0.161) \times 10^{-3}$$

$$= 0.237 \times 2.63 \times 10^{-3}$$

$$= 0.624 \times 10^{-3} \text{ H} \quad \text{or}$$

$$= 0.624 \text{ mH}$$

The capacitance is calculated as

$$C = \frac{0.0194 \times 0.237}{\log \dfrac{1.5}{0.032}} = \frac{0.00460}{\log 46.87} = \frac{0.00460}{1.671}$$

$$= 0.00275 \ \mu\text{F}$$

The inductance and capacitance of a transmission line varies with the type of line involved. Other types include coaxial line, parallel line with insulation between conductors, as with conventional television lead in line, and multiconductor insulated cable with radial and or concentrically placed conductors.

The inductance and capacitance is also affected by the frequency involved. A transmission line is therefore designed to most effectively carry the electrical energy at the frequencies involved.

The inductance and capacitance equations will vary for the various types of transmission lines used for various frequency ranges. They will be logarithmic equations, however. The procedures and equations used in the solution of the examples above are characteristic of those for other types of transmission lines.

EXERCISE 31–2

1. Calculate the inductance of a two-wire open-air transmission line with a length of 2,200 ft, a wire spacing of 2.2 in, and a wire size of 68 mils.

2. What is the capacitance of the transmission line of problem 1?

3. A two-wire open-air transmission line has a length of 672.5 ft. The wire size is 126 mils and the spacing is 3.16 in. What is the inductance?

4. Calculate the capacitance of the transmission line of problem 3.

5. Determine the inductance of a transmission line of 1,520 ft with a spacing of 1.86 in and a wire size of 0.32 in.

6. What is the capacitance of the transmission line of problem 5?

31–6 THE SLIDE RULE

The slide rule is a mechanical device used for multiplication and division as well as many other mathematical procedures. Prior to the modern hand-held calculators, the technician and the engineer would have been severely handicapped without a slide rule. The modern calculators have all but eliminated the slide rule as an engineering tool. Slide-rule operations involve the applications of logarithms and as such are of interest.

The slide rule has a number of logarithmic scales. The ones principally used are the C and D scales. The D scale is a part of the body of the rule, while the C scale is a part of the movable center slider as shown in Figure 31–1. The rule has a plastic or glass-faced runner with a hairline marker fitted over the body. This is for alignment and accurate indication of readings and settings.

The C and D scales are logarithmic scales. They start with 1 on the left and run to a 1, which we will consider 10, on the right. The

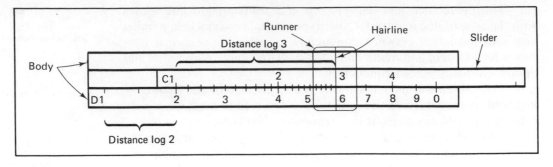

FIGURE 31-1
Slide-Rule Multiplication of 2 by 3

ranges of these scales may be varied to suit our convenience. For example, they may be considered to range from 10 on the left to 100 on the right, or from 0.1 to 1 or 100 to 1,000, and so on. The extremes of the scale are seen to represent, as desired, a variation of a power of 10. Thus we may use the scale to represent a number of any size.

Our work with logarithms established that to multiply 2 by 3 it was necessary to add log 2 and log 3 and take the antilog of the sum. Let us examine this operation on the slide rule. In Figure 31–1, this distance representing log 2 is shown on the D scale. To that distance log 3 is added, using the C scale. The addition of log 2 and log 3 is now shown in this figure. This total is shown by the hairline of the slider, which is over 3 on the C scale. The antilog of this sum is 6, and this value is found under the hairline on the D scale. In effect, then, our slide rule-operation established the logarithms of the two numbers, totaled them, and obtained the antilog of the sum.

The use of logarithms to divide 6 by 2 involved obtaining the antilog of the difference of log 6 minus log 2. Let us see how this operation is performed on the slide rule. It is seen in Figure 31–2 that the distance

FIGURE 31-2
Slide-Rule Division of 6 by 2

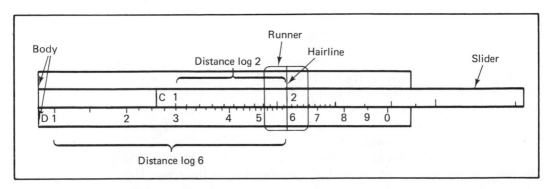

representing log 6 is laid off on the D scale. The distance representing log 2 is subtracted from it by using the hairline to align 2 on the C scale with 6 on the D scale. The distance representing log 2 on the C scale is "folded" back along the distance representing log 6 on the D scale. The result is that under the 1 on the C scale is found the antilog of this difference, or 3. It is seen, then, that the slide-rule operation, in effect, established the logarithms of the two numbers, subtracted them, and provided the antilog of the difference.

The above procedures have provided only a brief glimpse of this extremely valuable instrument. In addition to the above procedures the slide rule is capable of providing logarithms, squares, square roots, reciprocals, and trignometric functions. Also, most slide rules used by engineers and technicians contain a *log-log scale*, which permits the root or power of any number to be obtained, within certain limits. The slide rule is a truly remarkable instrument, as these capabilities will attest. In the hands of a skilled operator, many of the operations of the modern hand calculator can be matched in speed, if not in absolute accuracy, by the slide rule.

32

NUMBER SYSTEMS

The decimal system has been a part of our lives since our first attempts to count on our fingers. The advent of the computer has changed our lives in many ways. Its development has led to the need for additional numbering or counting systems. In this chapter, we shall examine number systems in general and those which are used in computer operations in particular.

The decimal system has been pretty well entrenched in our thinking since early youth. The procedures involved in its use have also been firmly established in our minds over the years. Let us look a little more carefully into the decimal system and how it operates.

The decimal system is based on the digits 0, 1, 2, 3, 4, . . . , 9. The numerical quantities with which we work are formulated with these digits. A number below 10 would require one of these digits. Numbers between 10 and 100 would require two of these digits, three would be needed to express a number between 100 and 1,000, and so on.

In this text, we have spent considerable time using scientific notation. We have become familiar with the process of expressing numbers in powers of 10. As we have seen that numbers between 1 and 1,000,000 may be expressed as

$$1 \times 10^0 = 1$$
$$1 \times 10^1 = 10$$
$$1 \times 10^2 = 100$$
$$1 \times 10^3 = 1,000$$
$$1 \times 10^4 = 10,000$$
$$1 \times 10^5 = 100,000$$
$$1 \times 10^6 = 1,000,000$$

Numbers below 1 may be expressed as

$$1 \times 10^{-1} = 0.1$$
$$1 \times 10^{-2} = 0.01$$
$$1 \times 10^{-3} = 0.001$$
$$1 \times 10^{-4} = 0.0001, \text{ etc.}$$

Using this system, we may consider that a number such as 683 is constructed as

$$6 \times 10^2 = 600$$
$$8 \times 10^1 = 80$$
$$\underline{3 \times 10^0 = 3}$$
$$\text{Number} \quad 683$$

Similarly, the number 0.275 is constructed as

$$2 \times 10^{-1} = 0.2$$
$$7 \times 10^{-2} = 0.07$$
$$\underline{5 \times 10^{-3} = 0.005}$$
$$\text{Number} \quad 0.275$$

Understanding these procedures will assist us in the development of other number systems.

32–2 THE BINARY SYSTEM

In the decimal system a base or radix of 10 was used. In Section 32–1, it was shown how the "weight" of the position of the digits was established using the powers of 10. In effect, though, years before we ever heard of the powers of 10, we assigned "weights" to numbers by virtue of their position. For example, in the number 1,286 we "weighted" the individual numbers by its position:

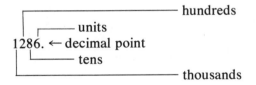

When we consider our decimal number system on this basis, it becomes apparent that there is no reason why a number system of any radix or base cannot be developed.

In electronics, switches are often used. These devices may be considered *binary* in nature, in that they have *two* operating positions, on and off. In a similar manner, certain electronics devices, such as diodes, are also binary in their operations. That is, they may be conducting current, on, or nonconducting, off. The digital computer uses hundreds of thousands of such devices.

If we were to use a decimal number system based on 10 with its 10 digits, the computer and its counting operations would become quite complex. This would result from the necessity for each digit, in each weight position, to have circuit arrangements to designate each separate digit. However, if we used a binary number system, with a base or radix of 2, our computer circuits would be greatly simplified.

A binary number system, which has a base of 2, uses a system of *powers of 2* to designate the weight of each position in the number. Using a similar arrangement as that used previously for powers of 10, we may represent powers of 2 as

$$2^0 = 1$$

$$2^1 = 2$$

$$2^2 = 4$$

$$2^3 = 8$$

$$2^4 = 16$$

$$2^5 = 32$$

$$2^6 = 64$$

$$2^7 = 128$$

$$2^8 = 256$$

In a similar manner as with powers of 10, powers of 2 may be used to represent any decimal number. For example, the decimal number 22 may be represented in the binary number system as

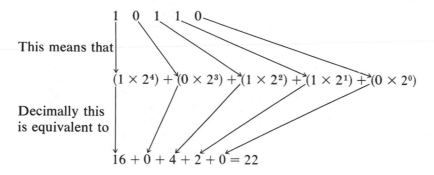

This means that

$$(1 \times 2^4) + (0 \times 2^3) + (1 \times 2^2) + (1 \times 2^1) + (0 \times 2^0)$$

Decimally this is equivalent to

$$16 + 0 + 4 + 2 + 0 = 22$$

In a similar manner, any decimal number may be so represented. For example, 349 in binary would be

1 0 1 0 1 1 1 0 1

This means that

$$(1 \times 2^8) + (0 \times 2^7) + (1 \times 2^6) + (0 \times 2^5) + (1 \times 2^4) + (1 \times 2^3)$$
$$+ (1 \times 2^2) + (0 \times 2^1) + (1 \times 2^0)$$

Decimally, this is equivalent to

$$256 + 0 + 64 + 0 + 16 + 8 + 4 + 0 + 1 = 349$$

In the binary system, then, the position of the 0 or 1 in the binary number represents its weighted value. For example, using the binary number for decimal 349, we show that

$$
\begin{array}{ccccccccc}
 & \overset{2^8}{\ulcorner} & & \overset{2^6}{\ulcorner} & & \overset{2^4}{\ulcorner} & & \overset{2^2}{\ulcorner} & & \overset{2^0}{\ulcorner} \\
1 & 0 & 1 & 0 & 1 & 1 & 1 & 0 & 1 & . \\
 & \underset{2^7}{\llcorner} & & \underset{2^5}{\llcorner} & & \underset{2^3}{\llcorner} & & \underset{2^1}{\llcorner}
\end{array}
$$

$\leftarrow$ binary point

In tabular form, a few binary numbers and their decimal equivalents are shown in Table 32–1. The table shows that decimal numbers from 0 to 15 may be represented in binary by the digits 0 and 1, using four positional locations.

TABLE 32–1 Binary–Decimal Equivalence

BINARY NUMBER	REPRESENTING	DECIMAL NUMBER
0000	$0 \times 2^0 = 0 =$	0
0001	$1 \times 2^0 = 1 =$	1
0010	$1 \times 2^1 = 2 =$	2
0011	$1 \times 2^1 + 1 \times 2^0 = 2 + 1 =$	3
0100	$1 \times 2^2 + 0 \times 2^1 + 0 \times 2^0 = 4 + 0 + 0 =$	4
0101	$1 \times 2^2 + 0 \times 2^1 + 1 \times 2^0 = 4 + 0 + 1 =$	5
0110	$1 \times 2^2 + 1 \times 2^1 + 0 \times 2^0 = 4 + 2 + 0 =$	6
0111	$1 \times 2^2 + 1 \times 2^1 + 1 \times 2^0 = 4 + 2 + 1 =$	7
1000	$1 \times 2^3 + 0 \times 2^2 + 0 \times 2^1 + 0 \times 2^0 = 8 + 0 + 0 + 0 =$	8
1001	$1 \times 2^3 + 0 \times 2^2 + 0 \times 2^1 + 1 \times 2^0 = 8 + 0 + 0 + 1 =$	9
1010	$1 \times 2^3 + 0 \times 2^2 + 1 \times 2^1 + 0 \times 2^0 = 8 + 0 + 2 + 0 =$	10
1011	$1 \times 2^3 + 0 \times 2^2 + 1 \times 2^1 + 1 \times 2^0 = 8 + 0 + 2 + 1 =$	11
1100	$1 \times 2^3 + 1 \times 2^2 + 0 \times 2^1 + 0 \times 2^0 = 8 + 4 + 0 + 0 =$	12
1101	$1 \times 2^3 + 1 \times 2^2 + 0 \times 2^1 + 1 \times 2^0 = 8 + 4 + 0 + 1 =$	13
1110	$1 \times 2^3 + 1 \times 2^2 + 1 \times 2^1 + 0 \times 2^0 = 8 + 4 + 2 + 0 =$	14
1111	$1 \times 2^3 + 1 \times 2^2 + 1 \times 2^1 + 1 \times 2^0 = 8 + 4 + 2 + 1 =$	15

As noted, solid-state diodes exhibit the characteristics of an electrical switch. These two state conditions, on or off, conducting or non-conducting, are ideal for representing numbers in the binary number system. The on, or conducting, condition may be designated as a 1, and the off, or nonconducting condition, may be designated as a 0. Thus we see that with four diodes, each representing a weight by virtue of its positional location, we may represent any number between 1 and

15. It is easy to see, then, that by expanding our table to include higher powers of 2 we can further expand the decimal numbers represented.

The binary number system may also be used to represent decimal fractions. In the decimal system the number 0.875 may be designated as

$$0.875 + (8 \times 10^{-1}) + (7 \times 10^{-2}) + (5 \times 10^{-3})$$

The binary number 0.1110 may be designated as

$$0.1110 = (1 \times 2^{-1}) + (1 \times 2^{-2}) + (1 \times 2^{-3}) + (0 \times 2^{-4})$$

As

$$1 \times 2^{-1} = \frac{1}{2}, \qquad 1 \times 2^{-2} = \frac{1}{4}, \qquad 1 \times 2^{-3} = \frac{1}{16}$$

These weights in decimal numbers are

$$1 \times 2^{-1} = 0.500, \qquad 1 \times 2^{-2} = 0.250, \qquad 1 \times 2^{-3} = 0.125$$

We than see that the binary number 0.1110 represents the decimal number

$$0.500 + 0.250 + 0.125 + 0 = 0.875$$

The examples above show how a decimal fraction is represented in both the decimal and binary systems. In the decimal system, positions to the right of the decimal point establish the weight of digit in each position. In the binary system, the position to the right of the binary point, equivalent to the decimal point in the decimal system, establishes the weight of the digit in each position. On this basis, a binary number may contain digits to the right and left of the binary point. For example, we saw how 101011101 in binary was equivalent to 349 decimal, and 0.1110 in binary was equivalent to 0.875 decimal. These may be combined to form 101011101.1110, which is equivalent to 349.875 decimal. Using similar procedures, any decimal number may be represented in the binary number system.

The process of converting a decimal number to its equivalent binary number requires the repeated *division* of the decimal number by 2. The remainder, 1 or 0, represents the binary digits, with the most significant digit representing the first digit of the binary number, while the last digit is provided by the least significant digit. This procedure is shown for the conversion of 284 decimal to binary:

Remainder

$284 \div 2 = 142$	0	Least-significant digit
$142 \div 2 = 71$	0	
$71 \div 2 = 35$	1	
$35 \div 2 = 17$	1	
$17 \div 2 = 8$	1	
$8 \div 2 = 4$	0	
$4 \div 2 = 2$	0	
$2 \div 2 = 1$	0	read up
$1 \div 2 = 0$	1	Most-significant digit

As noted, the most significant digit represents the first or largest digit in the binary number. Then we may write the binary number, reading up; we have

100011100

which represents 284 decimal. This is the same as writing in powers of 2:

$$(1 \times 2^8) + (0 \times 2^7) + (0 \times 2^6) + (0 \times 2^5) + (1 \times 2^4) + (1 \times 2^3)$$
$$+ (1 \times 2^2) + (0 \times 2^1) + (0 \times 2^0)$$

or

$$256 + 0 + 0 + 0 + 16 + 8 + 4 + 0 + 0 = 284$$

In a similar manner, this simplified procedure may be used to convert fractional decimal numbers to binary. This process requires repeated *multiplication* of the decimal numbers by 2. For each product that produces a 1 to the left of the decimal point, a binary 1 is recorded. For each 0 to the left of the decimal point of each product, a binary 0 is recorded. Each successive product to the right of the decimal point is multiplied by 2, until a zero result is obtained. This procedure is shown for the conversion of decimal 0.6875 to binary:

$$0.6875 \times 2 = 1.3750 \qquad 1 \qquad \text{Most-significant figure}$$

$$0.3750 \times 2 = 0.750 \qquad 0 \qquad \text{read down}$$

$$0.750 \times 2 = 1.500 \qquad 1$$

$$0.500 \times 2 = 1.000 \qquad 1$$

$$0.000 \times 2 = 0.000 \qquad 0 \qquad \text{Least-significant figure}$$

The binary equivalent of decimal 0.6875 is

0.10110

To check, writing in powers of 2, we have

$$0.10110 = (1 \times 2^{-1}) + (0 \times 2^{-2}) + (1 \times 2^{-3}) + (1 \times 2^{-4})$$
$$+ (0 \times 2^{-5})$$

When expressed as decimal numbers, this becomes

$$= \frac{1}{2} + 0 + \frac{1}{8} + \frac{1}{16} + 0$$

$$= 0.500 + 0 + 0.125 + 0.0625 + 0$$

$$= 0.6875$$

Subscripts are often used to designate the base used. For example, 0.10110 is binary with a base 2, while 0.6875 is decimal with a base 10. This is designated

$$0.10110_2 = 0.6875_{10}$$

It should be observed that using only the symbols 0 and 1 greatly simplifies the electronics circuits involved in a digital computer. This procedure is, however, not without cost. For example, the digital number, 349.875, in the example above, 101011101.1110 binary, requires 6 digits decimal and 13 digits binary to represent. The circuit simplification, then, is paid for in terms of the many more digits, called *bits* (from *bi*nary dig*its*). As your work with electronic circuits progresses, the great advantages of such a "trade-off" will become apparent.

EXERCISE 32-1 Convert the following binary numbers to their decimal equivalents.

1.	101	2.	11100
3.	011001	4.	10101
5.	111000	6.	101010
7.	01101	8.	00011

Convert the following decimal numbers to their binary equivalents.

9.	5	10.	62
11.	101	12.	139
13.	256	14.	321
15.	149	16.	220

Convert the following decimal fractions to their binary equivalents.

17.	0.375	18.	0.750
19.	0.09375	20.	0.1875

Convert the following binary fractions to their decimal equivalents.

21.	0.111	22.	0.010
23.	0.1101	24.	0.001

32-3 THE OCTAL SYSTEM

Often used in computer operations is a number system with a base or radix of 8, the *octal system*. As with the base 2 or base 10 number systems, the positional location of digits is based on the radix of the system, in this case powers of 8. In the octal system the symbols used would be 0, 1, 2, 3, . . . , 7. The number 462 in octal is represented as

$$462_8 = (4 \times 8^2) + (6 \times 8^1) + (2 \times 8^0)$$

$$= (4 \times 64) + (6 \times 8) + (2 \times 1)$$

$$= 256 + 48 + 2$$

$$= 306 \text{ decimal} \quad \text{or}$$

$$= 306_{10}$$

EXERCISE 32-2 In the following problems, convert the octal numbers to their decimal equivalents.

1.	16	2.	21
3.	36	4.	65
5.	101	6.	233
7.	432	8.	501

In this chapter, we have examined three number systems—the decimal system, the binary system, and the octal system. The procedures developed have established that a number system may be developed with any base or radix. As a matter of fact, there are many other number systems in current use. For example, in the computer field there is a system with a base or radix of 16, called the *hexadecimal system*. Clothing manufacturers sometimes use a numbering system with a base of 12, because of their involvement with items that are sold and manufactured on a dozen, gross, and great gross basis. All that is required is the need for a particular system. The process of developing such a number system is relatively simple, as we have seen.

A summary of number systems appears in Table 32–2.

TABLE 32–2 Number Systems Compared

DECIMAL	BINARY	OCTAL
0	0	0
1	1	1
2	10	2
3	11	3
4	100	4
5	101	5
6	110	6
7	111	7
8	1000	10
9	1001	11
10	1010	12
11	1011	13
12	1100	14
13	1101	15
14	1110	16
15	1111	17
16	10000	20
17	10001	21
18	10010	22
19	10011	23
20	10100	24

Conversion between systems is a relatively simple process. The procedure usually followed is to first convert the system to its decimal equivalent and then to change from the decimal system to the desired system. This is shown in the following examples.

example 32–1 Convert 220_8 to its binary equivalent.

solution: Initially, we would obtain the decimal equivalent as

$$0 \times 8^0 = 0$$
$$2 \times 8^1 = 16$$
$$2 \times 8^2 = \underline{128}$$
$$144$$

Then

$$220_8 = 144_{10}$$

Converting 144_{10} to its binary equivalent:

Remainder

$$144 \div 2 = 72 \qquad 0$$
$$72 \div 2 = 36 \qquad 0$$
$$36 \div 2 = 18 \qquad 0$$
$$18 \div 2 = 9 \qquad 0$$
$$9 \div 2 = 4 \qquad 1$$
$$4 \div 2 = 2 \qquad 0$$
$$2 \div 2 = 1 \qquad 0$$
$$1 \div 2 = 0 \qquad 1 \qquad \text{read up}$$

$$144_{10} = 10010000_2$$

example 32–2 Convert 100101_2 to its octal equivalent.

solution: Initially, convert the binary to its decimal equivalent:

$$1 \times 2^0 = 1$$
$$0 \times 2^1 = 0$$
$$1 \times 2^2 = 4$$
$$0 \times 2^3 = 0$$
$$0 \times 2^4 = 0$$
$$1 \times 2^5 = \underline{32}$$
$$100101_2 = 37_{10}$$

Converting from decimal to octal is performed in a similar manner to that of converting a decimal number to binary, except that the repeated division is by 8 instead of 2.

Remainder

591

Sec. 32–5
BINARY
ARITHMETIC—
ADDITION

$$37 \div 8 = 4 \qquad 5$$

$$4 \div 8 = 0 \qquad 4 \qquad \text{read up} \uparrow$$

Then

$$45_8 = 37_{10} = 100101_2$$

EXERCISE 32–3   Convert the following numbers to their binary equivalents.

1. 32_8 2. 16_8

3. 25_8 4. 111_8

5. 65_8 6. 132_8

7. 39_8 8. 136_8

Convert the following numbers to their octal equivalents.

9. 1101_2 10. 10111_2

11. 1001_2 12. 10101_2

13. 1000_2 14. 101011_2

15. 11010_2 16. 11101_2

32–5   BINARY ARITHMETIC—ADDITION

Addition in binary numbers is a relatively simple process. There are four basic rules to follow, which apply to addition. These are

$$0 + 0 = 0$$

$$0 + 1 = 1$$

$$1 + 0 = 1$$

$$1 + 1 = 0 \quad \text{with a carry forward of 1}$$

The carry is handled in a similar manner as in the decimal system. The addition procedure is shown in the following examples.

example 32–3   Add 1011011_2 and 110110_2.

solution: Convert to decimal for checking purposes:

$$1011011_2 = 91_{10}, \qquad 110110_2 = 54_{10}$$

Adding,

Binary		Decimal
1011011		91
110110		54
1101101	sum	
1 1	carry	
1001001	sum	
1 1	carry	
10010001	total	145

to check: $(1 \times 2^0) + (1 \times 2^4) + (1 \times 2^7) = 1 + 16 + 128 = 145$

The answer is correct.

example 32–4 Add 1110111_2 and 10001_2.

solution: Convert to decimal for checking purposes:

$$1110111_2 = 119_{10}, \qquad 10001_2 = 17_{10}$$

Adding,

Binary		Decimal
1110111		119
10001		17
1100110	sum	
1 1	carry	
1000100	sum	
1 1	carry	
10001000	total	136

to check: $(1 + 2^3) + (1 \times 2^7) = 8 + 128 = 136$

The answer is correct.

32–6 BINARY ARITHMETIC—SUBTRACTION

Four basic rules apply to the subtraction of binary numbers:

$$0 - 0 = 0$$

$$1 - 0 = 1$$

$$1 - 1 = 0$$

$$0 - 1 = 1 \quad \text{with a borrow of 1}$$

The subtraction of binary numbers is nearly always performed by changing the subtrahend to its complement and adding. The process that we use in our decimal-system subtraction is called the *10's complement*. In this procedure we first form the 9's complement by subtracting each digit of the subtrahend from 9; 1 is then added to this result, which forms the 10's complement. To subtract, we add the minuend and the 10's complement of the subtrahend. From this sum we subtract 1 from the left most digit. This is the answer.

This procedure is shown by subtracting 647 from 1,269. The 9's complement of 647 is first found by subtracting each digit from 9, which produces 352, to which 1 is added as $352 + 1 = 353$, which is the 10's complement of the subtrahend.

Conventional Subtraction   Complementary Subtraction

```
         1269  minuend            1269
        - 647  subtrahend        + 353   10's complement
answer    622  difference         1622
                                   -1
                           answer   622
```

With binary numbers, a similar procedure is used involving the 2's complement. Initially, the 1's complement of the subtrahend is formed by subtracting each binary digit from 1. To this result, 1 is added to form the 2's complement. The minuend and the 2's complement of the subtrahend are added. From this result, 1 is subtracted from the leftmost digit. For instance, to subtract 011011 from 101111, the 1's complement of 11011 is first found:

```
111111
011011    subtrahend
100100    1's complement
    +1
100101    2's complement
```

Adding,

```
101111    minuend
100101    2's complement
001010    sum
1  1 1    carry
1010100   sum
-1
010100    answer
```

To check:

$$101111_2 = 47_{10}$$
$$011011_2 = 27_{10}$$
$$20_{10}, \qquad 010100_2 = 20_{10}$$

The answer is correct.

example 32-5   Subtract 1101 from 10101.

solution: Forming the 1's complement of 1101:

```
  1111
 −1101
  0010   1's complement
   +1
  0011   2's complement
```

Adding,

```
  10101
+  0011   2's complement
  10110   sum
      1   carry
  10100   sum
      1   carry
  11000   sum
 −1
   1000   answer
```

to check: $10101_2 = 21_{10}$
$1101_2 = 13_{10}$
$\dfrac{}{8}$, $\qquad 1000_2 = 8_{10}$

The answer is correct.

example 32-6   Subtract 10001 from 101010.

solution: Forming 1's complement:

```
  11111
  10001
  01110   1's complement
+     1
  01111   2's complement
```

```
  101010
+   1111    2's complement
  100101    sum
    1 1     carry
  111001    sum
 −1
   11001    answer
```

to check:
$$101010_2 = 42_{10}$$
$$\frac{10001_2 = 17_{10}}{25_{10}}, \qquad 11001_2 = 25_{10}$$

The answer is correct.

A word of precaution is necessary in forming the 1's complement. The subtrahend must have the same number of binary digits as there are in the minuend. That is, if the minuend has six digits, the subtrahend must also have six digits, before the 1's complement is formed. This is shown in the following example:

example 32–7 Subtract 101 from 111011

solution: This would normally be set up as

```
111011   Minuend
   101   Subtrahend
```

However, the subtrahend does not have the same number of binary digits as the minuend. Adding zeroes to the subtrahend does not change the numerical value, and is written as

```
111011
000101
```

The 1's complement may now be formed, as both the minuend and the subtrahend have the same number of binary digits. This is shown as

```
 111111
−000101
 111010   1's complement
     +1
 111011   2's complement
```

Adding

$$
\begin{array}{l}
111011 \\
\underline{+111011} \quad \text{2's complement} \\
000000 \\
\underline{111\ 11} \quad \text{carry} \\
1110110 \quad \text{sum} \\
\underline{-1} \\
110110 \quad \text{answer}
\end{array}
$$

to check:

$$
\begin{array}{l}
111011_2 = 59_{10} \\
101_2 = 5_{10} \\
\hline
54_{10}
\end{array}
$$

$110110_2 = 54_{10}$ The answer is correct

32-7 BINARY ARITHMETIC—MULTIPLICATION

The rules that apply to binary multiplication are quite simple.

0 times any number $= 0$

1 times any number $=$ the number

In decimal multiplication, the multiplicand is added the number of times designated, starting with the least-significant figure of the multiplier. This process is continued using the next significant figure of the multiplier, shifting this result 1 place to the left. This process is continued through all digits of the multiplier, each time shifting the result one place to the left.

In binary multiplication a similar procedure to decimal multiplication is used, except that multiplication using each digit of the multiplier requires only multiplication by 0 or 1. For instance, multiplication of 10111 by 1001 is shown as

$$
\begin{array}{l}
10111 \\
\underline{\times\ \ 1001} \\
10111 \quad (\times 1) \\
00000 \quad (\times 0)\ \text{shift} \\
00000 \quad (\times 0)\ \text{shift} \\
\underline{10111} \quad (\times 1)\ \text{shift} \\
11001111 \quad \text{total}
\end{array}
$$

To check:

$$
\begin{array}{ll}
10111_2 = 23_{10} & (23)(9) = 207 \quad \text{and} \quad 11001111_2 = 207 \\
1001_2 = 9_{10} &
\end{array}
$$

The answer is correct.

example 32–8   Multiply 1111 by 101.

solution:

$$
\begin{array}{r}
1111 \\
\times\ 101 \\
\hline
1111 \quad (\times 1) \\
0000 \quad (\times 0)\ \text{shift} \\
1111 \quad (\times 1)\ \text{shift} \\
\hline
1001011 \quad \text{total}
\end{array}
$$

to check: $1111_2 = 15_{10},$ $(15)(5) = 75$ and $1001011_2 = 75_{10}$

$101_2 = \ 5_{10}$

The answer is correct. •

example 32–9   Multiply 110001 by 1111.

solution:

$$
\begin{array}{r}
110001 \\
\times\ \ 1111 \\
\hline
110001 \quad (\times 1) \\
110001 \quad (\times 1)\ \text{shift} \\
110001 \quad (\times 1)\ \text{shift} \\
110001 \quad (\times 1)\ \text{shift} \\
\hline
1011011111
\end{array}
$$

to check: $110001_2 = 49_{10},$

$1111_2 = 15_{10}$ $(49)(15) = 735$

and $1011011111_2 = 735_{10}$

The answer is correct.

32–8   BINARY ARITHMETIC—DIVISION

The rules for the division of binary numbers are quite simple. They are:

$1 \div 0 = 1$

$0 \div 1 = 0$

This procedure is similar to decimal-system division except that where subtraction is required, a change to 2's complement is made and then added. With each successive division, a shift to the right is made. For instance, the division of 1111 by 101 is shown as:

$$
\begin{array}{r}
1 \\
101\overline{)\ 1111} \\
-101
\end{array}
$$
this is changed to 2's complement and added

$$\begin{array}{r} 111 \\ \underline{101} \\ 010 \end{array} \text{1's complement}$$

$$\begin{array}{r} +\ \ 1 \\ \hline 011 \end{array} \text{2's complement}$$

We then show that

$$\begin{array}{r} 11 \\ 101\overline{)\ 1111} \\ +011 \\ \hline 1010 \\ -1\ \ \downarrow \\ \hline 0101 \\ -101 \end{array} \begin{array}{l} \text{2's complement} \\ \\ \text{changed to 2's complement and added} \end{array}$$

$$\begin{array}{r} 111 \\ \underline{101} \\ 010 \end{array} \text{1's complement}$$

$$\begin{array}{r} +\ \ 1 \\ \hline 011 \end{array} \text{2's complement}$$

We then have

$$\begin{array}{r} 11 \\ 101\overline{)\ 1111} \\ +011 \\ \hline 1010 \\ -1\ \ \downarrow \\ \hline 0101 \\ +\ 011 \\ \hline 1000 \\ -1 \\ \hline 000 \end{array} \begin{array}{l} \\ \\ \text{2's complement} \\ \\ \text{remainder} \end{array}$$

To check:

$$1111_2 = 15_{10}$$

$$101_2 = 5_{10}, \qquad 15 \div 5 = 3 \quad \text{and} \quad 11_2 = 3$$

The answer is correct.

example 32–10 Divide 1100 by 10.

```
              110
      10) 1100
          +10          2's complement
          101
          −1
          010
          + 10        2's complement
          100
          −1
          000
```

to check: $10_2 = 2_{10}$, $12 \div 2 = 6$ and $110_2 = 6_{10}$

$1100_2 = 12_{10}$

The answer is correct.

example 32–11   Divide 11000 by 110.

solution:
```
               100
      110) 11000
           +010          2's complement
           10000
           −1
           00000
```

to check: $110_2 = 6_{10}$, $24 \div 6 = 4$ and $100_2 = 4_{10}$

$11000_2 = 24_{10}$

The answer is correct.

EXERCISE 32–4   Add the following binary numbers.

1. 1010
    1111

2. 11011
    10110

3. 11100
    10001

4. 101010
    111111

5. 101111
    100101

6. 10101
    1101

7. Subtract 1110 from 101010.

8. Subtract 1001 from 100001.

9. Subtract 10010 from 101010.

10. Subtract 111 from 101110.

11. Subtract 1010 from 11111.

12. Subtract 1011 from 100010.

13. Multiply 111 by 1001.

14. Multiply 101 by 10101.

15. Multiply 1001 by 11101.

16. Multiply 1101 by 10010.

17. Multiply 1011 by 1111.

18. Multiply 101010 by 10101.

19. Divide 11100 by 111.

20. Divide 100100 by 110.

21. Divide 1000010 by 100001.

22. Divide 110000 by 1100.

23. Divide 100000 by 1000.

24. Divide 100000000 by 10000000.

APPENDIX

TABLE A Four-Place Logarithms of Numbers

N	0	1	2	3	4	5	6	7	8	9
10	0000	0043	0086	0128	0170	0212	0253	0294	0334	0374
11	0414	0453	0492	0531	0569	0607	0645	0682	0719	0755
12	0792	0828	0864	0899	0934	0969	1004	1038	1072	1106
13	1139	1173	1206	1239	1271	1303	1335	1367	1399	1430
14	1461	1492	1523	1553	1584	1614	1644	1673	1703	1732
15	1761	1790	1818	1847	1875	1903	1931	1959	1987	2014
16	2041	2068	2095	2122	2148	2175	2201	2227	2253	2279
17	2304	2330	2355	2380	2405	2430	2455	2480	2504	2529
18	2553	2577	2601	2625	2648	2672	2695	2718	2742	2765
19	2788	2810	2833	2856	2878	2900	2923	2945	2967	2989
20	3010	3032	3054	3075	3096	3118	3139	3160	3181	3201
21	3222	3243	3263	3284	3304	3324	3345	3365	3385	3404
22	3424	3444	3464	3483	3502	3522	3541	3560	3579	3598
23	3617	3636	3655	3674	3692	3711	3729	3747	3766	3784
24	3802	3820	3838	3856	3874	3892	3909	3927	3945	3962
25	3979	3997	4014	4031	4048	4065	4082	4099	4116	4133
26	4150	4166	4183	4200	4216	4232	4249	4265	4281	4298
27	4314	4330	4346	4362	4378	4393	4409	4425	4440	4456
28	4472	4487	4502	4518	4533	4548	4564	4579	4594	4609
29	4624	4639	4654	4669	4683	4698	4713	4728	4742	4757
30	4771	4786	4800	4814	4829	4843	4857	4871	4886	4900
31	4914	4928	4942	4955	4969	4983	4997	5011	5024	5038
32	5051	5065	5079	5092	5105	5119	5132	5145	5159	5172
33	5185	5198	5211	5224	5237	5250	5263	5276	5289	5302
34	5315	5328	5340	5353	5366	5378	5391	5403	5416	5428
35	5441	5453	5465	5478	5490	5502	5514	5527	5539	5551
36	5563	5575	5587	5599	5611	5623	5635	5647	5658	5670
37	5682	5694	5705	5717	5729	5740	5752	5763	5775	5786
38	5798	5809	5821	5832	5843	5855	5866	5877	5888	5899
39	5911	5922	5933	5944	5955	5966	5977	5988	5999	6010
40	6021	6031	6042	6053	6064	6075	6085	6096	6107	6117
41	6128	6138	6149	6160	6170	6180	6191	6201	6212	6222
42	6232	6243	6253	6263	6274	6284	6294	6304	6314	6325
43	6335	6345	6355	6365	6375	6385	6395	6405	6415	6425
44	6435	6444	6454	6464	6474	6484	6493	6503	6513	6522
45	6532	6542	6551	6561	6571	6580	6590	6599	6609	6618
46	6628	6637	6646	6656	6665	6675	6684	6693	6702	6712
47	6721	6730	6739	6749	6758	6767	6776	6785	6794	6803
48	6812	6821	6830	6839	6848	6857	6866	6875	6884	6893
49	6902	6911	6920	6928	6937	6946	6955	6964	6972	6981
50	6990	6998	7007	7016	7024	7033	7042	7050	7059	7067
51	7076	7084	7093	7101	7110	7118	7126	7135	7143	7152
52	7160	7168	7177	7185	7193	7202	7210	7218	7226	7235
53	7243	7251	7259	7267	7275	7284	7292	7300	7308	7316
54	7324	7332	7340	7348	7356	7364	7372	7380	7388	7396

N	0	1	2	3	4	5	6	7	8	9
55	7404	7412	7419	7427	7435	7443	7451	7459	7466	7474
56	7482	7490	7497	7505	7513	7520	7528	7536	7543	7551
57	7559	7566	7574	7582	7589	7597	7604	7612	7619	7627
58	7634	7642	7649	7657	7664	7672	7679	7686	7694	7701
59	7709	7716	7723	7731	7738	7745	7752	7760	7767	7774
60	7782	7789	7796	7803	7810	7818	7825	7832	7839	7846
61	7853	7860	7868	7875	7882	7889	7896	7903	7910	7917
62	7924	7931	7938	7945	7952	7959	7966	7973	7980	7987
63	7993	8000	8007	8014	8021	8028	8035	8041	8048	8055
64	8062	8069	8075	8082	8089	8096	8102	8109	8116	8122
65	8129	8136	8142	8149	8156	8162	8169	8176	8182	8189
66	8195	8202	8209	8215	8222	8228	8235	8241	8248	8254
67	8261	8267	8274	8280	8287	8293	8299	8306	8312	8319
68	8325	8331	8338	8344	8351	8357	8363	8370	8376	8382
69	8388	8395	8401	8407	8414	8420	8426	8432	8439	8445
70	8451	8457	8463	8470	8476	8482	8488	8494	8500	8506
71	8513	8519	8525	8531	8537	8543	8549	8555	8561	8567
72	8573	8579	8585	8591	8597	8603	8609	8615	8621	8627
73	8633	8639	8645	8651	8657	8663	8669	8765	8681	8686
74	8692	8698	8704	8710	8716	8722	8727	8733	8739	8745
75	8751	8756	8762	8768	8774	8779	8785	8791	8797	8802
76	8808	8814	8820	8825	8831	8837	8842	8848	8854	8859
76	8865	8871	8876	8882	8887	8893	8899	8904	8910	8915
78	8921	8927	8932	8938	8943	8949	8954	8960	8965	8971
79	8976	8982	8987	8993	8998	9004	9009	9015	9020	9025
80	9031	9036	9042	9047	9053	9058	9063	9069	9074	9079
81	9085	9090	9096	9101	9106	9112	9117	9122	9128	9133
82	9138	9143	9149	9154	9159	9165	9170	9175	9180	9186
83	9191	9196	9201	9206	9212	9217	9222	9227	9232	9238
84	9243	9248	9253	9258	9263	9269	9274	9279	9284	9289
85	9294	9299	9304	9309	9315	9320	9325	9330	9335	9340
86	9345	9350	9355	9360	9365	9370	9375	9380	9385	9390
87	9395	9400	9405	9410	9415	9420	9425	9430	9435	9440
88	9445	9450	9455	9460	9465	9469	9474	9479	9484	9489
89	9494	9499	9504	9509	9513	9518	9523	9528	9533	9538
90	9542	9547	9552	9557	9562	9566	9571	9576	9581	9586
91	9590	9595	9600	9605	9609	9614	9619	9624	9628	9633
92	9638	9643	9647	9652	9657	9661	9666	9671	9675	9680
93	9685	9689	9694	9699	9703	9708	9713	9717	9722	9727
94	9731	9736	9741	9745	9750	9754	9759	9763	9768	9773
95	9777	9782	9786	9791	9795	9800	9805	9809	9814	9818
96	9823	9827	9832	9836	9841	9845	9850	9854	9859	9863
97	9868	9872	9877	9881	9886	9890	9894	9899	9903	9908
98	9912	9917	9921	9926	9930	9934	9939	9943	9948	9952
99	9956	9961	9965	9969	9974	9978	9983	9987	9991	9996

TABLE B Natural Trigonometric Functions: Sine
Angles from 0.0° to 44.9°

	.0	.1	.2	.3	.4	.5	.6	.7	.8	.9
0°	.0000	.0017	.0035	.0052	.0070	.0087	.0105	.0122	.0140	.0157
1°	.0175	.0192	.0209	.0227	.0244	.0262	.0279	.0297	.0314	.0332
2°	.0349	.0366	.0384	.0401	.0419	.0436	.0454	.0471	.0488	.0506
3°	.0523	.0541	.0558	.0576	.0593	.0610	.0628	.0645	.0663	.0680
4°	.0698	.0715	.0732	.0750	.0767	.0785	.0802	.0819	.0837	.0854
5°	.0872	.0889	.0906	.0924	.0941	.0958	.0976	.0993	.1011	.1028
6°	.1045	.1063	.1080	.1097	.1115	.1132	.1149	.1167	.1184	.1201
7°	.1219	.1236	.1253	.1271	.1288	.1305	.1323	.1340	.1357	.1374
8°	.1392	.1409	.1426	.1444	.1461	.1478	.1495	.1513	.1530	.1547
9°	.1564	.1582	.1599	.1616	.1633	.1650	.1668	.1685	.1702	.1719
10°	.1736	.1754	.1771	.1788	.1805	.1822	.1840	.1857	.1874	.1891
11°	.1908	.1925	.1942	.1959	.1977	.1994	.2011	.2028	.2045	.2062
12°	.2079	.2096	.2113	.2130	.2147	.2164	.2181	.2198	.2215	.2233
13°	.2250	.2267	.2284	.2300	.2317	.2334	.2351	.2368	.2385	.2402
14°	.2419	.2436	.2453	.2470	.2487	.2504	.2521	.2538	.2554	.2571
15°	.2588	.2605	.2622	.2639	.2656	.2672	.2689	.2706	.2723	.2740
16°	.2756	.2773	.2790	.2807	.2823	.2840	.2857	.2874	.2890	.2907
17°	.2924	.2940	.2957	.2974	.2990	.3007	.3024	.3040	.3057	.3074
18°	.3090	.3107	.3123	.3140	.3156	.3173	.3190	.3206	.3223	.3239
19°	.3256	.3272	.3289	.3305	.3322	.3338	.3355	.3371	.3387	.3404
20°	.3420	.3437	.3453	.3469	.3486	.3502	.3518	.3535	.3551	.3567
21°	.3584	.3600	.3616	.3633	.3649	.3665	.3681	.3697	.3714	.3730
22°	.3746	.3762	.3778	.3795	.3811	.3827	.3843	.3859	.3875	.3891
23°	.3907	.3923	.3939	.3955	.3971	.3987	.4003	.4019	.4035	.4051
24°	.4067	.4083	.4099	.4115	.4131	.4147	.4163	.4179	.4195	.4210
25°	.4226	.4242	.4258	.4274	.4289	.4305	.4321	.4337	.4352	.4368
26°	.4384	.4399	.4415	.4431	.4446	.4462	.4478	.4493	.4509	.4524
27°	.4540	.4555	.4571	.4586	.4602	.4617	.4633	.4648	.4664	.4679
28°	.4695	.4710	.4726	.4741	.4756	.4772	.4787	.4802	.4818	.4833
29°	.4848	.4863	.4879	.4894	.4909	.4924	.4939	.4955	.4970	.4985
30°	.5000	.5015	.5030	.5045	.5060	.5075	.5090	.5105	.5120	.5135
31°	.5150	.5165	.5180	.5195	.5210	.5225	.5240	.5255	.5270	.5284
32°	.5299	.5314	.5329	.5344	.5358	.5373	.5388	.5402	.5417	.5432
33°	.5446	.5461	.5476	.5490	.5505	.5519	.5534	.5548	.5563	.5577
34°	.5592	.5606	.5621	.5635	.5650	.5664	.5678	.5693	.5707	.5721
35°	.5736	.5750	.5764	.5779	.5793	.5807	.5821	.5835	.5850	.5864
36°	.5878	.5892	.5906	.5920	.5934	.5948	.5962	.5976	.5990	.6004
37°	.6018	.6032	.6046	.6060	.6074	.6088	.6101	.6115	.6129	.6143
38°	.6157	.6170	.6184	.6198	.6211	.6225	.6239	.6252	.6266	.6280
39°	.6293	.6307	.6320	.6334	.6347	.6361	.6374	.6388	.6401	.6414
40°	.6428	.6441	.6455	.6468	.6481	.6494	.6508	.6521	.6534	.6547
41°	.6561	.6574	.6587	.6600	.6613	.6626	.6639	.6652	.6665	.6678
42°	.6691	.6704	.6717	.6730	.6743	.6756	.6769	.6782	.6794	.6807
43°	.6820	.6833	.6845	.6858	.6871	.6884	.6896	.6909	.6921	.6934
44°	.6947	.6959	.6972	.6984	.6997	.7009	.7022	.7034	.7046	.7059

	.0	.1	.2	.3	.4	.5	.6	.7	.8	.9
45°	.7071	.7083	.7096	.7108	.7120	.7133	.7145	.7157	.7169	.7181
46°	.7193	.7206	.7218	.7230	.7242	.7254	.7266	.7278	.7290	.7302
47°	.7314	.7325	.7337	.7349	.7361	.7373	.7385	.7396	.7408	.7420
48°	.7431	.7443	.7455	.7466	.7478	.7490	.7501	.7513	.7524	.7536
49°	.7547	.7559	.7570	.7581	.7593	.7604	.7615	.7627	.7638	.7649
50°	.7660	.7672	.7683	.7694	.7705	.7716	.7727	.7738	.7749	.7760
51°	.7771	.7782	.7793	.7804	.7815	.7826	.7837	.7848	.7859	.7869
52°	.7880	.7891	.7902	.7912	.7923	.7934	.7944	.7955	.7965	.7976
53°	.7986	.7997	.8007	.8018	.8028	.8039	.8049	.8059	.8070	.8080
54°	.8090	.8100	.8111	.8121	.8131	.8141	.8151	.8161	.8171	.8181
55°	.8192	.8202	.8211	.8221	.8231	.8241	.8251	.8261	.8271	.8281
56°	.8290	.8300	.8310	.8320	.8329	.8339	.8348	.8358	.8368	.8377
57°	.8387	.8396	.8406	.8415	.8425	.8434	.8443	.8453	.8462	.8471
58°	.8480	.8490	.8499	.8508	.8517	.8526	.8536	.8545	.8554	.8563
59°	.8572	.8581	.8590	.8599	.8607	.8616	.8625	.8634	.8643	.8652
60°	.8660	.8669	.8678	.8686	.8695	.8704	.8712	.8721	.8729	.8738
61°	.8746	.8755	.8763	.8771	.8780	.8788	.8796	.8805	.8813	.8821
62°	.8829	.8838	.8846	.8854	.8862	.8870	.8878	.8886	.8894	.8902
63°	.8910	.8918	.8926	.8934	.8942	.8949	.8957	.8965	.8973	.8980
64°	.8988	.8996	.9003	.9011	.9018	.9026	.9033	.9041	.9048	.9056
65°	.9063	.9070	.9078	.9085	.9092	.9100	.9107	.9114	.9121	.9128
66°	.9135	.9143	.9150	.9157	.9164	.9171	.9178	.9184	.9191	.9198
67°	.9205	.9212	.9219	.9225	.9232	.9239	.9245	.9252	.9259	.9265
68°	.9272	.9278	.9285	.9291	.9298	.9304	.9311	.9317	.9323	.9330
69°	.9336	.9342	.9348	.9354	.9361	.9367	.9373	.9379	.9385	.9391
70°	.9397	.9403	.9409	.9415	.9421	.9426	.9432	.9438	.9444	.9449
71°	.9455	.9461	.9466	.9472	.9478	.9483	.9489	.9494	.9500	.9505
72°	.9511	.9516	.9521	.9527	.9532	.9537	.9542	.9548	.9553	.9558
73°	.9563	.9568	.9573	.9578	.9583	.9588	.9593	.9598	.9603	.9608
74°	.9613	.9617	.9622	.9627	.9632	.9636	.9641	.9646	.9650	.9655
75°	.9659	.9664	.9668	.9673	.9677	.9681	.9686	.9690	.9694	.9699
76°	.9703	.9707	.9711	.9715	.9720	.9724	.9728	.9732	.9736	.9740
77°	.9744	.9748	.9751	.9755	.9759	.9763	.9767	.9770	.9774	.9778
78°	.9781	.9785	.9789	.9792	.9796	.9799	.9803	.9806	.9810	.9813
79°	.9816	.9820	.9823	.9826	.9829	.9833	.9836	.9839	.9842	.9845
80°	.9848	.9851	.9854	.9857	.9860	.9863	.9866	.9869	.9871	.9874
81°	.9877	.9880	.9882	.9885	.9888	.9890	.9893	.9895	.9898	.9900
82°	.9903	.9905	.9907	.9910	.9912	.9914	.9917	.9919	.9921	.9923
83°	.9925	.9928	.9930	.9932	.9934	.9936	.9938	.9940	.9942	.9943
84°	.9945	.9947	.9949	.9951	.9952	.9954	.9956	.9957	.9959	.9960
85°	.9962	.9963	.9965	.9966	.9968	.9969	.9971	.9972	.9973	.9974
86°	.9976	.9977	.9978	.9979	.9980	.9981	.9982	.9983	.9984	.9985
87°	.9986	.9987	.9988	.9989	.9990	.9990	.9991	.9992	.9993	.9993
88°	.9994	.9995	.9995	.9996	.9996	.9997	.9997	.9997	.9998	.9998
89°	.9998	.9999	.9999	.9999	.9999	1.000	1.000	1.000	1.000	1.000

TABLE B Natural Trigonometric Functions: Cosine
Angles from 0.0° to 44.9°

	.0	.1	.2	.3	.4	.5	.6	.7	.8	.9
0°	1.0000	1.0000	1.0000	1.0000	1.0000	1.0000	.9999	.9999	.9999	.9999
1°	.9998	.9998	.9998	.9997	.9997	.9997	.9996	.9996	.9995	.9995
2°	.9994	.9993	.9993	.9992	.9991	.9990	.9990	.9989	.9988	.9987
3°	.9986	.9985	.9984	.9983	.9982	.9981	.9980	.9979	.9978	.9977
4°	.9976	.9974	.9973	.9972	.9971	.9969	.9968	.9966	.9965	.9963
5°	.9962	.9960	.9959	.9957	.9956	.9954	.9952	.9951	.9949	.9947
6°	.9945	.9943	.9942	.9940	.9938	.9936	.9934	.9932	.9930	.9928
7°	.9925	.9923	.9921	.9919	.9917	.9914	.9912	.9910	.9907	.9905
8°	.9903	.9900	.9898	.9895	.9893	.9890	.9888	.9885	.9882	.9880
9°	.9877	.9874	.9871	.9869	.9866	.9863	.9860	.9857	.9854	.9851
10°	.9848	.9845	.9842	.9839	.9836	.9833	.9829	.9826	.9823	.9820
11°	.9816	.9813	.9810	.9806	.9803	.9799	.9796	.9792	.9789	.9785
12°	.9781	.9778	.9774	.9770	.9767	.9763	.9759	.9755	.9751	.9748
13°	.9744	.9740	.9736	.9732	.9728	.9724	.9720	.9715	.9711	.9707
14°	.9703	.9699	.9694	.9690	.9686	.9681	.9677	.9673	.9668	.9664
15°	.9659	.9655	.9650	.9646	.9641	.9636	.9632	.9627	.9622	.9617
16°	.9613	.9608	.9603	.9598	.9593	.9588	.9583	.9578	.9573	.9568
17°	.9563	.9558	.9553	.9548	.9542	.9537	.9532	.9527	.9521	.9516
18°	.9511	.9505	.9500	.9494	.9489	.9483	.9478	.9472	.9466	.9461
19°	.9455	.9449	.9444	.9438	.9432	.9426	.9421	.9415	.9409	.9403
20°	.9397	.9391	.9385	.9379	.9373	.9367	.9361	.9354	.9348	.9342
21°	.9336	.9330	.9323	.9317	.9311	.9304	.9298	.9291	.9285	.9278
22°	.9272	.9265	.9259	.9252	.9245	.9239	.9232	.9225	.9219	.9212
23°	.9205	.9198	.9191	.9184	.9178	.9171	.9164	.9157	.9150	.9143
24°	.9135	.9128	.9121	.9114	.9107	.9100	.9092	.9085	.9078	.9070
25°	.9063	.9056	.9048	.9041	.9033	.9026	.9018	.9011	.9003	.8996
26°	.8988	.8980	.8973	.8965	.8957	.8949	.8942	.8934	.8926	.8918
27°	.8910	.8902	.8894	.8886	.8878	.8870	.8862	.8854	.8846	.8838
28°	.8829	.8821	.8813	.8805	.8796	.8788	.8780	.8771	.8763	.8755
29°	.8746	.8738	.8729	.8721	.8712	.8704	.8695	.8686	.8678	.8669
30°	.8660	.8652	.8643	.8634	.8625	.8616	.8607	.8599	.8590	.8581
31°	.8572	.8563	.8554	.8545	.8536	.8526	.8517	.8508	.8499	.8490
32°	.8480	.8471	.8462	.8453	.8443	.8434	.8425	.8415	.8406	.8396
33°	.8387	.8377	.8368	.8358	.8348	.8339	.8329	.8320	.8310	.8300
34°	.8290	.8281	.8271	.8261	.8251	.8241	.8231	.8221	.8211	.8202
35°	.8192	.8181	.8171	.8161	.8151	.8141	.8131	.8121	.8111	.8100
36°	.8090	.8080	.8070	.8059	.8049	.8039	.8028	.8018	.8007	.7997
37°	.7986	.7976	.7965	.7955	.7944	.7934	.7923	.7912	.7902	.7891
38°	.7880	.7869	.7859	.7848	.7837	.7826	.7815	.7804	.7793	.7782
39°	.7771	.7760	.7749	.7738	.7727	.7716	.7705	.7694	.7683	.7672
40°	.7660	.7649	.7638	.7627	.7615	.7604	.7593	.7581	.7570	.7559
41°	.7547	.7536	.7524	.7513	.7501	.7490	.7478	.7466	.7455	.7443
42°	.7431	.7420	.7408	.7396	.7385	.7373	.7361	.7349	.7337	.7325
43°	.7314	.7302	.7290	.7278	.7266	.7254	.7242	.7230	.7218	.7206
44°	.7193	.7181	.7169	.7157	.7145	.7133	.7120	.7108	.7096	.7083

	.0	.1	.2	.3	.4	.5	.6	.7	.8	.9
45°	.7071	.7059	.7046	.7034	.7022	.7009	.6997	.6984	.6972	.6959
46°	.6947	.6934	.6921	.6909	.6896	.6884	.6871	.6858	.6845	.6833
47°	.6820	.6807	.6794	.6782	.6769	.6756	.6743	.6730	.6717	.6704
48°	.6691	.6678	.6665	.6652	.6639	.6626	.6613	.6600	.6587	.6574
49°	.6561	.6547	.6534	.6521	.6508	.6494	.6481	.6468	.6455	.6441
50°	.6428	.6414	.6401	.6388	.6374	.6361	.6347	.6334	.6320	.6307
51°	.6293	.6280	.6266	.6252	.6239	.6225	.6211	.6198	.6184	.6170
52°	.6157	.6143	.6129	.6115	.6101	.6088	.6074	.6060	.6046	.6032
53°	.6018	.6004	.5990	.5976	.5962	.5948	.5943	.5920	.5906	.5892
54°	.5878	.5864	.5850	.5835	.5821	.5807	.5793	.5779	.5764	.5750
55°	.5736	.5721	.5707	.5693	.5678	.5664	.5650	.5635	.5621	.5606
56°	.5592	.5577	.5563	.5548	.5534	.5519	.5505	.5490	.5476	.5461
57°	.5446	.5432	.5417	.5402	.5388	.5373	.5358	.5344	.5329	.5314
58°	.5299	.5284	.5270	.5255	.5240	.5225	.5210	.5195	.5180	.5165
59°	.5150	.5135	.5120	.5105	.5090	.5075	.5060	.5045	.5030	.5015
60°	.5000	.4985	.4970	.4955	.4939	.4924	.4909	.4894	.4879	.4863
61°	.4848	.4833	.4818	.4802	.4787	.4772	.4756	.4741	.4726	.4710
62°	.4695	.4679	.4664	.4648	.4633	.4617	.4602	.4586	.4571	.4555
63°	.4540	.4524	.4509	.4493	.4478	.4462	.4446	.4431	.4415	.4399
64°	.4384	.4368	.4352	.4337	.4321	.4305	.4289	.4274	.4258	.4242
65°	.4226	.4210	.4195	.4179	.4163	.4147	.4131	.4115	.4099	.4083
66°	.4067	.4051	.4035	.4019	.4003	.3987	.3971	.3955	.3939	.3923
67°	.3907	.3891	.3875	.3859	.3843	.3827	.3811	.3795	.3778	.3762
68°	.3746	.3730	.3714	.3697	.3681	.3665	.3649	.3633	.3616	.3600
69°	.3584	.3567	.3551	.3535	.3518	.3502	.3486	.3469	.3453	.3437
70°	.3420	.3404	.3387	.3371	.3355	.3338	.3322	.3305	.3289	.3272
71°	.3256	.3239	.3223	.3206	.3190	.3173	.3156	.3140	.3123	.3107
72°	.3090	.3074	.3057	.3040	.3024	.3007	.2990	.2974	.2957	.2940
73°	.2924	.2907	.2890	.2874	.2857	.2840	.2823	.2807	.2790	.2773
74°	.2756	.2740	.2723	.2706	.2689	.2672	.2656	.2639	.2622	.2605
75°	.2588	.2571	.2554	.2538	.2521	.2504	.2487	.2470	.2453	.2436
76°	.2419	.2402	.2385	.2368	.2351	.2334	.2317	.2300	.2284	.2267
77°	.2250	.2233	.2215	.2198	.2181	.2164	.2147	.2130	.2113	.2096
78°	.2079	.2062	.2045	.2028	.2011	.1994	.1977	.1959	.1942	.1925
79°	.1908	.1891	.1874	.1857	.1840	.1822	.1805	.1788	.1771	.1754
80°	.1736	.1719	.1702	.1685	.1668	.1650	.1633	.1616	.1599	.1582
81°	.1564	.1547	.1530	.1513	.1495	.1478	.1461	.1444	.1426	.1409
82°	.1392	.1374	.1357	.1340	.1323	.1305	.1288	.1271	.1253	.1236
83°	.1219	.1201	.1184	.1167	.1149	.1132	.1115	.1097	.1080	.1063
84°	.1045	.1028	.1011	.0993	.0976	.0958	.0941	.0924	.0906	.0889
85°	.0872	.0854	.0837	.0819	.0802	.0785	.0767	.0750	.0732	.0715
86°	.0698	.0680	.0663	.0645	.0628	.0610	.0593	.0576	.0558	.0541
87°	.0523	.0506	.0488	.0471	.0454	.0436	.0419	.0401	.0384	.0366
88°	.0349	.0332	.0314	.0297	.0279	.0262	.0244	.0227	.0209	.0192
89°	.0175	.0157	.0140	.0122	.0105	.0087	.0070	.0052	.0035	.0017

TABLE B Natural Trigonometric Functions: Tangent
Angles from 0.0° to 44.9°

	.0	.1	.2	.3	.4	.5	.6	.7	.8	.9
0°	.0000	.0017	.0035	.0052	.0070	.0087	.0105	.0122	.0140	.0157
1°	.0175	.0192	.0209	.0227	.0244	.0262	.0279	.0297	.0314	.0332
2°	.0349	.0367	.0384	.0402	.0419	.0437	.0454	.0472	.0489	.0507
3°	.0524	.0542	.0559	.0577	.0594	.0612	.0629	.0647	.0664	.0682
4°	.0699	.0717	.0734	.0752	.0769	.0787	.0805	.0822	.0840	.0857
5°	.0875	.0892	.0910	.0928	.0945	.0963	.0981	.0998	.1016	.1033
6°	.1051	.1069	.1086	.1104	.1122	.1139	.1157	.1175	.1192	.1210
7°	.1228	.1246	.1263	.1281	.1299	.1317	.1334	.1352	.1370	.1388
8°	.1405	.1423	.1441	.1459	.1477	.1495	.1512	.1530	.1548	.1566
9°	.1584	.1602	.1620	.1638	.1655	.1673	.1681	.1709	.1727	.1745
10°	.1763	.1781	.1799	.1817	.1835	.1853	.1871	.1890	.1908	.1926
11°	.1944	.1962	.1980	.1998	.2016	.2035	.2053	.2071	.2089	.2107
12°	.2126	.2144	.2162	.2180	.2199	.2217	.2235	.2254	.2272	.2290
13°	.2309	.2327	.2345	.2364	.2382	.2401	.2419	.2438	.2456	.2475
14°	.2493	.2512	.2530	.2549	.2568	.2586	.2605	.2623	.2642	.2661
15°	.2679	.2698	.2717	.2736	.2754	.2773	.2792	.2811	.2830	.2849
16°	.2867	.2886	.2905	.2924	.2943	.2962	.2981	.3000	.3019	.3038
17°	.3057	.3076	.3096	.3115	.3134	.3153	.3172	.3191	.3211	.3230
18°	.3249	.3269	.3288	.3307	.3327	.3346	.3365	.3385	.3404	.3424
19°	.3443	.3463	.3482	.3502	.3522	.3541	.3561	.3581	.3600	.3620
20°	.3640	.3659	.3679	.3699	.3719	.3739	.3759	.3779	.3799	.3819
21°	.3839	.3859	.3879	.3899	.3919	.3939	.3959	.3979	.4000	.4020
22°	.4040	.4061	.4081	.4101	.4122	.4142	.4163	.4183	.4204	.4224
23°	.4245	.4265	.4286	.4307	.4327	.4348	.4369	.4390	.4411	.4431
24°	.4452	.4473	.4494	.4515	.4536	.4557	.4578	.4599	.4621	.4642
25°	.4663	.4684	.4706	.4727	.4748	.4770	.4791	.4813	.4834	.4856
26°	.4877	.4899	.4921	.4942	.4964	.4986	.5008	.5029	.5051	.5073
27°	.5095	.5117	.5139	.5161	.5184	.5206	.5228	.5250	.5272	.5295
28°	.5317	.5340	.5362	.5384	.5407	.5430	.5452	.5475	.5498	.5520
29°	.5543	.5566	.5589	.5612	.5635	.5658	.5681	.5704	.5727	.5750
30°	.5774	.5797	.5820	.5844	.5867	.5890	.5914	.5938	.5961	.5985
31°	.6009	.6032	.6056	.6080	.6104	.6128	.6152	.6176	.6200	.6224
32°	.6249	.6273	.6297	.6322	.6346	.6371	.6395	.6420	.6445	.6469
33°	.6494	.6519	.6544	.6569	.6594	.6619	.6644	.6669	.6694	.6720
34°	.6745	.6771	.6796	.6822	.6847	.6873	.6899	.6924	.6950	.6976
35°	.7002	.7028	.7054	.7080	.7107	.7133	.7159	.7186	.7212	.7239
36°	.7265	.7292	.7319	.7346	.7373	.7400	.7427	.7454	.7481	.7508
37°	.7536	.7563	.7590	.7618	.7646	.7673	.7701	.7729	.7757	.7785
38°	.7813	.7841	.7869	.7898	.7926	.7954	.7983	.8012	.8040	.8069
39°	.8098	.8127	.8156	.8185	.8214	.8243	.8273	.8302	.8332	.8361
40°	.8391	.8421	.8451	.8481	.8511	.8541	.8571	.8601	.8632	.8662
41°	.8693	.8724	.8754	.8785	.8816	.8847	.8878	.8910	.8941	.8972
42°	.9004	.9036	.9067	.9099	.9131	.9163	.9195	.9228	.9260	.9293
43°	.9325	.9358	.9391	.9424	.9457	.9490	.9523	.9556	.9590	.9623
44°	.9657	.9691	.9725	.9759	.9793	.9827	.9861	.9896	.9930	.9965

	.0	.1	.2	.3	.4	.5	.6	.7	.8	.9
45°	1.000	1.003	1.007	1.011	1.014	1.018	1.021	1.025	1.028	1.032
46°	1.036	1.039	1.043	1.046	1.050	1.054	1.057	1.061	1.065	1.069
47°	1.072	1.076	1.080	1.084	1.087	1.091	1.095	1.099	1.103	1.107
48°	1.111	1.115	1.118	1.122	1.126	1.130	1.134	1.138	1.142	1.146
49°	1.150	1.154	1.159	1.163	1.167	1.171	1.175	1.179	1.183	1.188
50°	1.192	1.196	1.200	1.205	1,209	1.213	1.217	1.222	1.226	1.230
51°	1.235	1.239	1.244	1.248	1.253	1.257	1.262	1.266	1.271	1.275
52°	1.280	1.285	1.289	1.294	1.299	1.303	1.308	1.313	1.317	1.322
53°	1.327	1.332	1.337	1.342	1.347	1.351	1.356	1.361	1.366	1.371
54°	1.376	1.381	1.387	1.392	1.397	1.402	1.407	1.412	1.418	1.423
55°	1.428	1.433	1.439	1.444	1.450	1.455	1.460	1.466	1.471	1.477
56°	1.483	1.488	1.494	1.499	1.505	1.511	1.517	1.522	1.528	1.534
57°	1.540	1.546	1.552	1.558	1.564	1.570	1.576	1.582	1.588	1.594
58°	1.600	1.607	1.613	1.619	1.625	1.632	1.638	1.645	1.651	1.658
59°	1.664	1.671	1.678	1.684	1.691	1.698	1.704	1.711	1.718	1.725
60°	1.732	1.739	1.746	1.753	1.760	1.767	1.775	1.782	1.789	1.797
61°	1.804	1.811	1.819	1.827	1.834	1.842	1.849	1.857	1.865	1.873
62°	1.881	1.889	1.897	1.905	1.913	1.921	1.929	1.937	1.946	1.954
63°	1.963	1.971	1.980	1.988	1.997	2.006	2.014	2.023	2.032	2.041
64°	2.050	2.059	2.069	2.078	2.087	2.097	2.106	2.116	2.125	2.135
65°	2.145	2.154	2.164	2.174	2.184	2.194	2.204	2.215	2.225	2.236
66°	2.246	2.257	2.267	2.278	2.289	2.300	2.311	2.322	2.333	2.344
67°	2.356	2.367	2.379	2.391	2.402	2.414	2.426	2.438	2.450	2.463
68°	2.475	2.488	2.500	2.513	2.526	2.539	2.552	2.565	2.578	2.592
69°	2.605	2.619	2.633	2.646	2.660	2.675	2.689	2.703	2.718	2.733
70°	2.727	2.762	2.778	2.793	2.808	2.824	2.840	2.856	2.872	2.888
71°	2.904	2.921	2.937	2.954	2.971	2.989	3.006	3.024	3.042	3.060
72°	3.078	3.096	3.115	3.133	3.152	3.172	3.191	3.211	3.230	3.251
73°	3.271	3.291	3.312	3.333	3.354	3.376	3.398	3.420	3.442	3.465
74°	3.487	3.511	3.534	3.558	3.582	3.606	3.630	3.655	3.681	3.706
75°	3.732	3.758	3.785	3.812	3.839	3.867	3.895	3.923	3.952	3.981
76°	4.011	4.041	4.071	4.102	4.134	4.165	4.198	4.230	4.264	4.297
77°	4.331	4.366	4.402	4.437	4.474	4.511	4.548	4.586	4.625	4.665
78°	4.705	4.745	4.787	4.829	4.872	4.915	4.959	5.005	5.050	5.097
79°	5.145	5.193	5.242	5.292	5.343	5.396	5.449	5.503	5.558	5.614
80°	5.671	5.730	5.789	5.850	5.912	5.976	6.041	6.107	6.174	6.243
81°	6.314	6.386	6.460	6.535	6.612	6.691	6.772	6.855	6.940	7.026
82°	7.115	7.207	7.300	7.396	7.495	7.596	7.700	7.806	7.916	8.028
83°	8.144	8.264	8.386	8.513	8.643	8.777	8.915	9.058	9.205	9.357
84°	9.514	9.677	9.845	10.02	10.20	10.39	10.58	10.57	10.99	11.20
85°	11.43	11.66	11.91	12.16	12.43	12.71	13.00	13.30	13.62	13.95
86°	14.30	14.67	15.06	15.46	15.89	16.35	16.83	17.34	17.89	18.46
87°	19.08	19.74	20.45	21.20	22.02	22.90	23.86	24.90	26.03	27.27
88°	28.64	30.14	31.82	33.69	35.80	38.19	40.92	44.07	47.74	52.08
89°	57.29	63.66	71.62	81.85	95.49	114.6	143.2	191.0	286.5	573.0

TABLE C Symbols

SYMBOL	NAME	USE
α	Alpha (Greek lowercase letter)	Angles
β	Beta	Angles
γ	Gamma	Angles
ϕ	Phi	Angles
θ	Theta	Angles
Ω	Omega (greek capital letter)	Ohms
A		Area
C		Capacitance
D, d		Diameter
E, e, V, v		Voltage
$f, \sim$		Frequency
f_r		Resonant frequency
I, i		Current
j		Complex operator, $\sqrt{-1}$
L		Inductance
P, p		Power
Q		Charge
Q		Merit of Inductance
R		Resistance
t		Time
t		Temperature
X_L		Inductive reactance
X_C		Capacitive reactance
Z		Impedance

TABLE D Mathematical Signs

	MATHEMATICAL SIGNS
Add; positive	$+$
Subtract; negative	$-$
Multiply	$\times$ or $\cdot$
Divide	$\div$
Plus or minus	$\pm$
Equals	$=$
Does not equal	$\neq$
Is approximately equal to	$\cong$ or $\approx$
Is less than	$<$
Is much less than	$\ll$
Is greater than	$>$
Is much greater than	$\gg$
Is greater than or equal to	$\geqq$ or $\geq$
Is less than or equal to	$\leqq$ or $\leq$
Absolute value	$\vert\ \ \vert$
Perpendicular	$\perp$
Right angle	$\llcorner$
Angle	$>$ or $\angle$
Parallel	$\parallel$
Therefore	$\therefore$
Change of	$\triangle$
Proportional to	$\propto$
Infinity	∞

	ABBREVIATIONS
Alternating current	ac
Ampere	A
Angle whose $\begin{bmatrix} \text{sine} \\ \text{cosine} \\ \text{tan} \end{bmatrix}$ is	arcsin
	arccos
	arctan
Antilogarithm	antilog
Bel	B
Centi (1×10^{-2})	c
Centimeter	cm
Circular mil	cmil
Clockwise	CW
Cologarithm	colog
Cosecant	csc
Cosine	cos
Cotangent	cot
Coulomb	C
Counterclockwise	CCW
Cycles per second	Hz
Deci (1×10^{-1})	d
Decibel	dB
Decibel (reference level 1 mW)	dB_m
Degree	deg
Degrees Celsius	°C
Degrees Fahrenheit	°F
Diameter	diam
Direct current	dc
Electromotive force	emf
Farad	F
Feet	ft
Giga (1×10^{9})	G
Gram	g
Henry	H
Hertz	Hz
Highest common factor	HCF
Horsepower	hp
Hour	h
Inch	in
Kilo (10^{3})	k
Kilovolt-ampere	kVA
Kilowatt-hour	kWh
Logarithm (base 10)	log
Lowest common denominator	LCD
Lowest common multiple	LCM
Maximum	max
Mega (1×10^{6})	M
Megohm	$M\Omega$
Micro (1×10^{-6})	μ
Microfarad	μF
Mil (0.001 in)	mil
Mile	mi
Milli (1×10^{-3})	m
Milliampere	mA
Minute	min

TABLE E Abbreviations (*cont.*)

	ABBREVIATIONS
Nano (1×10^{-9})	n
Ohms	Ω
Pico (1×10^{-12})	p
Pound	lb
Power factor	PF
Radians	rad
Radius	r
Revolutions per minute	r/min
Root mean square	rms
Secant	sec
Second	s
Sine	sin
Square foot	ft^2
Square inch	in^2
Tangent	tan
Tera (1×10^{12})	T
Var (volt-ampere reactive)	var
Volt	V
Volt-ampere	VA
Watt	W
Yard	yd

ANSWERS
TO SELECTED
ODD-NUMBERED
PROBLEMS

EXERCISES 2–1
1. 22
5. 114

EXERCISES 3–1
3. -77
7. 438

EXERCISES 3–2
3. 0
7. -1

EXERCISES 3–3
3. -3
5. 78

EXERCISES 3–4
5. 78
7. 400 volts

EXERCISES 3–5
1. 832
5. 288

EXERCISES 3–6
1. x^{18}
7. 4^{2+y+x}

EXERCISES 3–7
1. 1.148
7. 1.834

EXERCISES 3–8
1. x^{13}
5. a^2

EXERCISES 3–9
3. 3^{-23}
7. 14^{-3}

EXERCISES 4–1
1. $-3a - 3y$
5. $-5R + 8T - 11Z$

EXERCISES 4–2
1. $-22a + 20b$
7. $-18a + 6b - 4c + 4d$

EXERCISES 4–3
1. $-26x^3$
5. $-48a^3xy$

EXERCISES 4–4
1. $-6xy + 8y^2$
3. $6a^2b - 12ab^2 + 9abc^2$

EXERCISES 4–5
1. $-3x^2 - 7xy - 4y^2$
5. $x^2 + 4xy - 2x + 3y^2 - 2y$

EXERCISES 4–6
3. $2.33x^2y^2z$
5. $1.08m^{-1}n^{-1}p^{-1}$ or $\dfrac{1.08}{mnp}$

EXERCISES 4–7
1. $-6abc + 2a^2b^2c^2$
3. $3a^{-1}c^{-1}x^{-1} + 4ac^{-1}x^{-3}$ or $\dfrac{3}{acx} + \dfrac{4a}{cx^3}$

EXERCISES 4–8
5. $C^2 - D^2$
7. $D^2 + CD + C^3$

EXERCISES 5–1
1. $4x - 5 = 2x + 10$
5. $x - 2 = \dfrac{x}{2} + 2$

EXERCISES 5–2
1. $x = 6$
5. $c = -2$
7. $e = -60$
15. $c = -5$

EXERCISES 5–3
1. $f = \dfrac{X_L}{2\pi L}$, $L = \dfrac{X_L}{2\pi f}$

3. $R_1 = \dfrac{1}{\dfrac{1}{R_T} - \dfrac{1}{R_2}}$, $R_2 = \dfrac{1}{\dfrac{1}{R_T} - \dfrac{1}{R_1}}$

5. $I_1 = \dfrac{I_2 N_2}{N_1}$, $I_2 = \dfrac{I_1 N_1}{N_2}$

7. $I = \sqrt{\dfrac{P}{R}}$, $R = \dfrac{P}{I^2}$

EXERCISES 5–4

1. $x = 64$

5. $x = 9.09$

9. $R = kE$

13. $X_L = 2\pi f L$

EXERCISES 6–1

3. 3.575×10^6

5. 4.25×10^{10}

EXERCISES 6–2

3. 6.7×10^{-3}

7. 3.7×10^{-3}

EXERCISES 6–3

3. 6.32

5. 0.1422

EXERCISES 6–4

3. 5.624×10^{10}

7. 1.701×10^8

EXERCISES 6–5

3. 2.138×10^1

7. 6.14×10^6

EXERCISES 6–6

3. 1.97×10^1

7. 1.44×10^{-13}

EXERCISES 6–7

1. 1.65 MHz. 1.65×10^{-3} GHz

5. 1.35×10^{-2} mW, 1.35×10^{-5} W

EXERCISES 6–8

3. 3,080 ft/min

7. 1.666×10^{-3} MΩ

EXERCISES 7–1

1. 729 c mils

7. 0.0228 in.

EXERCISES 7–2

1. 141,000 mils^2

5. 1.394×10^6 c mils

EXERCISES 7–3

3. 30 Ω/c mil-ft

7. 0.000358 in.

EXERCISES 8–1

1. 0.005 A or 5 mA

5. 41.66 Ω

EXERCISES 8–2

1. $E_1 = 150$ V, $E_2 = 300$ V, $E_T = 450$ V

3. $I = 2.5$ A, $R_2 = 40$ Ω, $E_{R_1} = 150$ V

EXERCISES 8–3

1. $19.60

7. 1219.5 A, 128,860 W

EXERCISES 9–1

3. $R_1 = 133.33$ Ω

7. $R_T = 60.02$ Ω, $R_{T_{oc}} = 66.66$ Ω

11. $E = 29.03$ V

15. $R_T = 9.42$ Ω, $I_T = 12.73$ A, $I_1 = 0.4$ A
$I_2 = 0.2$ A, $I_3 = 0.133$ A, $I_4 = 12$ A

EXERCISES 9–2

1. $I_T = 7.79$ A

5. $R_T = R_3 = 400$ Ω, $I_T = 0.25$ A
$R_T = R_1 + R_3 + R_4 = 1,100$ Ω, $I_T = 0.091$ A

EXERCISES 10–1

1. $a(b + c + b^2)$

5. $xyz(4 + z + yz^2)$

9. $2cd^2e(2 + cde^4 + 2c^4d^2e^2)$

EXERCISES 10–2

1. $(x + 2y)(x - 2y)$

7. $(3w^2 + 2)(3w^2 - 2)$

9. $(6ab^2 + 1)(6ab^2 - 1)$

EXERCISES 10–3

1. $(2x - y)(2x - y)$ or $(2x - y)^2$

5. $(0.5m + 0.2n)(0.5m + 0.2n)$ or $(0.5m + 0.2n)^2$

9. $16d^2$

11. y^2

EXERCISES 10-4

1. $(x + 4)(x + 3)$

7. $(2s - 3)(3s - 2)$

9. $(9a + 3)(4a - 4)$

EXERCISES 10-5

1. 360

5. $(m + 4)(m - 4)(m - 2)$

EXERCISES 11-1

3. $4a$

5. $\dfrac{9}{20}$

9. $\dfrac{5c^2}{44ab^2}$

11. $\dfrac{2}{(x - y)}$

15. $\dfrac{3}{(5s + 4t)}$

EXERCISES 11-2

1. $1^{4/15}$

5. $\dfrac{-2}{x}$

7. $\dfrac{b + 4a}{ab}$

9. $\dfrac{49}{6s}$

13. $\dfrac{3s + 25}{(s + 3)^2}$

EXERCISES 11-3

3. $\frac{3}{5}$

5. $\dfrac{9w^2}{10}$

7. $\dfrac{4vxy}{13w}$

9. $\dfrac{(a + b)^2}{(a - b)^2}$

11. $c - d$

EXERCISES 11-4

1. $3^{1/5}$

7. $\dfrac{x + y}{2}$

EXERCISES 11-5

3. $y = \frac{11}{32}$

5. $w = 2^{2/5}$

EXERCISES 12-1

1. $R_1 = 15,000\ \Omega,\ R_2 = 7,500\ \Omega,\ R_3 = 4,500\ \Omega,\ R_4 = 3,000\ \Omega$

5. $I_T = 55\ \text{mA},\ R_1 = 1818.2\ \Omega,\ R_2 = 2727.3\ \Omega,\ R_3 = 30,000\ \Omega$

EXERCISES 13-1

1. $R_s = 10.101\ \Omega$

5. $R_{s100\,\text{mA}} = 0.300\ \Omega,\ R_{s250\,\text{mA}} = 0.120\ \Omega$

EXERCISES 14-1

1. $R_{\text{mult.}} = 9900\ \Omega$

7. $R_{1V} = 8000\ \Omega,\ R_{10V} = 98,000\ \Omega,\ R_{25V} = 248,000\ \Omega$

EXERCISES 15-1

1. $R_x = 16.14\ \Omega$

7. $R_3 = 76.01\ \Omega$

EXERCISES 16-1

1. $E = 21.15\ \text{V},\ r = 4.65\ \Omega$

3. $E = 1.34\ \text{V},\ r = 0.158\ \Omega$

EXERCISES 16-2

1. $V_t = 15.05\ \text{V}$

3. $V_t = V_L = 35.12\ \text{V}$

EXERCISES 17-1

3. $e = -\frac{3}{2}$

5. $k = 3$

9. $v = -4^{3/4}$

EXERCISES 17-2

1. (a) II ; (b) IV ;

(c) III ; (d) I ;

(e) II ; (f) III

EXERCISES 17–3

1. (a) $y = 4$; (b) $y = -1$; (c) $y = 0$;

(d) $y = -5$; (e) $y = -\frac{5}{3}$; (f) $y = \frac{5}{6}$

7. $E = 50\,I$, $M = \dfrac{1}{R}$, $R = \dfrac{1}{50} = 0.02\ \Omega$

EXERCISES 18–1

1. $a = 15$, $b = 6$

7. $e = 3$, $f = 5$

EXERCISES 18–2

1. $x = -1$, $y = 3$

3. $e = -6$, $f = -3$

EXERCISES 18–3

1. $a = -1$, $b = 3$

5. $n = 8$, $m = 2$

EXERCISES 18–4

1. $w = 3$, $z = 2$

3. $c = 7$, $d = 3$

EXERCISES 18–5

1. $p = 1$, $q = -3$

EXERCISES 18–6

1. $y = \dfrac{5}{-f + g}$, $x = \dfrac{2g + 3f}{ge - fe}$

EXERCISES 18–7

1. $x = 1$, $y = 4$, $z = 1$

3. $R_1 = 20$, $R_2 = 20$, $R_3 = 25$

EXERCISES 18–8

1. $C_1 = 7\ \mu\text{F}$, $C_2 = 15\ \mu\text{F}$

7. $L_1 = 9\ \text{H}$, $L_2 = 6\ \text{H}$

EXERCISES 19–1

1. $-M_1N_2 - M_2N_1$

5. 28

EXERCISES 19–2

1. $c = 3$, $d = 5$

7. $r = -12$, $s = -13$

EXERCISES 20–1

1. $\pm 9\sqrt{2}$

5. $\pm 11c\sqrt{c}$

EXERCISES 20–2

3. $\pm\dfrac{7b^2c^3}{9d^4}$

5. $\pm\dfrac{g\sqrt{6g}}{3h}$

EXERCISES 20–3

1. $3\sqrt{2}$

5. $16\sqrt{2}$

EXERCISES 20–4

3. $140\sqrt{6}$

5. $5 + 2\sqrt{5}$

EXERCISES 20–5

3. $8\sqrt{2}$

7. $10\sqrt{5}$

11. $24\sqrt{3}$

13. $\dfrac{9 + \sqrt{3}}{13}$

17. $-1 + j7$

21. $80 - j15$

23. $\dfrac{30 - j20}{13}$

EXERCISES 21–1

1. $a = \pm 8$

5. $e = \pm 14$

EXERCISES 21–2

3. $c = 0$, $c = -5$

5. $d = 6$, $d = -3$

EXERCISES 21–3

1. $a = -2 \pm \sqrt{19}$

3. $c = -9 \pm \sqrt{29}$

EXERCISES 21–4

1. $x = -6$, $x = 2$

5. $x = -4$, $x = -2$

1. $16 - (4)(1)(16) = -48$
3. $36 - (4)(1)(8) = 4$

EXERCISES 22–1

5. $I_{R_{30}} = 5.36$ A
7. $I_{R_1} = I_{R_2} = 0.717$ A

EXERCISES 22–2

3. $R_1 = R_2 = 57$ Ω, $R_3 = 89.06$ Ω
7. $R = 191.49$ Ω

EXERCISES 22–3

5. $R_N = 2.22$ Ω, $I_N = 1.2$ A
7. $E_{oc} = 15.1$ V, $R_{TH} = 11.53$ Ω

EXERCISES 23–1

1. $25.5°$, $67.083°$, $5.534°$
3. Reflex, Reflex, Acute
7. 0.636, 2.75, 4.73

EXERCISES 23–2

3. $c = 23.88$ ft
7. $h = 147.17$ ft

EXERCISES 24–1

1. $\sin \alpha = 0.8538$, $\cot \beta = 1.64$, $\csc \alpha = 1.17$
3. $\cos \alpha = 0.520$, $\tan \beta = 0.609$, $\cot \alpha = 0.609$
9. $\tan \alpha = 1.176$, $\csc \beta = 1.544$, $\cos \alpha = 0.647$
13. $\csc \alpha = 1.776$, $\sec \beta = 1.98$, $\cot \alpha = 1.468$
15. $\tan \beta = 0.568$

EXERCISES 24–2

1. $\sin 95° = 0.996$, $\cos 95° = -0.087$, $\tan 95° = -11.43$
5. $\sin -300° = 0.866$, $\cos -300° = 0.50$, $\tan -300° = 1.732$
9. $\sin -604° = 0.898$, $\cos -604° = -0.438$, $\tan -604° = -2.05$
11. Quadrants II and IV
15. $\sin \theta = -0.780$, $\cos \theta = -0.624$, $\tan \theta = 1.25$

EXERCISES 25–1

1. $\sin 52° = 0.788$, $\cos 52° = 0.615$, $\tan 52° = 1.28$
   $\sin 38° = 0.615$, $\cos 38° = 0.788$, $\tan 38° = 0.781$
   $\sin 89° = 0.999$, $\cos 89° = 0.0174$, $\tan 89° = 57.29$

EXERCISES 25–2

1. $\theta = 42.22°$
5. $\alpha = 27.71°$

EXERCISES 25–3

1. $\sin = 0.259$, $\cos = -0.966$, $\tan = -0.268$

EXERCISES 25–4

1. $b = 26.2$, $c = 31.1$, $\phi = 57.5°$
7. $c = 31.9$, $\theta = 31.5°$, $\phi = 58.5°$
11. $b = 49.8$, $\theta = 41.8°$, $\phi = 48.2°$
15. $a = 73.7$, $c = 92.8$, $\phi = 37.4°$

EXERCISES 25–5

3. Anchor distance = 96 ft
   $l_{120} = 153.6$ ft
   $l_{60} = 113.2$ ft
   $l_T = 1412.4$ ft
   $\text{Angle}_{180} = 61.9°$
   $\text{Angle}_{120} = 51.3°$
   $\text{Angle}_{60} = 32°$

EXERCISES 25–6

1. $\alpha = 78.1°$, $\beta = 71.9°$, $a = 39.1$
5. $a = 79.63$, $\beta = 55.48°$, $\gamma = 28.32°$
7. $A = 97.53$ ft²

EXERCISES 26–1

1. $40.4 + j29.4$
5. $66.7 - j38.5$
7. $-18 - j31.2$
13. $19.2 \underline{|-38.6°}$
17. $214.9 \underline{|135°}$
23. $-25 - j25$
29. $186.6 + j223.2$

EXERCISES 26–2

1. $\omega = 1{,}570$ rad/sec
3. 34.27 rad, 11.56 revolutions
11. $A = 15.5$, $\omega = 4{,}678$ rad/sec
   $f = 744.9$ Hz, $T = 0.00134$ sec
13. $A = 26$, $\omega = 12.56$ rad/sec
   $f = 2$ Hz, $T = 0.5$ sec

EXERCISES 27–1

3. $I_{max} = 64.07$ mA
7. $I = 16.94$ mA

EXERCISES 27–2

3. $e = -147.7$ V, $i = -24.3$ mA
7. $e = 169$ V, $i = 22.65$ A

EXERCISES 28–1

3. $X_L = 87.96\ \Omega$
5. $X_L = 2.356$ MΩ

EXERCISES 28–2

3. $I = 1.428 \times 10^4$ A
7. $C = 2994\ \mu\mu$F

EXERCISES 28–3

3. $Z = 15 + j23.56$
7. $Z = 25000 - j1500$, $I = 99.8$ mA, $\theta = -3.43°$

EXERCISES 28–4

1. $Z = 6666.6\ \Omega$, $L = 17.57$ H, $X_L = 6624.3\ \Omega$
5. $X_c = 17.68\ \Omega$, $Z = 200.78\ \Omega$, $I = 1.24$A
9. $f_r = 654000$ Hz

EXERCISES 29–1

1. $I_T = 4.13 \underline{|-90°}$ mA, $\theta = -90°$
   $P = 0$ W, $Z = 72.639$ Ω

5. $I = 100.7$ A, pf $= 0.663$ leading
   $P = 133.45$ kW, $Z = 19.86$ Ω

EXERCISES 29–2

3. $I_1 = 0.632 \underline{|-71.5°}$ A, $I_2 = 0.732 \underline{|23.76°}$ A, $I_T = 0.921 \underline{|-19.15°}$ A

5. $I_1 = 3.33 \underline{|0°}$ A $= 3.33 + j0$ A
   $I_2 = 1.24 \underline{|-8.55°}$ A $= 1.23 - j0.184$ A
   $I_3 = 4.72 \underline{|26.56°}$ A $= 4.22 + j2.11$ A

EXERCISES 29–3

1. $I_1 = 1 \underline{|-90°}$ A, $I_2 = 1 \underline{|60°}$ A, $I_T = 0.517 \underline{|-14.73°}$ A, $Z = 580.3 \underline{|14.73°}$ Ω

5. $Z = 12.39 \underline{|73.74°}$ Ω, $R = 3.47$ Ω, $X_L = 11.89$ Ω

7. $pf_1 = 0.384$ lagging, $pf_2 = 0.761$ leading

11. $C = 0.064 \ \mu$F

13. $f_r = 649$ Hz

17. $L = 0.479 \ \mu$H in parallel

21. $408 \underline{|-1°}$

EXERCISES 30–1

3. $\log_{16} 4096 = 3$

5. $\log_x a = b$

11. $15^4 = 50,625$

13. $361^{0.5} = 19$

EXERCISES 30–2

1. 1.5441

5. 6.4150

9. $8.4742 - 10$

13. $6.3222 - 10$

17. 10.6294

19. $9.5328 - 10$

21. 2.5563

EXERCISES 30–3

3. 6.1170

5. 0.01663 or 1.663×10^{-2}

9. 7970.8

13. 1.0856

EXERCISES 30–4

3. 8.5928

5. $8.5689 - 10$

9. 6.2197

13. 2.7017

EXERCISES 30–5

3. 6292

7. -1.14×10^7

9. -5.608

11. 0.626

15. 4.55×10^{-4}

19. $8.2503 - 10$

EXERCISES 30–6

3. 5.639

7. 12.96

11. 5.159

13. 23.49

EXERCISES 30–7

3. 0.1135

7. 2.4321

9. 2.511

13. $y = 9.120$

EXERCISES 31–2

1. $L = 1.183 \times 10^{-3}$ H = 1183 mH

5. $L = 0.5 \times 10^{-3}$ H = 500 mH

EXERCISES 31–1

1. 12.42 dB

7. −1.076 dB

11. $P_2 = 1143.2$ mW

EXERCISES 32–1

3. 25

5. 56

9. 101

13. 100000000

17. 0.0110

19. 0.000110

21. 0.875

EXERCISES 32–2

3. 30

7. 282

EXERCISES 32–3

1. 11010

5. 110101

9. 15_8

13. 10_8

EXERCISES 32–4

1. 11001

5. 1010100

9. 11000

13. 111111

17. 10100101

21. 10

INDEX

a

j

k

l

m